THE Μετάνοία Method

How the Brain, Body, and Bible Work Together

Kent McKean
Heather McKean

The Metanoia Method

All Greek and Hebrew words and definitions are from Bible Hub, unless otherwise notated.

Medical Disclaimer — The contents of this work are based on personal experiences, research conducted by the authors (unless otherwise noted), and experiential data collected from work with clients. The authors present this information for educational purposes only. Concerning the complex and highly individualized nature of any health problem, this book and the ideas, methods, procedures, and suggestions herein are not intended to replace the advice of trained medical professionals. All matters regarding an individual's physical or mental health require medical supervision. A medical professional should be consulted prior to adopting any program, programs, or methods described in this book or any information shared by the Mind Change Institute® and its affiliate programs. The authors disclaim any liability arising directly or indirectly from the use of this book. Anyone reading this book or using methods suggested in this book acknowledges that they have read and understood the details of this disclaimer and take complete responsibility for the outcome of any implementation of the material herein.

Anonymity of Testimonials and Client Stories — We have found that sharing our clients' stories and journeys is a powerful way to help people understand the mindset of the work we do. We also understand the necessity and value of keeping our clients' identities and stories confidential. We have chosen to take both these views into consideration. All the case studies are based on real client experiences. Please know that all names have been changed. Some subjects are compilations of client experiences, and some are modified to focus on a particular element. Though many of our clients are happy to share their personal successes and stories, we have chosen, in all cases, to ensure that the identity of the client is protected. Therefore, details/genders/timelines may have been altered in each story.

McKean, Kent, 1981-
McKean, Heather, 1976-
The Metanoia Method: How The Brain, Body, And Bible Work Together

www.MindChange.com

TABLE OF CONTENTS

A Note To The Readers

However you came to read this book, with purpose or by chance, we are thankful that you are taking the time to dive deeper. This book will help you discover, uncover, and transform. As it says in Romans 12:2: "*Be transformed by the renewing of your mind. Then you will be able to test and approve what God's will is—his good, pleasing and perfect will.*"

We are very thankful to have you join us on this journey. The truth is, you are fully capable, knowledgeable, and have unique gifts that will add to the concepts in this book. Please utilize all that God has given you. For some of you, this information will be brand new. For others, you may have a background or expertise in science or the Bible. Regardless, we have one request: no matter how much you believe you know about anything held within these pages, we ask that you keep an open mind. As we all know, this kind of heart will help us grow to our fullest capacity.

> *Simon Peter, a servant and apostle of Jesus Christ, to those who through the righteousness of our God and Savior Jesus Christ have received a faith as precious as ours: Grace and peace be yours in abundance through the knowledge of God and of Jesus our Lord.* ***His divine power has given us everything we need for life and godliness through our knowledge of him*** *who called us by his own glory and goodness. Through these,* ***he has given us his very great and precious promises, so that through them you may participate in the divine nature****, having escaped the corruption in the world caused by evil desires. For this very reason,* ***make every effort to add to your faith*** *goodness; and to goodness, knowledge; and to knowledge, self-control; and to self-control, perseverance; and to perseverance, godliness; and to godliness, mutual affection; and to mutual affection, love. For if you* ***possess these qualities in increasing measure****, they will keep you from being ineffective and unproductive in your*

> *knowledge of our Lord Jesus Christ. But whoever does not have them is nearsighted and blind, forgetting that they have been cleansed from their past sins. Therefore, my brothers and sisters, make every effort to confirm your calling and election.* ***For if you do these things, you will never stumble****, and you will receive a rich welcome into the eternal kingdom of our Lord and Savior Jesus Christ.*
>
> **2 Peter 1:1–11,** emphasis added

So, then, why are you reading this? Hopefully, to add to your faith and knowledge of God so that you will be increasingly effective and productive. In this way, we can participate in the divine nature of God: life to the full with abundant peace and transformation. Get ready to dive in!

Both of us love God, love his church, and love to explore the domain of change and continual transformation. You may notice that most portions of the book, although it is written by two people, are told from the first person. This was our solution for helping the reader stay focused instead of adding the repetitive "I, Kent..." or "I, Heather..." Although our personal stories may be quite different, we have helped each other find our needed areas of growth, and we continue to build on one another's strengths. As for our beliefs and convictions contained within this book, we remain united and speak as one. We have both experienced these truths and methods of transformation in our own lives and witnessed them in thousands of others. It is with great honor and pleasure that we can share all this with you in the pages to come. Our hope is that you find your truest and most authentic self as you see more clearly and more evidently the amazing being God created in you. You *can* overcome. You *can* be victorious. The power is already within and transformation is at hand.

Prologue

Have you noticed that religion has become (and probably always has been) a complicated topic? I have. I don't think that was the plan. Paul tells us in 1 Corinthians that God is not a God of confusion or disorder but a God of peace. Interesting that the converse of peace here is confusion. Though there are countless manifestations of the "human condition" concerning sin and religion, I have identified one that I think is at the root of all the rest. Let me explain. If we call ourselves Christians, it is likely that we do not align with the doctrine of original sin, at least at first glance. The theory of original sin has its roots in pagan philosophy. As it evolved, it was made a dogma of the Roman Catholic Church in the fifth century CE, primarily by Augustine's influence.

Most people are grossly unaware of the extraordinary amount of influence the early church philosophers have over our current theology as modern-day Christians. It's important to understand how far we have traveled from the gospel's original intent, especially in Western culture. We would do well to remember that much of what we believe today has been filtered through generations of those who came before us. Augustine himself was deeply influenced by the expanding heathen philosophies of his day. He first became a student of the Manichaeans, who were a Gnostic-Christian sect that had done away with many of the foundational Christian basics. It was their core belief and teaching that *all matter* is inherently evil. This indoctrination led to the denial that Jesus was the real incarnation of Christ, saying that he did not actually come in the flesh, since their view held that all physical things are inherently evil. After spending nine years under the tutelage of the Manichaeans, Augustine firmly viewed human nature as fundamentally evil. Meanwhile, he viewed true freedom from sin as a delusion.

If you had asked me 10 years ago (possibly even five years ago) if I believed that we, as humans, are inherently evil, I would likely have said no. But I cannot say that my doctrine matched my life in this area. I think this is why the Christian mantra of the last decade has been, "Well, we are all sinners!"

Prologue

I never thought to question this until I started to do the work I talk about in this book. I never set out to challenge my faith. I wanted to heal my body and mind. I had no idea how connected they are. I know now that I am not alone. Why is it so much easier to adhere to a belief that there is something *wrong* with us? Why do more and more people want to hear "relatability in struggle and sin" from the pulpit? If we were to get extremely honest, most of us feel like there is something wrong with us. Rather than believing and feeling like we are inherently good, we seem to be much more comfortable with the idea that we are bad. Over the years, I have spoken to countless Christians who cherry-pick a handful of scriptures that make them feel justified in this idea of their awfulness. But if I could sum up my current "elevator speech" regarding God, Jesus, and the Bible, it would go a little something like this:

> *While God was creating the universe and everything in it, he decided that he would like to create something incredibly special. Not just something, but someone to enjoy this creation with! So he created man and woman in his image to be with him and share the beauty of his creation. But these beings were influenced by their surroundings and soon began to doubt God's ability to take care of them and all their needs. That lack of trust ended up with these treasured children choosing to allow sin into their world. Ever since that time, God has been trying to reconnect with his children—to help them remember* ***who*** *they are and to* ***whom*** *they belong. After hundreds of years of mostly failed attempts at winning them back, God had one last plan: to* ***show*** *them how to do it. So he came back to them, in their own form, to give up the only thing he had left to give: himself. Hoping that this grand display of love and self-sacrifice would finally convince them that they could stop doing, trying, arguing, and fighting in order to earn God's love and acceptance, and just remember that accepted is already what we are. God knew that if we could feel his heart for us, know his hope for us, and produce*

> *fruit in accordance with his love for us, we would never settle for anything less.*

Sound simple? What if it is? What if the best motivation for our daily walk with God *isn't* because we are just so darn awful and quick to sin? What if the best motivation is understanding just how loved we are and what amazing creations we are?

Why is this so hard? *Especially* for Christians? We are going to talk about that. In fact, that is the undercurrent of this entire book. To understand this, we are going to put this book into the framework that God used with his people from the beginning: the first and greatest commandment. What if the entire Bible and knowledge of God can be summed up in this command?

> *Hear, O Israel: The Lord our God, the Lord is one. Love the Lord your God with all your heart and with all your soul and with all your strength.*
>
> **Deuteronomy 6:4–5**

What if the message of God, Jesus, and the Bible can be found in this one verse? God says, "The first and most important thing you need to hear and know is that I am God. The only one. That means I created you, and you can trust me. The best way for you to know that is to focus your heart, soul, strength (and mind) on how much I love you. When you know this, you can begin to love me back. Then we can really get this thing going! After that, you can truly take the overflow of my love for you and love other people the same way you have learned to love yourself *as I have loved you*. It's going to be great. Just stay focused."

For God's people, since the days of being set free from captivity in Egypt, there has been a scriptural foundation from which everything else flows in our relationship with the Creator. This passage, for the Jews, is known as the Shema. Thousands of years later, Jesus himself even uses a portion of the Shema to emphasize the greatest command.

FIRST AND GREATEST COMMANDMENT

When God speaks the Shema into existence, his people have just been freed from slavery, and they have a journey ahead of them before entering the promised land. God *wants* everything to go well with these people. He *wants* them to enjoy a long life. But he also knows what will prevent them from having joy, peace, and freedom. So before he continues to guide and provide, God gives the Israelites a charge. He tells them how to live in accordance with the way he created them from the start. So let's break this down a bit.

This idea of "Hear, O Israel" was an address to the people to listen up! Pay attention! What you are about to hear is of the utmost importance. Are you ready?

Moses relays that the Lord is our God. He is the *one* true God. This one-God emphasis is needed because the Israelites were inundated with so many gods from the Egyptian culture. Even after they had recently been set free, they worshiped a golden calf in the desert, similar to what they had witnessed and had been surrounded by in Egypt. So God is trying to remind them that there is only one Creator, one overseer, one true Lord and God over all. He is communicating that he really does know how they will be the happiest and most fulfilled and will thrive in the best possible way.

Moses lays it out for the people in one simple statement, which Jesus repeats in the Gospels as the greatest command: *"Love the Lord your God with all your heart and with all your soul and with all your strength."* Moses tells the people that the idea here is to be whole within yourself, to love and live as God created us. And then to teach, train, and exemplify this to the next generation so that they, too, can live life to the full.

Now these three categories (*heart*, *soul*, and *strength*)—and in two cases in the New Testament, the added *mind*—are not distinct elements of our make-up, but instead, they are overlapping facets of every human being.

Each time God gives them a directive of *how* to love, he uses the word "all," which in the Hebrew is *kol* (כֹּל), meaning whole. So no matter how you read this, God is trying to convey that when we give our love to him in various ways, it is to be our full self, our whole self, an "all-of-self" aspect of us.

The first component of loving the Lord starts with all our *heart*—the word here is from the Hebrew word *leb* (לֵבָב), and it means the inner man, mind, or will. Next, it says to love the Lord with all our *soul*—the Hebrew word used here is *nephesh* (נֶפֶשׁ), meaning the life force, the desire, passion, appetite, and emotional drive. Finally, this concept closes with loving the Lord with all our *strength*—in Hebrew, the word used is *meod* (מְאֹד), which in context means the use of muchness, abundance, and might.[1]

Today, the world has caught on to this idea of the mind-body connection. Some have even gone so far as to say there is a mind-body-soul connection. In this passage, we have God helping us understand, from the beginning, that we have always been made up of these threefold elements: heart, soul, and strength.

Heart: the inner self, the intellect's will, the mind
Soul: the seat of desire, passion, emotion, and life
Strength: the abundance, the outcomes of life, the fruit of what is sown

There is a distinguishable flow in this teaching: Everything stems from our inner self, our thought life (heart), and then overflows into the outer self, the emotions and desires and passions we let drive us (soul). Finally, we find the outcome of our choices, desires, and thoughts in the fruit of our life (strength). It makes sense, then, that the Israelites would wear tablets around their necks, etch God's truths on their doorposts, and speak freely to their children about his precepts.

How easily we fragment our whole being. But God is trying to tell us that wholeness is exactly what he is providing. God didn't ask us to love him in three distinct temporary behavior-modification ways. Instead, he gave us the map of how to be the *whole* person he originally designed to love and grow and give.

Why, then, do two of the Gospel writers add a fourth word (mind) when Jesus speaks about the greatest command? Remember that the Old Testament was translated into Greek (in the Septuagint) before the Gospels were written (by a few hundred years). As with any language translation, the translators had to adjust some words and concepts to the best of their capacity. To fully grasp the meaning behind the three Hebrew words for heart, soul, and strength, the Greek language (and English) needed to expand these into four different words. Scholars kept the English words for heart and soul as such. Matthew substituted mind for strength, while Mark and Luke added to the three original Hebrew

---

[1] Went, K. J. Love the lord your God with all of your what? *https://www.studylight.org/language-studies/difficult-sayings?article=520.html,* 2007

words to give us a better grasp on the fullness of the Shema that Jesus was reciting: heart (*kardia*), soul (*psuché*), mind (*dianoia*), strength (*ischus*).[2]

Kardia – καρδία – the heart, mind, character, inner self, will, intention, center

Dianoia – διάνοια – the mind, disposition, thought, understanding, intellect, insight

Psuché – ψυχή – the breath of life, the soul as the seat of emotions, individuality; it is the direct aftereffects of God breathing his gift of life into a human being

Ischus – ἰσχύς – absolute strength, power, might, force, ability

Kardia (Greek) and *leb* (Hebrew) refer to the heart as the center that governs our somatic, mental, and emotional attributes. And although we typically relate the heart to emotions, the Bible's intention of the word is related primarily to our thoughts.

Dianoia (Greek) is an added word to help the reader understand this concept further of what the OT heart represented in the Shema. All desires, feelings, and outcomes stem from our *dianoia* (heart-mind). As Proverbs 4:23 says, *"Above all else, guard your heart* (leb), *for everything you do flows from it."* Some other translations help us understand it even further:

> *Guard your heart above all else, for it determines the course of your life.* (NLT)
>
> *Guard your heart above all else, for it is the source of life.* (CSB)
>
> *Carefully guard your thoughts because they are the source of true life.* (CEV)

Loving God with all our *psuché* (soul) means to love him with the very essence he breathed into Adam. The word here is more like spirit than soul. It is not the immortal soul we think of, but rather the individual gift of life. It is our

---

[2] Brown, Francis, 1849–1916. *The Brown, Driver, Briggs Hebrew And English Lexicon*. Peabody, Mass. Hendrickson Publishers, 1996.

very being, which constitutes our life, our emotions, or the essence of being made in the image of God.

Finally, the *ischus* is the Greek word translated as "strength." This is when we do something with all our ability, might, or power. If our child were stuck under a car or tree branch, we would lift it with all our *ischus* (strength). If we were determined to get that job or get into a certain university, we would give it all our *ischus* (strength). For the Gospel writers, translating the Hebrew word for strength (*meod*) was one of the more difficult aspects.[3] Ultimately, this word can be translated as "very" and can be found over 300 times in the Old Testament. As we will discuss later, it shows up in God's statement about his amazing and perfect creation after creating humans in his own image: *"And...it was very good"* (Genesis 1:31). It was abundantly, mightily, fiercely good. God had put all his force, everything he had, into making us. We were the outcome, the fruit of his love and creation and desire. More on that later. But the issue here was figuring out how to sum up what God originally intended for his people to understand about the greatest command. Understanding this is the key to understanding life to the full, to live exactly as we were created to live, not only in a relationship with the Father, but with others. God's intent is for us to live congruently and in alignment with our original design.[4]

All in all, the idea that God, Jesus, and the Gospel writers are trying to convey as they replicate the Shema in Jesus' own words is that God wants us to know him, to love him, and to have a relationship with him to the full, with our all.

Just as God provided freedom for the Israelite slaves out of Egypt, he has also provided a way out of spiritual slavery for us. He has already loosed the chains of sin, and salvation is already at hand. The prison gates are already open! This instruction is simply the map for stepping out into the freedom of a meaningful relationship—one with the full spectrum of complete freedom and true love.

---

[3] Strong's Exhaustive Concordance: New American Standard Bible. Lockman Foundation. *http://www.biblestudytools.com/concordances/strongs-exhaustive-concordance, 1995.*

[4] Thayer, Joseph Henry, Carl Ludwig Wilibald Grimm, and Christian Gottlob Wilke. *A Greek-English Lexicon of the New Testament.* New York: American Book Co. 1889.

SECOND-GREATEST COMMAND

If my kids ask for $5 to buy ice cream, but I only have $3, can I give $5 to them? No. Even if I really, really want to and even if I understand that I would have to have $2 more, I cannot give them $5, because I do not have it. We can only give what we already possess. This is why God's first and greatest command is for us to learn and live true love for him. We must first understand and learn to offer our whole selves (thoughts, emotions, passion, and full strength). Then we can truly love how he created us to connect with him, know him, live freely in him, and be fully known. Only then will we be able to do the same with someone else.

When Jesus is asked about the greatest command, he not only shares the Shema, summing up four of the ten commandments, but he also sums up the final six, using Leviticus 19:18, by telling us to *"love your neighbor as yourself."* This is the second greatest command. Why? Because you need to have that kind of love inside you before you can give it to someone else. In other words, the more we love God in the truest agape form, the more we will have that love inside us to love others, to give to others.

We can only give what we already hold within. Loving God to the full teaches us how to see ourselves in his image and from his perspective, allowing us to love and accept ourselves fully. In so doing, we can give that kind of full, unfiltered, unstoppable, strength-based kind of love to others.

LET'S GET THIS THING STARTED

God's plan of redemption was set into motion from the beginning. He loves us and wants us to be made whole. He continues to do whatever it takes to show us the truth about how valuable we are. God sees us for who we really are, and all he wants is a relationship with us. He wants us back! Unfortunately, the trust has been broken. But God isn't surprised. He knew it was coming. He had a plan. It is finished. Now the ball is in our court. Will we believe him? Or will we believe what the world says about him? Let's get this thing started…

Part 1
How It All Began

INTRODUCTION

Pretty words aren't always true, and true words aren't always pretty.
— Frank Mohanna

I'm going to be honest. I can't promise it will be pretty. I am a Christian. I love God. I believe in the Bible. I used to think that those phrases meant the same thing to most people and would ultimately result in a similar life and doctrine outcome. I know differently now. Having previously not realized this led to a long period of disillusionment in my walk with God and, for a time, disrupted my faith in the Christian church.

I will save some of you a good deal of time and energy now by letting you know that I do not possess a doctorate in theology or a master's in psychology. If you will only listen to someone who has letters after their name, this is not the book for you. I wholeheartedly respect those whose life journey took them down the road of academia, but that was not to be my path. I am an "armchair expert," if you will. Fortunately, bound to no particular creed or set standard of practices, this has allowed me to bumble my way through both sides of each argument and find the truth that usually exists somewhere in the middle. Trust me—I would love to have spent time with some of the top minds in the fields from which I borrow knowledge, but due to the many interests needed to approach these subjects and the late date at which I stumbled upon them, it would have taken more lifetimes than I possess.

If I were to have a doctorate in theology and a doctorate in psychology and also have been a student of the mysteries of the Spirit as well as the way that our mind communicates through our body, I would be a rare individual, indeed! I'm not saying that person isn't out there, but I have yet to meet them personally.

In my efforts to pull myself from the trenches of my own physical misery, emotional disconnect, and spiritual confusion, I have found some fascinating information. I have done my best to vet this information biblically, scientifically, and experientially. The Metanoia Method is a result of this journey.

For those of you who are willing to join me, this will be an incredible adventure. My goal with the Metanoia Method is to start a conversation. I'm going to be fully transparent and radically honest. I'm asking you to do the same.

CAN YOU FEEL IT?

You can feel it, right? Something isn't right. We've gone a little off course somewhere. And try as we might, we cannot seem to get back on track.

I (Heather) came to Jesus because I was lost. I felt broken. I had made a complete wreck of my life, and I wanted another chance. I felt beyond hope, and then I heard the Good News. And for a while, it *was* good. After a while, it was less good. And after a while longer, it looked a heck of a lot like it did before I became a Christian, except I didn't really curse anymore, and I went to church most Sundays, and I had *a lot* more to feel guilty about. I told you I was going to be honest.

Over and over, I would recommit. Read more, pray more, reach out more. I shared my faith, studied my Bible, served, tithed, and *tried*. It seemed like everyone around me "got it" except me. So I tried harder. Eventually, I learned to say the things that *they* did, act like *they* did, and do the things *they* did. And it helped, for a while. Until it didn't anymore. Some of the same behaviors that I dealt with outside the church started to happen within the church: conflict, judgment, gossip. This only made me feel worse. Like there was something wrong with me that I was missing. I needed to *try harder*. Guilt was a powerful motivator for me too. So I used it and perceived it in every message I heard, every song that we sang, and in every hang-out time I had with someone. I thought it was a victory to feel guilty. I started to try to make others feel guilty, to help them "do better."

An interesting thing was happening to my body physically, as I (Heather) dealt with all this spiritually and emotionally—I got sick. I mean, really sick. I started having accidents. Breaking bones, falling through windows, passing out while driving. I began getting diagnosis after diagnosis of autoimmune disorders and diseases. My mental health suffered greatly, and I ended up back on antidepressants.

I (Kent) came into the realm of mind/body/Bible from a much different perspective and mindset. I grew up in the church—I could sing the names of the books of the New Testament in order by age three. I could recite 100 scriptures by the age of 10. At the age of 12, I made Jesus the Lord of my life and was baptized into Christ. By the age of 14, I had spoken in front of 10,000 people on a stage at Madison Square Garden about my convictions in Jesus and the full life he had in store for us. I never smoked, drank, or cursed. I kept myself far away from impurity and bitterness and anger. I learned to be who God intended me to be—the good kid, the kind gentleman, a leader among my peers. I had a stable family life, one in which I can recall no yelling or fighting, except for the momentary disagreement or frustration. I had a great relationship with my sister. I helped people at school become Christians. I became an intern for the ministry while in college and found my wife-to-be at the end of college. I even went into the ministry about a year after I was married. I have traveled internationally, preached to thousands and thousands of people...yet somewhere along the journey, I cracked. Not in an obvious way, but in a way like you'd see in concrete that has been there a long time, that is "no big deal"—except that it *became* a big deal very fast. My kids harped on the fact that I wasn't listening and began to pull away. My passion for people started draining my life force. And my marriage began to seriously and swiftly unravel. "*But I did everything right! How can this be happening to me?*"

It took me years to realize that the way I was embracing "the perfect life" was its own set of coping skills that was actually damaging me. You see, many people who have had issues, traumas, or problems go headfirst into addiction, depression, bitterness, or chronic this or that—but not me. I had somehow figured out a way to see my whole life as *the perfect life*. Any issues in my path were because of "other people." But not me! I was living and doing and feeling and helping "just the way I was supposed to, just the way God would be proud of me," yet my life was finally crumbling. My past and my unconscious coping skills were finally catching up to me.

Although I could argue that my life had many good outcomes, I was finally hitting critical mass. Although having the perfect Christian exterior, I was driven by fear, shame, and guilt. I was living my "ideal life"—but in actuality, it was just a clever way to avoid the negative emotional drivers that kept me stuck. In truth, my fear, shame, and guilt were driving me and every aspect of my life. I had nowhere else to turn—except inward.

We'll go into more detail later regarding our physical, mental, emotional, spiritual, and relational health, but let me ask you a question: Does this sound familiar? If you were to look around your church, do you see it? Maybe this is you.

I'll tell you right now: shame, blame, guilt, and judgment have no place here. Nothing good will come of it. Let's agree to leave that right here, right now. I'll have none of it. Without placing blame, without assigning fault, can you hear the cry of the church? So many people are sick, medicated, addicted, guilty, and ashamed. You can keep turning a blind eye or accept this and begin to talk about what to do.

I hope this book is a starting place for you. It's not going to be comfortable. It will push boundaries, and it will challenge strongholds. It might be painful at times. But overall, I hope it is refreshing, like a cool stream on weary feet.

> *So repent—change your mind and purpose; turn around and return to God, that your sins may be erased, blotted out, wiped clean, that times of refreshing may come from the presence of the Lord.*
>
> **Acts 3:19** AMPC

CHAPTER 1

WHAT HAPPENED TO THE PLAN?

Then I repented of my sins and won the victory.
Oh, victory in Jesus, my Savior forever.
He sought me and bought me with his redeeming blood.
He loved me ere I knew him, and all my love is due him,
He plunged me to victory beneath the cleansing flood.

I think many of us are familiar with this 1939 classic hymn written by Eugene Monroe Bartlett.[5] This was the plan, right? The goal. The hope and vision of God for his people, for his church. So what happened to the victory? What happened to the people, the church?

I have full faith in God, that he is divine, all-powerful, all-knowing, and all-seeing. I am full of hope that we can overcome *anything*, transform *everything*, and become the likeness of Christ, individually and collectively. And I *love* the church, the body of Christ, God's treasured possession, his flock. I have faith, hope, and love, but I must be missing something, because when I look at the church as a whole—where is the victory?

YOU CANNOT HEAL WHAT YOU WON'T REVEAL

And not a creature exists that is concealed from his sight, but all things are open and exposed, and revealed to the eyes of him with whom we have to give account.

Hebrews 4:13 AMP

For whatever is hidden is meant to be disclosed, and whatever is concealed is meant to be brought out into the open.

Mark 4:22

---

5 Bartlett, Eugene Monroe. *Victory In Jesus*. Gospel Choruses, Paperback. 1939.

If you have ever tried to help someone with something, you would agree that it becomes very difficult to help if you do not have the whole story. Getting the full picture is an essential part of addressing the problem.

Think about a medical analogy: People generally come to a doctor for help. They have a symptom or a condition that requires assistance beyond their ability. For a doctor to provide the best treatment, they will usually require a good deal of information. They will ask questions relevant to the person's health history, eating habits, level of exercise, drug and alcohol usage, sexual encounters, and especially their use of prescribed or over-the-counter medications. Each one of these answers is vital information for the doctor. Major decisions will be made based on the portrayal of the situation.

Imagine a man is admitted to the ER with a broken wrist. When interviewed about his health history, out of shame and perceived stigma around his mental health issues, he neglects to mention he's on Xanax, a popular antidepressant. He figures that he's only in for his wrist, so his Xanax use should have no bearing on the treatment. The doctor prescribes Vicodin to deal with the pain of the break. The man takes it as prescribed, as well as his regular dose of Xanax. He also neglected to mention that he is a casual drinker, so he washes his meds down with a beer each night to relax. In the next few days, the man begins to lose mental and physical functions. Within a week, he finds himself back in the ER, but this time he is nearly in a coma due to a potentially fatal overdose.

Would you be surprised to know that between 60 and 80 percent of patients admit to lying about information that could be relevant to their health or treatment?[6] How does this analogy relate to the Metanoia Method?

"HOUSTON, WE HAVE A PROBLEM"

Before moving on, I feel compelled to explain what I mean when I say "church." For me, this term is intended to signify the church as a body of believers. I cannot possibly address the church without understanding that the

---

[6] Scherer, A., Barnes , G., and Larkin, K. *Most Patients Are Not 100 Percent Honest When Talking to Their Doctors*. https://news.umich.edu. 2018, November 13.

church is the people. It is easy to fault a particular movement, denomination, or even the clergy when we realize that something in our collective religious culture needs to be reevaluated. But I would caution you to refrain from that thinking. If there is a "problem" within a church, we can be assured that it is a problem within the people that make up that church. My goal here is not to place blame on any particular organization, but rather to take an inward look at ourselves and any incongruencies that we may find, and then look around to see that we are likely not alone in these feelings and experiences. If, at any time, you find yourself turning toward a narrative of "the church is the problem," I invite you to pause and look inward to see if you may be personally contributing to this story.

In the last section, I used the analogy of an ER patient to illustrate the need for transparency and a thorough assessment of the problem. This is a crucial component to adequately formulate a plan for healing. I'm compelled to mention this analogy because I have perceived some resistance in Christian circles to fully assess and address the crisis I see in our churches. The crisis I speak of is the degradation of the holiness of the church, "holy" meaning set apart. Though we say that we are different from the world, and at one time may have been, things are looking a little too similar these days. Many people, myself included, were drawn to the church because of feeling lost, broken, and/or helpless. We longed for the promise of freedom, forgiveness, and safety in the arms of a sovereign Lord. The church was meant to be an extension of that safety and love, where we could each find fellow travelers in the journey to becoming more like Jesus. We were called to be set apart, a light, salt of the earth, an ambassador for Christ, and a student of the truth. Consider Paul's encouragement to the church in Corinth:

> *And we all, who with unveiled faces contemplate the Lord's glory, are being transformed into his image with ever-increasing glory, which comes from the Lord, who is the Spirit.*
>
> **2 Corinthians 3:18**

Not for the sake of shame, judgment, blame, or criticism, but in the spirit of full disclosure for the condition that we may be facing, I want you to look around you. How is this going in your fellowship? I can tell you what I see. I see marriages disintegrating, addictions increasing, chronic states of disease and poor health, a significant rise in mental health issues, and people who are burned out and fed up. But without a solution or answer, we continue to slightly modify or rehash something that seemed to have worked before. Sometimes we blame. Sometimes we just press on. Sometimes we ignore the issue entirely. Yet we still end up landing in roughly the same spot spiritually, emotionally, and physically.

For the sake of space and time, I will not rehash the large amount of statistical data associated with the rate of divorce, addiction, and prescription drug use pertaining to those who claim to be Christians. It's out there if you look carefully for unbiased information. Suffice it to say, it's dismal. I'm not a fan of being a Debbie Downer, but ignorance is not always bliss. It is my belief that if we truly have a good idea of what the problem is, it can generally be fixed. But glossing over, neglecting symptoms, and just-ignore-it-until-it-goes-away mentalities are no longer working (not that they ever really did).

And this isn't just within the membership. Many of the leaders are in the same boat. Many churches have become less a place of healing and transformation and more of a "support group" structure. Many fellowships have become a collection of problem-specific ministries: grief ministry, addiction ministry, sexual identification ministry, chronic illness ministry, etc. Many see this as progress, a way to continually meet the needs of the members. Please hear me say this: I am not against supporting people in their struggles. I'm a firm believer in meeting people where they are at. But I want us to be very careful that in our effort to support, we do not cross over into enabling. Do we believe that God is a God of healing? Or is he just a divine entity with unlimited Band-Aids to hand out? What doctrine have we accepted in our minds to make sense of what we are seeing in this day and age? Consider this warning to the shepherds of Israel issued through the prophet Ezekiel:

> *The word of the Lord came to me: "Son of man, prophesy against the shepherds of Israel; prophesy and say to them: 'This is what the Sovereign Lord says: Woe to you shepherds of Israel who*

> *only take care of yourselves! Should not shepherds take care of the flock? You eat the curds, clothe yourselves with the wool and slaughter the choice animals, but you do not take care of the flock. You have not strengthened the weak or healed the sick or bound up the injured.'"*
>
> **Ezekiel 34:1–4**

I believe in people. And I believe that most people are genuine. I believe that most church leaders really do have a genuine heart for God and the flock. But I also know myself. When I don't have a solution, I still want people to be taken care of. The dilemma ensues when I, as a church leader, let the flock's pain, hurt, and problems become the foothold for the next step in growth. When we, as a church (or as church leaders) are navigating how to move a church forward, we can many times be fueled by the issues in that church. If we continuously treat fear, sickness, division, addiction, etc., then we will become a spiritual ICU. Instead, the church must transform into a wellness center for the soul. We will have a first-aid station, to be sure. But we must not be stuck dealing with problems forever. Instead, we must be a church that is full of healing, growing, maturing, and overcoming. And as a church leader, I do not want us to be a spiritual hospice for society. Is this really what the church was created to be? Is this really God's plan for his creation?

CAUTION REGARDING CONFORMING

> *Do not conform to the pattern of this world, but be transformed by the renewing of your mind. Then you will be able to test and approve what God's will is—his good, pleasing and perfect will.*
>
> **Romans 12:2**

It is my guess that, if you are reading this book, you are no stranger to the issues that our churches are facing. Let me reiterate: I genuinely believe that ministers, pastors, and most church leaders mean well and are trying desperately to find answers to the increasing physical and emotional demands of the members. In churches across the world, we see a monumental effort to bridge the gap between the members' rising needs and the clergy's spiritual fatigue. Many of us would say that we believe in God's ability to heal, yet how many of us (or those around us) are being profoundly impacted by this belief?

One of the biggest concerns that I have is the church turning to the secular world to find the answers to these issues. A trend that began in recent years was the thought that pastors/evangelists/ministers must just need more education. The worldly belief that years of schooling unilaterally equal skill and proficiency is a limiting belief system. Often, the indoctrination of longstanding traditions and outdated learning materials requires conformity to a system rather than a conviction. I am not saying that education does not have its place. One of my core values is learning, and I consider myself a student for life. I love education and knowledge gathering! But I don't believe our church issues are a result of a lack of education in religious studies.

As always, I will go back to the word of God. Let us remember those whom Jesus chose to be his personal trainees: many fishermen, a tax collector, a zealot, and a thief. Most were blue-collar workers with little education.

> *When they saw the courage of Peter and John and realized that they were unschooled, ordinary men, they were astonished and they took note that these men had been with Jesus.*
>
> **Acts 4:13**

Another identifiable trend is the perceived need for mental health professionals within a church. I cannot count the number of lay leaders, church leaders, and members alike who are turning toward careers in counseling and therapy as a way to serve the needs of the church. Again, not a bad thing. In fact, I think this can be a great addition to our ministries in most cases: learning how to listen, validate, and have greater compassion for people. But here we see another rub. The world of psychiatry and psychology is not known for being a place of great change or healing, by their own admission. A Yale psychologist named Alan Kazdin addresses problems regarding therapy in an article written in

2011, saying there is little or no evidence that the talk-therapy model of psychology even works. Although this is the most prevalent model of therapy taught to students of counseling and therapy today, it is the current consensus that patients seeking help for mental health conditions are finding talk therapy/ counseling typically isn't working as a long-term solution. For some, it can even make things worse. In a *Time Magazine* article, Maia Szalavitz has this to say about our current relationship with the counseling/therapy model: "Psychotherapy doesn't have an 'image problem': it has an evidence problem. The treatments provided by most therapists are not those shown to work, and the treatments shown to work are hard to find because therapists don't practice them."[7]

Over the years, I have seen more of the problems and sin. I have become more aware of the issues at hand in my relationships, marriage, and parenting. I have even begun to understand *how* these came to be. Awareness is an important first step. It is imperative to *see* the problem before we can *change* the problem. But awareness and talk do not always *solve* the problem. Just like confession does not create repentance, more awareness does not always create solutions.

In Romans 12, we are warned *not* to conform to the patterns of the world, yet this is what I see occurring within our churches. Within the Christian doctrine, we are quick to blame "the world" for the condition of people, yet we turn to the world for the answers! This is a problem.

THE "PROBLEM" IS NOT THE PROBLEM: RETURN TO THE VISION

Okay, it's pretty clear that we have an issue. So, what do we do about it? Honestly, that is the purpose of this book. It's the beginning of a conversation. It's an invitation to an open-ended discussion about what is the root cause of this collective sense of unease, this "dis-ease," of those who claim Christianity, and what we can do about it.

---

[7] Szalavitz, M. *The Trouble With Talk Therapy.* https://www.healthland.time.com. November 27, 2012.

See, it's my belief that "problems" are not really the problem. Problems are usually just undesired feedback that results from the way we are doing something. If you get up every morning and stub your toe on the huge vanity that is ill placed in your room, what do you see as the problem? Is the stubbed toe the problem, or is the stubbed toe a way of communicating that the vanity would be better placed in a less-traveled part of your room?

The way I see all of this is feedback. The church, as the body of Christ, isn't feeling well. Many symptoms are popping up throughout. How do we view this? From a current worldview, we will probably look for a pill or course of action to "treat" the dis-ease. Rather than look for the root cause or the possible source of the issue, we see the "problem" as a problem. What if this is not a problem, but instead, a message? What if, rather than finding a way to *work around* the issue, we instead find a way to get to the heart of what is causing the disruption? We can either cope with it, cope *around* it, or *heal* it.

What if we, the individuals who make up the church, really could look like and function as it says in the Bible? What if we could be a people who experienced some of the same miracles that the Word promises we would have access to? What if people came to Jesus and found healing, peace, comfort, and joy? What if people found freedom from addiction, obesity, pain, chronic illness, and suffering? What if friendships, marriages, and families were not merely refereed in church, but truly transformed? I'm not talking about a temporary change in behavior, but lasting transformation and true freedom in Christ! I believe we can. I believe it was meant to be. I already know many people who are taking personal responsibility within their own lives to make it happen. I hope to show you how to begin this process through the rest of this book. Do you still believe this is all possible?

> *Every day they continued to meet together in the temple courts. They broke bread in their homes and ate together with glad and sincere hearts, praising God and enjoying the favor of all the people. And the Lord added to their number daily those who were being saved.*
>
> **Acts 2:46–47**

Everyone was filled with awe at the many wonders and signs performed by the apostles.

Acts 2:43

The whole assembly became silent as they listened to Barnabas and Paul telling about the signs and wonders God had done among the Gentiles through them.

Acts 15:12

To make her holy, cleansing her by the washing with water through the word, and to present her to himself as a radiant church, without stain or wrinkle or any other blemish, but holy and blameless.

Ephesians 5:26–27

Instead, speaking the truth in love, we will grow to become in every respect the mature body of him who is the head, that is, Christ. From him the whole body, joined and held together by every supporting ligament, grows and builds itself up in love, as each part does its work.

Ephesians 4:15–16

CHAPTER 2

THE HEATHER STORY

I'm going to brief you on my personal "creation story" and show you how it impacted me and my personal view of God and religion. I'll also show how dealing with that has allowed me to change *everything*.

When I was 22 years old, I found myself at a relatively rock-bottom place. I had recently moved to California, a dream of mine since I was quite young. I had never even been to California before I packed up my little red car with all my worldly possessions and set out to follow my dream. Truth be told, I had "stars" in my eyes. Hollywood stars! Like many young girls before me, I thought I would be an actress. I had been involved with acting for many years, and it made perfect sense in my naïve mind that because I was an "actress" in a small theatre in Nebraska, I would naturally transition to the LA acting scene. Cue the old cliche: "Small town girl moves to the big city to become a star!" From the outside, it looked as though I was following a dream. But a more in-depth look would reveal that I was on the run, yet again.

I was a broke and depressed 22-year-old girl with no real direction or support. A year prior, I had ended a relationship with my fiancé. He was my high-school sweetheart and first love. As with most breakups, I lost a lot more than just the relationship. We had bought a house together and fixed it up. His family had become very dear to me, and I considered them my family, especially his nieces, who had already begun calling me "Aunt." Our circle of friends was mainly his friends and their wives or girlfriends. He had a family member who didn't think too highly of me and eventually convinced him that I was "up to no good" or some silly thing. I will say that I was in no shape to be in an intimate relationship. I had lots to learn about love and myself. But at the time it was devastating. I left him, the house, the friendships, and the family, and "started over." I also dropped out of college and began working on the horse-racing circuit. This started a downward spiral of drinking, sleeping around, and depression.

So in October 1998, I moved to California. I was going to be staying in Redondo Beach with an older cousin whom I had not remembered meeting before. I was determined to start over (again). No drinking, no guys, no partying. I was going to do it! I had to.

My cousin turned out to be *amazing!* Though old enough to be my mother, she provided friendship, inspiration, and support to me. I lived with her and her preteen son. I quickly got a job managing a ranch in the Malibu mountains and found an agent to manage my "budding acting career." I was living the dream! I had maintained my promise to myself: no drinking, no guys, no partying. Considering I was spending about three and a half hours in traffic every day, working full time, and auditioning, who had time for the other stuff?

Over a short amount of time, "real life" eclipsed the "dream life." The only auditions I was called for involved me being half naked, even after I had clearly explained to my agent that I wasn't looking for *that* kind of work. After one particular Cinemax audition, I was fed up. My agent explained, "This is the only way to the top" and "Everyone starts here." I was so angry and discouraged that I yelled, "Then I guess I'll *never* make it!" and slammed down the phone. I never went on another audition in LA.

The commute was killing me, so I found a room for rent in a large house in Malibu. I was paying $750/month back in 1999 for a small room in a six-bedroom house. It seemed a small price to pay to live next door to movie stars and franchise owners!

I went back home to Nebraska for Christmas. I hung out with family and old friends and realized how lonely I was in LA. I saw my ex at a party, and it reopened old wounds. I decided that I would give LA one last try, and if something didn't change, I would move back home.

On my trip, I received a phone call from someone named Steve. He said he was the manager at a hotel in Malibu. He was calling me to set up a job interview. I thought it was strange because I hadn't applied for a job. I had hotel experience but had never even heard of the hotel he mentioned. I listened to the voicemail with some curiosity but quickly forgot about it. When I arrived back in Malibu after Christmas, I felt more depressed than ever. One day, I remembered the strange voicemail and decided to follow up on it. I called and got hold of Steve. He asked me to come in to interview for the front desk manager position. I was already working full time managing a horse ranch, but it wouldn't hurt to do an interview. Besides, addiction runs rampant in my family as a coping mechanism, and my drug of choice was work. I was a workaholic.

Soon, I was working at the ranch from 8am to 4pm, and then the hotel from 5pm to 12am. The more I worked, the less I focused on the loneliness and dissatisfaction with my life. Sometimes, Steve would sit with me in the evenings and we would chat. We didn't get much traffic at the hotel. Even though it was right in the middle of Malibu, directly across from one of the best surf breaks around, it was old and run-down. I came to know that Steve was a Christian. Inevitably, conversations would turn theological, and I would spout off all my "knowledge."

I knew about Christianity. My mother's side of the family were all "Christians." My mom's uncle was a pastor, and at least one of her brothers attended seminary (or intended to). This was much to my father's chagrin. My father is and has always been agnostic. He mocked my mother and her family for their "Christianity." Of course, he was referring to the same things that I had come to witness in my family: self-righteousness and hypocrisy, drug and alcohol abuse, sexual abuse, physical abuse, and much more. To hear my dad tell it, in one moment they would be chasing the televangelist, Jimmy Swaggart, across the country and in the next moment lighting a joint and dropping acid.

I thought I knew Christianity. It was guilt, shame, hiding. It was wearing a nice dress on Sunday and sitting next to the very people you were out smoking, cussing, and drinking with the night before. It was counting each boring minute until you could get out of there and get on to what Sundays were really all about —football and naps. It was living the life you wanted until you had so thoroughly screwed it up and had burned every bridge that the only possible thing left was to turn to Jesus. Then it was rinse and repeat.

The first real metanoia (mind change) experience I had was realizing that everything I knew and deeply believed might be wrong. The debates around religion and spirituality have been raging for centuries, to the point that millions and millions of people have lost their lives over some zealous belief or conviction. Our personal beliefs around God, the Bible, the afterlife, and any other relevant teaching are intrinsically wrapped up in our upbringing. Some people so dogmatically hold to the values and "truths" passed down from the previous generations that they are willing to die for them. Others were so turned off by what their parents taught or believed that they completely turned away from anything that held a vague reminder of those beliefs. Either way, we cannot deny that our upbringing influenced and shaped our beliefs (not only concerning religion, but everything else too).

MY UPBRINGING

My parents did not have easy lives. They both grew up in a tiny town in Kansas, where the population is fewer than 2,000 people. In the year 2000, the median income for a household in the town was $26,857. Raised by a well-respected, "standard" American family, my father lived close to extended family who all had good, stable jobs and took regular vacations. But my quick-tempered and critical grandfather was not an easy man. He was quite bigoted, which was not uncommon in those parts. From what I gather, encouragement and approval were rare, and affection was nonexistent. I witnessed harshness in my relationship with my grandfather but was told that he had softened tremendously over the years. That was hard to imagine as I watched my brother and various cousins get belittled and spanked by him!

My mom's family was another story altogether. Her father (my other grandfather) was a known alcoholic and would disappear for months, leaving my grandmother to raise and support four kids independently. His family and close relations around town were known to be wild and unruly. A common lament around town was, "Those Williams and Timmons kids are making trouble again." My maternal grandfather was one of the worst alcoholics I have seen to this day. He passed away from alcohol-related liver cirrhosis.

My parents went to school together, my dad being a few years ahead. When he returned home from serving in the Vietnam War, he started a relationship with my mother. At 19, she became pregnant (with me), and they married shortly after. Drugs, cigarettes, and alcohol use were common. There are many colorful stories of those early years. One of the stories that I heard over the years from a family friend was about the day my mom went into labor with me. Supposedly, my mom (at nine months pregnant) was riding a horse and smoking a joint when she went into labor. I didn't know it at the time, but this story helped subconsciously fuel a belief that I was never nurtured or cared for growing up (more on that later).

My mom and dad divorced when I was four years old and my brother was two. This precipitated the agonizing experience of being caught in the middle between two unresolved adults. As if it wasn't hard enough to lose the stability of having two parents at home, I also was faced with moving away from extended family. My mom became a single mother who had to work extra hard and long to support two children by herself. What ensued were endless fights about child support and "who got who" for holidays and summers. Divorce is more the rule than the exception these days. With over half of marriages ending in divorce and with the glorified celebrity version of coparenting, this childhood trauma is grossly normalized. It is only within the last few years that I began to understand the impact it had on my childhood and adult life.

As a single parent, my mother was faced with even more guilt, stress, and uncertainty. Given that her coping mechanism was drugs and alcohol, you can imagine the spiral that readily followed. She met my first stepfather when I was five. Though I don't believe she was consciously aware of it at the time, this man fit perfectly the trajectory of pain, abuse, and trauma that my mother was familiar with from her past. Like my mother, he came from a family of addiction and abuse. Though charismatic and gregarious, his mood could turn dark and dangerous quickly. I don't remember when the physical abuse started. Likely, it was very early on. Calls to 911 became commonplace, as were screaming, bruises, broken dishes and furniture; the all-too-familiar background occurrences in an abusive home. Neighborhood BBQs, fueled by laughter and alcohol, would devolve over the course of the evening. My little brother and I huddled in the closet, waiting to see how the chaos would play out and hoping we would all emerge alive the next day.

Without words (that I remember anyway), we instinctively knew that we couldn't talk about it. From the outside, things must have seemed okay. It wasn't until later, when I was around 10, that things took a more sinister turn. One afternoon, while looking for fingernail clippers, I found something on the top of the bathroom cabinet in my mom and stepdad's room. I didn't know what it was at the time, but somehow I perceived that *it* was responsible for some of the more troubling events: increased paranoia, new groups of "friends," the electricity being shut off repeatedly, and running out of propane in the middle of a Colorado winter. The "weekend trips" that they would take sometimes lasted three or four days, leaving my brother and me behind without food or expectation of when they would return. It didn't seem to make sense that a little mirror with a razor blade and strange white dust could be contributing to the problems, but somehow I knew: things were about to get much worse.

I hated my stepfather. I'm sure that, on some level, I also loved him. But I didn't feel it. I felt a fierce need and responsibility to protect my mother and brother. To my recollection, nobody ever gave me that charge, but I took it anyway. I made it my sole purpose in life. I saw my mother in an interesting way, almost like a child herself—more than I was, even. All the anger, hurt, and pain came much later. Though I desperately wanted her to leave my stepfather and the drugs and alcohol, I somehow knew she couldn't. She seemed so lost, and it was somehow my responsibility to "fix" all this for her. Of course, I know now that this is a common phenomenon in the addiction cycle. But back then, as a little girl, I lived for my mother. My stepfather, in my mind, was the problem. My mother was the victim. I don't remember feeling any pain when he would hit me. I vaguely remember thinking, "*If he's hitting me, at least he's not hitting my brother or mother.*" I found peace in that. My mom, of course, denies that my brother and I were ever abused. I know that she probably really believes this. I think she *has* to believe it. The more I have learned about abuse and addiction, the more fascinated I have become with the way our brain chooses to represent these traumas.

Through a course of events that are a bit fuzzy to me, my stepfather ended up in jail and court-ordered rehab. We had to visit the rehab facility for "family" sessions. I hated this. I remember that one of the therapists at the facility did individual sessions with family members. He brought me in to ask me how I was doing. I said I was fine. As he probed a little more, I simply stated that my stepfather was an abusive alcoholic, and my mother was a weak woman who believed she needed him. They were both sick and needed help, but I doubted that either of them would ever take it. I told him that my main job was to keep myself, my brother, and my mom alive and that if they let my stepfather out, that job would be harder. The therapist closed his notebook and looked at me for a minute in silence. He told me that I was a smart girl and then dismissed me. I never had to go back. Of course, they did let my stepfather out. And things did, indeed, get more challenging.

In my sixth-grade year, the school office called me in. I was always a stellar student, so this was odd, and I feared that I was about to receive terrible news. As a child of abuse, you are hypervigilant regarding disaster. It's always around the corner, waiting to take you out. The best you can hope for is to be as prepared as possible. When I arrived at the main office, I was escorted into the principal's office. Along with the principal, a female guidance counselor was there. The counselor asked me if I would please lift up my shirt. I was genuinely puzzled by this request but never questioned someone in authority. As I lifted my shirt, they studied my back and then asked me to lower it. I noticed that neither would look me in the eye after that, but I genuinely could not make out what it was that I had done wrong. The counselor asked me where I had gotten the bruises. "Oh! The bruises!" I felt relieved that I hadn't made some sort of grievous mistake at school, but I had completely forgotten that I had bruises on me. I calmly explained that my stepfather was a drug addict and alcoholic and that he hit us. They asked how long it had been going on, and I said I wasn't sure, but as long as I could remember. I remember feeling vaguely guilty and disappointed. My one job was to protect my mother, and these bruises told the story of my failure. I felt ashamed that they knew. I had tried so hard to keep it all together, but now they knew that I had failed. The facade was up. I felt like they now knew the one thing that I was too afraid to admit: my mother loved him more than she loved me. I could not be good enough, strong enough, or *enough* for her to choose me. I noticed the pity in the school officials' eyes, and I knew. I knew that they saw it too: I could never be worth choosing.

Not long after this, my brother and I were sent to live with my father and his new family. I was miserable. Nobody seemed to understand that my mother was in danger and that I was the only one who could help her. My father's wife wasn't thrilled with our arrival. Did she see my failure too? Did she already know how worthless I was? I made things miserable for everyone. My brother dealt with things in his own way. He was angry, violent, and emotional. I was moody, manipulative, and had venom in my words and my looks. My stepmother was a drug addict as well, though I don't believe she was actively using at the time. She later devolved into the addiction, and my father ended up raising my half-sister on his own. This living situation did not last very long. After I had gotten news that my mother had been hospitalized from being pushed down a flight of stairs, I upped my efforts at making the situation of living with my father and his new family intolerable, so they would have no choice but to send me home. It worked. We were sent back to live with my mother shortly after.

My stepfather was back in jail, and my mom promised that she had left him for good this time. She had a restraining order and had begun dating other men. One evening, after I had gone to sleep, I was awakened by an impossible sound: my stepfather's truck in the driveway. I knew that sound all too well. "It couldn't be!" He was supposed to be in jail. I heard the front door slam open and then the curious sound of kitchen drawers being violently opened and shut. I had gone to sleep in my mother's bed that night. Her room was at the end of the hall, and the door was open. From the hall light, I could see the outline of my stepfather approaching the door. His arm was raised, and with mounting dread, I noticed that he held something in his hand. It was a large kitchen knife. In that moment, everything turned to slow motion. I saw my mom running behind him and screaming, "*No!*" I saw the look on his face and registered somehow that the darkness had complete control over him, and no reason remained. I saw the knife, and I knew. He was there to kill me.

I didn't feel scared, just sure. Sure that I would die, and devastated that I would never get the chance to prove that I was worthy of love. All at once, the slow motion switched to fast-forward. In an instant, he had lifted me off the bed by one arm. He still had the knife raised in one hand, and me hanging from the other. My mom was screaming and clawing at his back, but he seemed 10 feet tall and unaware of her. I was certain the knife would be plunged into me, but he unexpectedly threw me aside into the closet. With fury in his movements, he attacked the waterbed with the knife. I was dazed and couldn't quite get my bearings, when I heard my mom yell, "RUN!!" My feet were in motion before my brain realized what was happening. I ran down the hall and out the front door, heading for the neighbors' house, but blindly ran face-first straight into a tree. Stunned but unfazed, I made it to their front door and was shocked to find that the horrible screams that I was hearing were coming from me. My neighbors—my best friend and her family—were accustomed to my family's drama. But this time was different. Whether it was the blood all over my face, thanks to the massive oak tree that I had just gotten intimate with, or the agonized scream emerging from my very soul, they looked nearly as shocked as I felt. I don't remember much after that. I know that many police vehicles arrived and that my stepfather was nowhere to be found, having taken off when my neighbor went to help. Also missing were my mother and brother. They were later found hiding beneath the horse trailer outside, unharmed. The only victims of this brutal attack were my mother's waterbed and my bloody nose. My stepfather had sliced the bed to shreds, leaving behind a flooded bedroom and long-lasting emotional devastation.

After this, two realizations occurred to me. The first was that nobody could protect us. Even the police, handcuffs, and jail cells had failed to keep my stepfather at bay. The second was that my mother was never going to leave. So I made up my mind. In a last-ditch effort to save her and my brother, I made one of the hardest decisions of my life. I decided to leave. I was 11 years old when I boarded a Greyhound bus to Texas. At the time, it made perfect sense to me. Because my stepfather was never going to leave us alone, *we* had to be the ones to leave. I knew that my mother couldn't. So I decided to show her how. Many years later, nearly 30 years later, I realized what this decision was really about. It was the final test. I was leaving, and the questions remained in my mind: Would she come after me? Would she finally choose me over him? Of course, she didn't. This event would solidify into stone the belief that I was not worthy of love, no matter how much I put my own life on the line for another.

The next two years were very low times for me. I jumped around to many extended family members, traveling to Texas, Louisiana, Virginia, and finally to Nebraska, living with my grandma, my mother's mother. I was depressed and contemplated suicide almost daily. My life's purpose, to protect my mother, hadn't worked out. Even worse, it seemed like she was doing better since I left. Not only did she not need me, but she also didn't seem to want me either. I missed most of my seventh-grade year. Only briefly attending school in Texas, I spent my days writing melancholy poems and tragic diary entries. By the time I arrived in Nebraska to live with my grandma, I was a shell of my former self.

The early days with my grandmother were healing. She introduced me to Patsy Cline and the Bee Gees. We would spend hours sitting over a cassette player belting out "Crazy" and "I Fall to Pieces," with the familiar starts and stops of trying to rewind the tape and find the spot where the song began. We would bake together and make wild plum jam. She would take me to the horse races and taught me how to bet (little did I know that I would work on that same race track many years later). I started eighth grade at the nearby middle school, determined to fit in with the kids who were the same age physically but a lifetime behind me in emotional baggage. In the middle of my eighth-grade year, I received news that my mom and brother were moving to Nebraska. She had finally left my stepfather and was moving away for a new start. Surprisingly, I had mixed feelings about this. I didn't really want her to be back in my life. I could have never articulated it at the time, but I think it was nice to be taken care of for a while. The only responsibility that I had was to go to school and help out around the house. There was always food, electricity, and love. I didn't feel responsible for keeping my grandmother alive or safe. She seemed to already know how to do that herself. Strangely enough, she seemed to want to do that for me! I wasn't sure I wanted that to end.

Soon, as if nothing had ever happened, my mom and brother arrived. It quickly became apparent that things were different. The anger I had stored up for years had no focus now that my stepfather was out of the picture. Shouldn't my mom be able to be "normal" now? Happy? Why did she seem sadder than ever? Now she could love my brother and me and focus on us, right? What was my role? I couldn't very well "mother" her when *her* mother was living under the same roof. I became even more confused and aimless. My grandmother now had two more people to look after. Her attention was divided, and I was lost.

Before long, my mom found a job in a nearby small town called Central City. She rented a house by the train tracks (wrong side, of course). I was set to begin high school, and my mom wanted us to be a family again. So the three of us moved into the little house and started our new life. As with all fresh starts, the beginning was exciting, and the future was ripe with promise. Albert Einstein had a great way to explain this new chapter of our lives' eventual dismal outcome: *"No problem can be solved with the same way of thinking that created it."*

What I didn't know then (a truth that I now hold dear) is that "You can only give what you hold within." We may want desperately to change. We can change our situations, locations, vocations, and even our appearance, but if we do not change what *we hold within us*, we eventually end up back in the same place. Over the years, I have witnessed this time and time again in my own life. The common denominator in all my "problems" is *me*. If I want to change my life, I need to change *myself*. More specifically, I need to change what I think makes "me" me.

Regardless of fresh starts, new jobs, new men, different houses, and various cars, my mom continued what she knew and was good at: avoidance through addiction. Now, without an evil protagonist to blame for all our problems, I started to view my mom as the main culprit. I couldn't shake the self-imposed responsibility I felt for protecting her. But now, instead of mothering her, I "parented" her. I hounded her about her decisions, her whereabouts, her friends. I questioned how the money was spent and "punished" her emotionally when she inevitably screwed up. I shamed her about her lack of job performance, ridiculed her choice of men, and tried (in vain) to keep her on a responsible life schedule.

You can imagine how this all went down! It was a nightmare. She became increasingly sneaky with her behavior, and I became more and more suspicious and resentful. So much happened in those four years before I graduated high school, including a surprise visit by my ex-stepfather on the night of my senior prom. My date (who would become my fiancé years later) couldn't quite comprehend my repulsion and indignation at the appearance of this figure from my past. Seeing him with his arm around my mom, as if he belonged in this picture, asking obligatory "dad" questions of my date, I was speechless. I viewed my mother with a newfound disgust and disrespect that evening. He stayed for a few days, but I stayed away from the house. My brother was spared this injustice. He had been caught selling pot on school property during middle school and had subsequently moved to Kansas to live with my dad.

After graduating from high school, I joined the Army. Another story for another book! Away from my mom, all I could think about was how she was managing. I could always tell, even on the phone, whether she was high or not. She had been hanging out with my aunt more and more (her brother's ex-wife), and they were best friends. I loved my aunt dearly. She was a special person. But she also came from a very troubled upbringing, and the influence they had on each other was toxic. I would talk to my mom, and she would relay her concern to me for my aunt and her three young daughters. My mom would weave stories of reckless behavior, drugs, and men. Talking to my aunt revealed chilling tales of my mother's lifestyle and choices. They were worried about each other; I was worried about them. I was eventually discharged from the Army, early and honorably, and went home to try to take care of my mom and aunt.

Things were worse off than I had realized. I moved back in with my mom to the little farmhouse we had bought outside of town when I was in high school. She rarely stayed at the house and spent most of her time with my aunt. I would spend time with all of them, trying to help take care of my nieces, who were more like daughters to me than anything. I recognized the desperate cycle of guilt, shame, and addiction that both of them were caught in and attempted to reason with them. But they were on the run from facing the rubble of their lives. The responsibility was too great to handle. My mom had not been paying her bills for many months. As I tried to assess the magnitude of the situation, I realized that bill collectors were hounding her. The house was in foreclosure, and she had lost her car and her job. The electricity was shut off, and the cops even showed up at the house one day looking for her. They had found piles of rubbish that had been dumped on a country road. Among the trash items they found numerous personal items and mail that had my mom's name and address. With the refuse collection being cancelled for lack of payment, I now knew what my mom had been doing with the trash. I confronted her about it and, not surprisingly, she denied it. Taking responsibility has never been a skill that I witnessed in my mother. I saw less and less of her. It became clear that she was giving up on everything that she had built.

I was not in a position to save something she didn't seem to want saved, so I moved into my own apartment in the town where I was working, about 30 minutes away from her. I returned to the house about a month later to pick up a few items. The stench was detectable from outside. With the electricity shut off, the food left in the refrigerator and freezer had spoiled. The house smelled of death. Appropriately so, I imagine. This was the first house my mother had ever bought and was supposed to be her new start—a sign of her maturity and capability. All those dreams had died a slow, agonizing death, and the smell of those crushed hopes was devastating. I had begun dating the man who would later be my fiancé, and we decided to get an apartment together. This relationship and its eventual end bring me nearly full circle to where I began chatting with Steve about Christianity and my beliefs.

I mentioned before that at this time in my life, I "knew" Christianity. A more in-depth look into that statement would reveal a more accurate sentiment, which would have been, "I know what I know of Christianity." See, I only had my own experiences to draw from, and with what I had witnessed, I felt strongly that "if those people are Christians, then I don't want to be one." By "those people," I was referring to my family and other people who had helped shape my opinion. To me, Christians were fake, two-faced, self-righteous, judgmental people who used God and the Bible to manipulate others. Maybe you share my former beliefs?

When I was sitting at the hotel during the night shift, I knew I needed something. I knew that something was missing in my life. I felt lost and confused. I had tried so hard to "be good." I tried hard to help others and to do the right things, making different choices in my life. Yet I felt more miserable, lost, and alone than ever. I had moved very far away from all the people I knew and the places I grew up. I made different choices than my parents had, doing everything to show that I was worth loving, yet I felt emptier than ever before. I knew I needed something, but I also knew that I didn't need "Christianity" (or at least what I believed to be Christianity).

Imagine if you were told when you were young that your parents would take you to Disneyland. You had no idea what Disneyland was, so you didn't really know what to expect. Then they packed you in the car and drove you to the dentist's office. From the minute you walked in, you began to build your knowledge base of what "Disneyland" is like. First off, nobody seems to want to be there. The mood is grim as people sit, blankly flipping pages of a magazine. Soon, a door opens, and a little boy emerges with his cheeks stuffed with cotton; dry, cracked lips; and red-rimmed eyes—telltale signs of crying. Hmm... Disneyland is not looking like the "happiest place on earth." Next, sounds emerge from behind the door.

Even as a child, you can identify the apparent sounds of torture! Grinding, buzzing, high-pitched screeches. The little boy who recently emerged is standing, dejected and defeated, next to his mother while she checks out. He cringes when he hears the sounds, clear signs of PTSD-related trauma from what he just endured. You look up at your mother, and she gives you a weak smile and small knee pat that tells you that you are in for something that you are not going to enjoy but have no hope of escaping. Entirely too soon, you hear your name being called. You rise, hesitantly, with one last glimpse toward your mother, hoping for a glorious pardon. You shift your gaze to the little boy, now leaving the office with a "goody bag" of tooth-torture for home use. He looks back at you and shakes his head slowly, signaling without words that "resistance is futile." You take a big gulp and head to your own "Disneyland" experience. You emerge 30 minutes later, dazed and confused, but sure of one thing: I *hate* Disneyland! Of course, I am poking fun (and at the dentist's expense). I am blessed to say that this is *not* the way I feel about the dentist. But the illustration should provide a powerful point. You may be thinking that was a terrible trick played by the parents. But what if it wasn't a trick? What if, for generations, the family had called this Disneyland? What if the mother didn't know any better? What if she just called it what her mother had called it, and *her* mother before her? I know—it's silly to think of in the context I explained, but no less true.

You may have heard the old story of the Sunday pot roast. A mother is preparing a Sunday pot roast meal, and her teenage daughter is watching. The mother preheats the oven, prepares the spices, and washes and pats down the roast. Just before putting it in the pan to cook, she cuts the end of it off. The daughter, curious about this last step, inquires as to why the end is cut off. The mother stops and thinks briefly and then answers, "I'm not sure. It's just the way my mother taught me." Later in the day, the question lingering in her mind, the mother calls her own mother and asks her the same question. Her mom is also perplexed by the question and relays that she has never really thought about it. She, too, learned it from her mother. Later that evening, the teenage girl's great-grandmother is called and asked the same question. Expected to finally solve the mystery, the aged woman exclaims, "I had to cut the end off because my pan wasn't big enough to fit the whole thing!" Though it may be difficult to see how a dentist and a pot roast are analogies for my story, it has helped me better explain what I went through in my first metanoia experience.

So back to Malibu. Steve eventually spoke to me about his experiences with God and the Bible, telling me about his own studies and consequential beliefs. Though I found it intriguing, I still saw it like "Disneyland" from the illustration: something people say is good, but that is actually torture. Steve was patient with my skepticism. He continued to invite me to join them for activities and services, which I always declined or made up excuses. As he shared his convictions and journey to belief, I made a logical decision. What do you do with all people who call themselves Christians? You watch them closely until they inevitably mess up and show their true colors, of course. So I watched. Closely. And I had many opportunities. Steve was very involved with his local congregation, helping to serve in the teen ministry with his girlfriend, Holly. Many of their other friends from the church would often visit the hotel. The teenagers that Steve worked with would also come around, and they would surf and hang out. So I had plenty of people to judge...I mean *observe*. This began to play at the edges of my former belief system. They certainly seemed to live what they claimed to believe, unless it was all a ruse for my benefit (of course, I wasn't suspicious *at all*). But how could they possibly know that I was watching them? Could it be real?

Eventually, after attending a Women's Day event (which they promised me was *not* church), I broke down and cried. It was not typical for me to cry, especially in front of strangers, especially women! But the topic had cut me deeply as it described women searching for worth and love in all the wrong places. I agreed to study the Bible for myself and find out what it really said. This was the beginning of my first crucial metanoia moment. I had spent 23 years up to that point developing a belief about "Christianity," and I was about to find out that I had been wrong. Very, very wrong. Nobody likes to admit they are wrong. A large majority of people will continue in something that they have always done, even if they suspect it could be wrong, just to avoid facing the change (and subsequent responsibility). As I began to read the Bible, I began to see that it did not say most of the things I had heard growing up, at least in the context in which they were written. Scriptures that formerly struck fear, guilt, and shame in me now felt like loving encouragements. I began to see that my previous understanding was immature and uninformed. Though women helped point me in the right direction, using the Bible to teach me about building a foundation with God, I realized that it was up to me to listen to God's word and learn what it was saying to me and about me.

One of the most refreshing studies I did was on the topic of sin. While most people may want to shy away from this thorny topic, I dove right in. I was thrilled to see such black-and-white direction with such clear boundaries. Morality and "right and wrong" had been grossly manipulated and twisted in my childhood. It was oddly comforting to hear that clear lines *had* been drawn, and it sounded like people even figured out how to stay on the "right side" of those lines. Soon after, the group of women helping me make sense of everything studied out the cross of Jesus with me. My main takeaway from this was that "I killed Jesus." Though it sounds a little harsh to my ears now, it resonated strongly with me then. *Yes! Of course, I killed Jesus. Look at all the awful things I've done*. It seems strange to me now that my primary motivation for changing my entire life hinged on the guilt I felt for killing the Son of God. I was 100 percent convinced that I deserved death and that the cross represented my only possible escape. Looking back, I see that my upbringing and view of the world shaped my understanding of this at the time. I was very punitive. Justice and punishment for wrongdoing were high on my moral compass. I used *my* eyes and *my* understanding of the world and projected this on God.

Regardless, I truly believed that my baptism would be a death of the old and birth of the new. I firmly believe that I was not wrong in thinking that, but what needed to "die" was mixed up in my mind and clouded by immaturity. What needed to die was my way of thinking, my past, my coping mechanisms, and my pain. I know now what I didn't then: becoming a Christian meant I needed to unburden myself from the years (and generations) of identities, beliefs, and subsequent actions that I had picked up in my childhood. Christianity wasn't about merely modifying my behaviors. Following Jesus was about figuring out where those behaviors originated and why I was still holding on to them and how they were keeping me "safe." It was about letting go of my earthly hold on reality and grabbing onto our Creator's supernatural love and his vision for me.

But like many, I focused solely on changing my "doing" rather than my "being." I was a bit of a hot mess in the first few years of my Christian journey. I had to learn many things. Though I functioned quite independently as a human and could assume a put-together facade fairly easily, the truth was that I had very few emotional skills to lean on. I carried with me the secret core belief that I was unlovable and somehow needed to earn love, even from God. Thankfully, many women stepped up in my life and patiently stood by me as I fumbled my way through "becoming more Christlike." The problem was, I never really addressed *why* I was doing what I was doing or *why* it seemed so hard for me to trust, feel, or healthily connect with others.

Eventually, I learned enough from the people around me to begin playing the part. I didn't know I was playacting. I thought I was learning to be more like Jesus. Truthfully, I was just adapting to my surroundings so that I could survive, a skill that I had perfected in childhood. The more I fit the mold of the good Christian, the easier life became. It is important to note that this process was a natural one for me. Nobody asked me to settle for behavior modification rather than core change and transformation. I don't think most people knew the difference. I definitely didn't.

A funny thing happened. The more "spiritual" I became, the more my health declined. I share my declining health journey in great detail in my first book, *Mind Change*; therefore, I won't recount all the details here. I will, however, share with you where I ended up. I was living in Northern Virginia, and I was sick. Not with the flu, but with a myriad of rare and "incurable" diseases that were threatening to take my life in relatively short order. I was in debilitating pain. I had lost a large portion of my physical and mental capacity. I was under the almost constant care of a rheumatologist, a cardiologist, an infectious disease doctor, a Lyme disease specialist, and a spinal surgeon. I was on almost 180 pills/ injections/tinctures every day. My body was systematically shutting down. More details later in the book, but suffice it to say, I was dying.

It progressively worsened until I found myself, in December 2012, at home on an IV drip. My liver and kidneys showed signs of failure, and I looked (and felt) like the walking dead.

I had seen every doctor imaginable and tried every treatment possible. After exhausting the limits of Western medicine, I eventually tried a more holistic approach. At times I would see slight improvements in one or two symptoms, but eventually, I always got worse. Many well-intentioned friends gave me advice or offered up personal "cures" or recommendations. I was willing to try anything, but nothing seemed to work.

Throughout the years of my declining health, a few wise and dear friends had mentioned that maybe all my illness could be linked to my past. But I had adopted the common sentiment that "It all made me stronger," "I am who I am today because I made it through," and "Hey, the past is in the past." When I was in the full-time ministry, I was often chosen to speak and share specifically *because* of my illnesses! There were so many other sick and chronically ill people, in and out of the full-time ministry, that I served as a great example of "strength in suffering." In my desperation, I heard every imaginable consolation from well-meaning Christian brothers and sisters:

"God must think you are strong enough to handle all this."
"What a blessing for you to be an inspiration to so many others."
"God must be trying to teach you something."
"Just think of all the people who can relate to you through this."
"Maybe this is your ministry."
"God must be saying no for a good reason."
"God is in control."
"Now you really know how much you need God."

The list goes on. I prayed, begged, and bargained for my healing. But ultimately, I knew the truth. It all came full circle: I wasn't lovable enough or worthy of healing. I hadn't tried hard enough, and I couldn't be good enough. God was saying no, and he must have a good reason. I must not have learned my lesson yet. Interestingly, throughout this time, I never felt anger toward God. Why? Because I deeply believed that I somehow deserved all this. And I also believed the lie that God was "using my illness for his glory." How much glory was there going to be in me dying and leaving my husband widowed and my two little girls without a mommy? This should have been profoundly confusing and concerning for me, but I dutifully accepted that I deserved nothing less…until I didn't anymore.

The rest of these pages will take you on the same journey I took to heal, not just my body, but my mind, and ultimately my spirit. Changing my mind was indeed the "death" that needed to happen. It was the death of old identities, beliefs, legacies, and lies. When I began to address the "how" and "why" behind the things that were driving me, I quickly began to heal. It was miraculous. At the time, I thought it was only my body that needed healing. I now know it was much more. The healing was spiritual, emotional, and physical. Today, the cross of Jesus means so much more to me than it ever has before. My relationship with God has been completely transformed. Jesus makes sense. The freedom that was so appealing to me when I first read John 8:32, Acts 13:39, and Romans 6 and 8 (and more) is finally mine. I can't wait to share more with you.

CHAPTER 3

THE KENT STORY

Heather's story was predominantly about her life transformation when becoming a Christian. She also explained her spiritual transformation *as* a Christian, while overcoming physical maladies. My wife's conversion to Christ, as well as her healing journey, were turning points in her life. My life, however, has been more of a continual un-layering, an evolution of deeper transformation, and I continue to recognize and take off any filters to find truer freedom in Christ. My story (along with yours) doesn't end at one pivotal metanoia moment. Instead, God takes us on a journey of continual change and transformation, should we choose to accept it. He is molding and nudging my heart even as recently as this present moment. Change is like time: it never stops.

My intention in this chapter is to share how my life view has been flipped upside down and sideways on numerous occasions. From a young age, I saw my upbringing as the "perfect" life, and throughout my adolescence and young adulthood, I held onto that belief. Everything that seemed out of whack, I filtered through my perfect-life lens, which saved me a lot of grief and hurt. But it also prevented me from feeling safe enough (on a subconscious level) to deal with and embrace everything that I encountered. This is not always a bad thing. Most of the time, our mind will go to great lengths to keep us safe. The only reason I blocked out anything too traumatic and created some fantasy worldview was to keep on living and moving forward. It was my way of surviving. But I could not and would not become fully authentic until there was nowhere left to run.

It took many years after becoming an adult, getting married, and having kids, before I finally was able to see that life is not all rainbows and butterflies. Once I gave myself permission to feel those raw emotions of anger and disappointment, I was finally able to step into the one-and-only real me. The problem was that I couldn't begin to grasp just how much Jesus loved me. After all, who could love someone who, deep down, could never measure up? And so my life was a journey of seeking validation. Along the way, others would affirm me, but it didn't matter, because I couldn't see my own value. One of my life's goals has always been to love people as Jesus has loved me. But how could I possibly love others like Jesus if I couldn't even stand to look at and love everything about myself?

Part of life's adventure is the transformation process that happens as we learn and overcome. This is the story of my evolution, my transformation. I am ever changing and ever growing. And that is precisely what makes my story a conquest of freedom and victory. Let us begin.

GOLDILOCKS AND THE THREE BEARS

Life was great. I grew up in stable family, in a solid church, with a sister I admired, parents who were there for me, and mentors who helped support me as I became a man. As I said, life was great. We moved around, saw the planet, served the world. We weren't poor, and we weren't spoiled. I went to one of the top 10 public schools in the nation, graduated from prestigious Boston College, and was married to my dream girl directly afterward. My wife and I have raised two beautiful daughters, who have also been able to see the world through the mission work we have done. I served in the ministry for 17 years, closing out my final five years of ministry leading a church in Maui, Hawaii. Currently, my wife and I run and operate our Mind Change® business and see clients in our private practice. My life has truly been the story of The Three Bears, and I was Goldilocks. Everything was "just right."—until it wasn't. The bears had finally found me.

LIFE AS I KNEW IT

So let me start from the beginning. My parents met at the University of Florida, where they both became disciples of Jesus in an emerging group of fiery college students who became bent on preaching the gospel as far as the ends of the earth. After my parents were married, my dad was hired as a campus minister in Columbia, South Carolina, my birthplace. My sister, Summer, was born three years before me, and by the time I rolled around, I was the perfect closing to a family of four. Soon, my dad became the lead minister of the congregation we were a part of, and I was loving life. We had awesome neighbors, friends, and babysitters. As a tow-headed 4-year-old, I rode my Gizmo Big Wheel like I was a man on a mission. I was ready for any adventure that came my way.

Other than a few cuts and scrapes, life was sweet. I was never in need and felt very cared for by my family. And then we moved. We moved around a lot!

We first moved to Tokyo, Japan, leaving behind everything we knew. In general, Japanese culture is quite a contrast from life in the USA. In 1985, relatively few Americans even visited there, let alone lived there. But as kids, we always seemed to find ways to enjoy the present moment no matter what barriers were there. Some people who had only seen blond hair in American movies and magazines would come up to me and rub my platinum blond hair, saying "kawaii," which means cute. I remember every morning rolling up the mats that we slept on in the living room. I remember learning to sit on the floor at a shortened table for meals, in the traditional Japanese eating style. And I absolutely remember going to Disneyland Tokyo, feeling the warm memories of classic American entertainment while in a foreign land.

After time spent in Tokyo, helping to start a church and building roots and ties there, we moved to Needham, Massachusetts for my parents to have more training as future missionaries. We moved twice in that year within the same town, but to me, it was all part of the experience.

Before we headed overseas again, my parents were given a short ministry opportunity in Orlando, Florida. It was summertime, so my sister and I were at the condominium pool most days with the other kids in the community.

About six months later, our family decided that we would "sell everything for the sake of the gospel," and we went on the mission field to Munich, Germany. Wow! Different culture, different food, different mindset of life. We did a lot of fun outings as a family, going to Octoberfest, singing hymns in the square, and inviting people to church. I learned a couple of phrases in those six months, including "Ich liebe dich" (I love you), "Du bist eingeladen" (You are invited—for when we passed out church invites), and "Apfelsaft bitte" (apple juice, please). The food, the gardens, the festivities, the church planting, the mission were all an adventure. We even got to move to four different apartments in just a handful of months. What an excursion we were on!

We finally received our visas to move to Paris, France. *Paris!* The Eiffel tower, the crêpes, the street fairs, the subway system, the old-city feel. I went to a French school and acclimated reasonably well. The church was small, but many people were coming out to hear God's word in what had become an essentially atheistic society. The gospel was being spread, and my family was at the front lines. Paris was extraordinary for sure, and I felt special.

When we moved back to the Boston area, we landed in Lexington, Massachusetts. We lived in a parsonage house that had been owned by the church for decades. Again, we had sold most of our belongings and were starting fresh, starting anew. I could have my own room, my own space, and grow up for 10 years in one place. This was incredible, considering I had lived in four countries, within seven different cities, inhabiting thirteen different houses/apartments, all by the age of eight! In Lexington, my parents were overseeing a large church consisting of several campuses surrounding the city center. It was exciting to see so many different Christians who were all of one mind and spirit, fully giving their lives to Jesus. I met many other kids my age, from different communities, races, and family lifestyles, and would get to be backstage for every event since my dad was running most of them. I interacted with the key players in leadership and the music ministries and participated in nearly everything the churches hosted.

At the age of 12, I went to my first Teen Camp: a one-week overnight camp setting consisting of several lessons each day about the Bible and Jesus. We also had team building, games, and a plethora of activities. I remember one speech given by Wyndham, the father of one of my best friends. That was the tipping point for me to come home and tell my parents that I wanted to study the Bible on a personal level with some mentors and learn to follow Jesus for myself. A few months later, I got baptized, making Jesus the Lord of my life. I didn't know all that would follow, but I knew that I now had my destination set and my map laid before me. I loved this new Christian life, feeling the support of God all the time and strengthened by the church, my peers in the fellowship, and my mentors who loved me. I knew that God and the church would support me no matter what —after all, I had God on my side!

Many victories ensued throughout my teenage years: deep friendships, international service projects, leadership training, rock bands, commercials, modeling and movie sets, girlfriends, and of course, helping others become Christians.

When I moved to NYC for college, I absolutely loved the independence and freedom of being my own man out of the house. I also valued the interdependence of my relationships within the church. That first year, I was an intern in the campus ministry. I met many new friends in my dorm, one of whom became a disciple of Jesus as well. Life continued to take off for me, and the view was amazing. I had best friends and freedom, and I was able to significantly impact those around me.

I moved back to Massachusetts to finish my final two and a half years of university at Boston College. During this time, there was a deconstruction in my church and a lot of uncertainty surfaced. Many of my friends seemed to desert God and the church to which they once were so devoted. My parents, along with my sister and her husband, were all nudged out of the ministry. And although I voluntarily led two small-group Bible discussions on campus and headed up the church's music ministry, I too was forced to let go of those responsibilities after one emotional collision with my campus minister. There were some things that were being taught and expected in my church ministry that I did not agree with, and I finally stood up and communicated my disagreements. What was going on? What was this seemingly major hiccup in my life? Soon, all this disappointment was completely sideswiped by a new discovery in my path as I took a trip across the country.

Within a week of moving to LA that summer, I met my future wife at a church bonfire event on the beach on June 5, 2003. Following my final year of college, we were married on June 5, 2004. That's right! We met and were married within a year. And although we had tough moments, we made it through that year. We married in the mountains of Malibu in an outdoor amphitheater surrounded by wild peacocks and eucalyptus trees. Pretty magical.

Speed up the story a bit. We worked random jobs before entering the ministry a year later in Savannah, GA, working secularly to support ourselves financially. We took full-time ministry positions when Heather was pregnant with our first daughter, moving us back to California. After both our girls were born, we moved to the northern part of Virginia, near Washington DC, to be close to my parents, who had decided to work in the ministry again. We were hired to work in the same church with them, focusing on the youth ministry. During those years, we helped with family ministries throughout the mid-Atlantic and Western European churches until we moved our family to the mission field of South Africa. What an adventure that was! After the mission field, we finally landed at our permanent place of residence—and my favorite place in the whole world—the amazing island of Maui in the Hawaiian Islands. Here, we led the church, and our oldest daughter, Cadence, was baptized, making Jesus the Lord of her life. We seemed to be living the ideal Christian family life.

UNPLUGGING FROM THE MATRIX

I want you to remember back to the beginning of this chapter when I was describing how every moment in life is another layer to discover and uncover. Even before moving to Maui, God had been continuously trying to get me to see the walls I still had and filters I still used. I had changed many things about my life, but was still overlooking some of the deeper-rooted issues. Finally, the three bears found me. Just like in the story, I had finally run out of chairs to sit in, beds to sleep in, or excuses to make. I kept on trying new things, new friendships, new places, new jobs, new houses, new "adventures," only to find that nothing really satisfied me for very long. You see, I wasn't really looking for happiness. I was searching for myself.

My exceptional coping skills ("everything is perfect," "look on the bright side," etc.) had finally caught up to me, and I faced the same choice Morpheus gave Neo in *The Matrix*:

> *"This is your last chance. After this, there is no turning back. You take the blue pill—the story ends, you wake up in your bed and*

believe whatever you want to believe. You take the red pill—you stay in Wonderland, and I show you how deep the rabbit hole goes. Remember: all I'm offering is the truth, nothing more."[8]

I had been in "the matrix," if you will, for way too long. I did not want to realize that something was off, that something was amiss, that something was scratching at my door for a very long time. I had chosen to look the other way for years and years. For too long, I had ignored the voices, the signs, the nudges from the Holy Spirit. I had created a livable, bearable, believable world, "good enough" to continue in this ideal. From the outside, I think most would have thought we had it all together, that my family, marriage, and work were on track as God would have them. And then one day, seemingly out of nowhere, I was faced with the hard truth.

My wife had started her journey of healing and mind work years before me. I was thankful that she was physically well again—better than she'd ever been, in fact. She was happy and continuously becoming the best version of herself. In 2013, something was displaced in me when Heather began to heal from the inside out. She started to see life, health, and happiness—even God—in a completely different light, through new eyes and a different lens. But that meant seeing life, marriage, parenting, ministry, church, and everything else from a different point of view, while I was still living that "perfect" life. Any changes meant deconstructing my entire world. But I also realized that changes would have to occur for this "new" Heather to still fit into my world. So I changed...but not really. I simply learned (as I had most of my life) to modify my behavior in order to be whoever and whatever I needed to be. I buried my real emotions, desires, and fears down even deeper. I didn't realize it then, but I was coping even more than before.

Now don't get me wrong. Throughout my life, I had hit walls in the past. But I always came out on top by perseverance. Unfortunately, most of the growth was driven by fear and shame, instead of trust and confidence; I appeased my guilt by

---

[8] Wachowski, L., and Wachowski, L. *The Matrix.* Warner Bros. Copy, 1999.

asking myself questions of comparison: "*Doesn't everyone have sin to deal with at times? Doesn't everyone hit walls and run into marriage or life issues? Didn't I do enough?*" My excusatory questions did not help.

I continued to defend myself: "*I raised daughters who loved God. I kept my marriage together. I started ministries and trained churches. I brought many friends to Jesus. I facilitated others in the transformation of their traumas and chronic health issues. We traveled the world. We evangelized the nations. We served the people. We lived in Maui, for goodness sake; the most beautiful and special place in the world!*" Yet there was still this looming dis-ease inside. Not a physical disease, but an emotional one (and come to find out, spiritual as well).

No matter where I moved or what behaviors I modified or what I was doing for my career, or how many people I helped, there was still one constant that I couldn't seem to shake: me! It reminds me of Paul's directness in 1 Corinthians 13:2–3: " *If I have the gift of prophecy and can fathom all mysteries and all knowledge, and if I have a faith that can move mountains, but do not have love, I am nothing. If I give all I possess to the poor and give over my body to hardship that I may boast, but do not have love, I gain nothing.*" This scripture then got me thinking of the second greatest command in Matthew 22:39: "*Love your neighbor as yourself.*" How could I possibly love people to the max if I couldn't even stand to look at and love everything about myself? I suppose I was loving people as I loved myself, and it showed up in various little ways throughout my life, but it was rearing its ugly head in my relationship with Heather.

You see, some people are so good at focusing on what's wrong that they become victims of everything in life. Others (like me) are so good at "looking past" the negative issues that they not only avoid the problem, but they bypass the solution and opportunity to change. I was so good at "the positive" and the "well, at least it's not as bad as...," I became so skilled at seeing the bright side of things (needing to be happy all the time) that I was unable to accept anything negative happening around me. I couldn't face the fact that I might have done something unfavorable. Instead, I needed to be "righteous" and "perfect," and that meant I could not look too deeply at anything, because I was riddled with guilt and shame and fear of who I thought I really might be. Trying so desperately to be the person I wanted to be, I missed the opportunity to grow and become all that I could. Rather than deep change and growth, I continued to change as much as I *needed* to in order to feel better or make others happy.

I also created a buffer in my relationships with others to keep myself safe from the hurt and pain of my reality. The pain was too much. I learned that it was safer to stay emotionally neutral (numb) rather than be full of passion or despair at any given moment. I scaled down my emotional limits, which then limited who I could become.

HITTING CRITICAL MASS

The time came when I hit "critical mass." This is a term used by David Schnarch, marriage and sex therapist guru. In the world of physics, it represents the amount of energy necessary to create a self-sustaining reaction. You see, I had been living in a cycle for a long time that would give me just enough energy to deliver what was needed to sustain my "perfect" life. But the truth is that below the surface was a very hurt and self-discarded little boy. Then it happened: my wife let me know that she couldn't "do this" anymore. We had previously spoken many times about the need for change in different areas of our lives and relationship. We even had completed an uncountable amount of marriage courses/trainings/workbooks/therapy. You name it—we tried it. And yes, there were times of improvement and growth in certain ways (most likely behavior modifications). But my wife couldn't stay married to someone who kept holding her (and himself) down in this state of constant emotional gridlock. Schnarch defines critical mass in a marriage as the moment at which pressure and anxiety become so intense that gridlock collides with emotional intensity, stimulating the motivation for change.[9] All this to say that *I was stuck*, and I was holding my wife, and ultimately, the potential for my entire life, captive, chained, restricted, and pressed down.

So what did I do? I fasted, prayed, and spent hours and hours working on myself (using the tools we will later teach in this book). It wasn't about changing

---

[9] Schnarch, David. *Passionate Marriage,* W. W. Norton & Co., New York, 2009

my surroundings, changing my church, changing my accomplishments, changing my direct or indirect circumstances. It wasn't about proving that I was good enough, strong enough, righteous enough. It was never about being who I was "supposed" to be, or who Heather and others wanted me to be. The answer did not lie in modifying my behaviors, formulating better habits, or putting into practice the next best-selling seven steps to...fill in the blank.

The answer lay within. The answer was always within. The power to change, to overcome, to be victorious, was always there, hidden behind the walls of my biggest fear: Kent, exposed. You see, the truest me, the Kent created in God's image, the little baby Kent whose parents held in their arms and saw as perfect, the Kent for whom Jesus laid down his life, the real Kent whom Heather married, the Kent whom God smiled and shined upon every single day—that Kent was always there. But where had he been hiding?

During that crucible of life, I had an enlightening talk with my wife about the "dummy" self I had been living through—an extension of myself through whom I lived, without full authenticity. Completely subconscious and unaware, I hid behind a limited self in order to stay neutral, to stay "safe" from harm's way (relationally, emotionally, spiritually). I had lived this way to protect all that I was. It was too vulnerable to put my authentic self out there, so at some point, I unconsciously created an avatar version of myself. This way, no matter what happened in life, no matter how scary or disappointing or problematic life might become, I could never truly be injured. The problem was, just as Neo (from *The Matrix*) was living his life as full and real as he thought while stuck in the matrix, his true self was in a little body capsule tucked away for safekeeping. He was never really moving, feeling, or connecting with others. In the same way, my emotional muscles were atrophied. For however long, I had not deeply, emotionally, vulnerably connected with my wife (or myself). I was living in my own world that fit into the programs of my mind. Like Neo, I finally decided to stop merely adding new programs and software upgrades into my life—I needed and wanted to unplug from my own matrix. And that was scary! (If you haven't seen *The Matrix*, please put this book down after this chapter and watch the 1999 ahead-of-its-time film—you will thank me later.)

SWALLOWING THE RED PILL

I found the truth, but that can conjure up realities we aren't yet willing to face. Thanks be to God, I was finally ready! I prayed the prayer that I always tell other people is dangerous: Psalm 139:24—"*See if there is any sinful way in me and lead me in the way that lasts forever*" (NLV). You know what happens when you ask God to show you your stuff, and you are ready for it? He brings it to you in surround sound, with a digitally crystal-clear picture. You are then confronted with the choice to either turn face or fully embrace—blue pill or red pill—stay asleep or wake up—live a lie or face the truth.

I went full tilt into this work, going through my life, character, memories, beliefs, and coping skills. Anything that came up in my mind as something that I was not entirely at peace with, I wrote down and used the Metanoia Method to overcome. And it was awesome! I felt like Neo when he was first plugged into the training programs and was learning Kung Fu and every other fighting skill out there. I would go for hours working on myself, seeing my eyes open more and more to who I was, changing my mind, changing myself to who I really am, letting go of my past negative experiences and current realities.

And then it happened. God answered my prayer. As I stepped out on a sea of gratitude, vulnerability, and growth, I reached out to someone from my past. This person had been a part of my life during my formative years, and I felt compelled to reach out after a couple of decades of our lives diverging on different paths. We had no ill departure in our friendship, but we had just each floated our own way as life took us to different places and different interests. Kids grow up, right? As I reached out online to find this person, I sent what I thought to be an encouraging reminiscence of some childhood memories. In my message, I built up this person's character of genuineness and authenticity. I let them know that I hoped one day our paths would cross once again. I did not expect a reply. My intention was to put love and encouragement out into the world where I felt it. It was simply a desire to express my true feelings.

The next day I woke up, and to my surprise, there was a message from this person. I opened it up, excited to hear about how they had lived the second half of their life. Remember that prayer I prayed earlier in the week? Yep—here was another healing opportunity of a lifetime. The words spat back were some of the harshest and most demeaning statements I had ever encountered. They hit fast and they hit hard, especially considering how vulnerably I had put myself out there.

I took the time to work on myself until I felt nothing but compassion for this person—and it took some time. But when I wrote back, I let them know that I understood how much they must be feeling and that if I had ever done anything to hurt them, I was so sorry and that I would be more than happy to listen to anything they needed to possibly work out with me. This person, again, sent another destructive message. I left it at that. I felt hurt, discouraged, confused, repulsed, and uncertain about what all this meant. But I still decided to work on my feelings about all of it and where it might be coming from.

A day later, I shared this with my wife, of course, expecting (or rather hoping) for consolation. My wife did verbalize how she thought that this person must be stuck in some unhealthy thought patterns about people and life, *but* (wait for it...) that she could totally relate to several of the feelings this person had about me. What?! My own wife, turning against me!! Is all really fair in love and war? For that moment, which felt like an eternity, I felt defeat, loss, failure, confusion, and discouragement. Again, I had to remember that prayer I had prayed. I was asking God to reveal *anything* in me that needed to change, and here was another answer.

Remember when I said that I was excellent with my coping skills? I was almost ready to sink right back into them, when something shifted inside me. All that work I had done on myself changed my thought patterns, changed my reactions, changed my go-to "woe-is-me" attitude. All this self-work had changed my "put on a good face and be who I need to be" mentality. How? My mind was finally willing to see the truth. What if something in me needed to change, something about me that needed healing, something surrounding my relationships that could use mending? So I went on to listen.

I listened to my wife's heart—she *was not* against me. She was, is, and always will be *for* me. She was not teaming up on me. She was expressing a thought, a feeling—something that I had learned a long time ago to tuck away. She was being authentic, and the crazy thing was that I was too! I told her all that I felt. But I also told her how I was ready and willing to seek out the truth about myself, about my past, about who I really am. You see, normally, I had taken on the problems others felt or the negative remarks they had as personal hits. Not this time! I was beginning to see people and situations as *feedback*. The feedback itself is not weaponry or danger. It is just feedback. What I *do* with that feedback is what matters. *This* was a healing moment.

I ended that conversation by telling my wife that although healing and growing are not always easy for me, I was thirsty for it because it always—*always*—makes me a better me. I always come out on top when I decide to grow and overcome. I wanted to heal.

Weeks later, I had the first *real* talk I'd had with my sister, Summer, since we were teenagers. We talked about life growing up, things that were great, things that were crazy, and things that were hard. My main objective was to bring realness, gratitude, and connection to the relationship. The secondary objective was to ask her about her version, her view, her perspective of who I was growing up. The conversation was amazing, enlightening, and encouraging. Although the talk lasted for hours, she was able to give me incredible feedback about who I was as a kid. She said that I was very authentic, that I did what I wanted, and that I spoke out against anything I did not like or think was right. She commented on my ability to read into the heart of people or situations but that I wasn't listened to and that my perceived selfishness as a child was simply a way of fighting to be who I was instead of fitting the mold. In my sister's mind, people would sort of shove my ideas or thoughts or opinions to the side because they were not mainstream. So over time, I stopped speaking up, due to increasing repercussions, and my assertiveness diminished over my lifetime. What she saw in me as a kid, as a brother, and as a friend was a sensitive, in touch, genuine (and sometimes stubborn) person who always remained true to who I was and what I felt.

This was not just a time to validate the good in me. It was a time for me to hear about the real me and to connect with and get a better grasp on life growing up. Maybe it was all good because of who it was coming from (although my sister can be brutally honest, so I don't think that was it). I think I was ready to hear feedback and truth without personalization/victimization because I had taken my filters off; I had taken my walls down. And the real me, in the words of my dad, is "*aw-w-we*some!"

I continued my journey of seeking truth and liberty within myself, calling up my old friends to ask for their viewpoints. And you know what? I found out that I had some quirks! But you know what else? I was a kid doing the best I could with what I had. And my learning and growth and change will continue for the rest of my life—and that's a good thing.

LIFE, REVISITED

Let's revisit my life. I was born as a preacher's kid. I was told who I was supposed to be as an imitator of Christ. I didn't always feel free to feel what I wanted to feel. I often needed to put on a good face going to places I didn't feel like going to and doing things I didn't feel like doing. And that caught up to me later, being whoever I needed to be in any given situation, but not necessarily able to be completely vulnerable. But I learned obedience and respect, and I learned the importance of being giving. When I felt grumpy, I learned to keep some of those grumpy feelings inside for a safer time. So I learned to hold many of my feelings in and did not learn how to have healthy anger or raw emotions. I became analytical of everything about myself and was in my own head way too much!

We moved around a lot, which was exciting because my parents made it an adventure. But, yes, it was hard to give up my things and leave my friends so often. I realize that I have not been sensitive enough with my own children, letting them keep what means a lot to them. I have been subconsciously doing to them what felt so hard for me. I now see that giving up special things and special friends with an uncertain next step is scary for kids.

I got used to a life of traveling abroad, and it gave me a sense of pioneering and stepping out in faith that I may not have had otherwise. Moving to places with such different cultures, such different people and languages, although exciting and educational, also left me feeling isolated and misunderstood. I still learned to connect to many people in many different situations, but it wasn't always easy to be the one who would need to make new friends, try new things, and still be full of happiness and gratitude all the time. Part of me felt a complete lack of control over my life, so I tried to find control by overly organizing my things, by being neat and tidy. And this has continued in my parenting. When I feel uncertain about anything in life or what the next steps are, or when I feel a bit out of control or overwhelmed, I notice that I am more controlling of my children: *what* they are doing, *how* they are doing it, and how *quickly* they are doing it. When I speak sharply to them, it is because I am still reliving that fear and uncertainty from my childhood.

Interestingly, the main thing that cut me to the heart when studying the Bible as an adolescent was *not* the love of Christ. It was the guilt of my sin. Yes, I had sinned, but guilt and shame can only produce more guilt and shame. I felt this on the inside while becoming more and more "righteous" in how I lived on the outside. The less sin in my life, the better I felt about myself—which is why I became so defensive, needing to play the victim and the good guy all the time. Even in my marriage, I would find any way possible to be "the good one." This came in the form of judgment, blame, or cutting Heather down just so that I could stay above water. The more my wife grew, changed, and shined, the more my issues showed up. Why? Because if I was not "the good one," then what I felt deep down about myself (how terrible and sinful and shameful I am) must be true. And that was too much for me to bear. So I would try to take her down and come out on top just so that I didn't have to experience those feelings. This is *not* what God says when he talks about metanoia. It's not a behavior change while continuing to feel wretched on the inside. True repentance is a *mind change*, which starts from within. It's a complete shift away from the way of thinking that I once had. Instead of doing the right thing or else I would feel even lousier about myself, I had to learn to love God because he first loved me (1 John 3).

As I look at the formative years of my Christian life, I realize the atmosphere of pressure I was under. With good intentions, many of the people in my life who were mentoring me had created a dynamic that caused me to perform in certain ways and be who or what I was "supposed to be." I was in an environment that compounded my own sense of fear, shame, and guilt. As a teenager in small-group church settings, I would become terrified when talking about any aspect of my life where I recognized needed growth and change. Crazy, right? The environment that I was in contributed to my inability to accept myself. Why? Jesus had saved me—what was I to fear? People's reactions. I had been getting subtle (and sometimes not-so-subtle) reactions to my behavior all my life. I froze in most circumstances in order to be "who I needed to be," because if I was not who they wanted me to be, there *would be* repercussions. And if it was anything having to do with impurity—forget it! If you faltered in any way by even confessing your attraction to a girl, it was as if you had already had sex with her! I remember a teen minister telling us that even getting erections meant that we were in sin. Seriously? All men get at least three to five per night, and now you are talking about teenage boys with pulsing hormones. But I internalized much of what I heard and perceived. So I got really good at shutting that sexual part of me down. If anything aroused me, I ran the other direction, I stopped it on a dime, I went somewhere else, somewhere "pure" in my mind. And I became an expert at it. So when I got married, I was one of the "purest" men I knew—yet that's when all my sexual dysfunctions surfaced. I was full of judgment against myself, against my wife, against sex (mostly subconsciously)—no wonder I had so much performance anxiety! It took years of therapy to even get to the point of admitting there was a problem. When I started dealing with my subconscious programming, I could begin to clear these massive issues and twisted core beliefs from my life.

What I want to convey more than anything else is that I had filtered so much of my life through an idealistic, nonconfrontational, "everything-is-great" lens for so long that I held myself captive in fear and shame. And instead of moving through the normal aspects of grief, sadness, anger, hurt, and disappointment, I coped by living in a fantasy world and presenting a version of myself that was not fully authentic. When I finally discovered the tools, the ability, and the safety within myself, I could finally accept the aspects of my life that were difficult and disempowering. The power was back in my court.

THE CONCLUSION OF THE MATTER

My whole life was amazing! "What? I thought you just revealed that much of it was a farce, a matrix, a dummy-self trying to survive." Well, yeah, you could look at it like that. Or you can see it through the eyes of a victor. Jesus knew what he was here to do, and he knew the only way was to see through his Father's eyes: "*For the joy set before him, he endured the cross, scorning its shame*" (Hebrews 12:2). You see, the cross, the blood, the torture, and what happened to him was not what he focused on. Jesus had his heart, mind, and eyes set on all that he had done. He remembered all those he had helped while on earth and all who would come to him because of his life, death, and resurrection. Jesus did not pretend that bad things had not happened to him. I believe his clarity of being the Son of God drove him to be his true and perfect self. He was *not* a victim. He was always the *victor*. He felt it. He knew it. He saw it. And he listened to the voice of truth.

So how does God commission us? "*Let us throw off everything that hinders and the sin that so easily entangles. And let us run with perseverance the race marked out for us, fixing our eyes on Jesus, the pioneer, and perfecter of faith*" (Hebrews 12:1-2). We *can* throw off everything that hinders and *run* (with joy) the race marked out for us.

My life was, is, and always will be amazing! Here I am today, changed, because God has given me the opportunity to take the scales off my eyes and see my past through his eyes. Thank you, God, and thank you, past! Every day onward is another opportunity to get up and keep moving forward. I now see (and continue to work on seeing) everything that comes into my life through God's eyes, through his perspective.

God has already won the war, and every battle belongs to him. If he is the victor, so am I. If he is the conqueror, so am I. If he is the creator of life, true life, life to the full, then I can create that full life I want to live in him. If he is the Great I AM, then that must mean I am pretty great too.

For this son of mine was dead and is alive again… So they began to celebrate.

Luke 15:24

CHAPTER 4

IS THIS THE WAY IT'S SUPPOSED TO BE?

People assume a lot in life—more than anyone can account for or even realize on a day-to-day basis. Some call this faith, while others may call it naïveté. I call it normal. We assume that when we eat our food, we will no longer be hungry. We have faith that the car will indeed come to a halt when we hit the brakes. We assume going to marriage retreats, reading books to enhance our understanding of one another, and spending the time to talk and enjoy life together will inevitably lead to a healthy, stable relationship. We believe that if we teach our kids about God, bring them to church, and set a good example, it follows that they will become disciples of Jesus too. Work hard; get rewarded. Love others, and they will love you in return. If I follow God, then life will work out the way it should. Is this the way it's supposed to be? These and many more are all assumptions, beliefs, values. Call it faith, call it naïveté—call it whatever you want. But one thing I will tell you that every reader will agree with: life doesn't always turn out "the way it's supposed to be."

We typically do one of two things with that fact. Some of us withdraw from God, from people, from a happy life. We may become distant, nostalgic, escapists, bitter. Others of us stuff it all down: the disappointment, frustration, anger, confusion, uncertainty, shame, guilt, blame, passion, and even love. We keep all of it tucked away inside while we live in a fantasy life that is never quite real, where we are never quite able to be fully present.

When it finally sets in that life is *not* supposed to be this way, but it still is, we face this dilemma: we live distanced from the world or distanced from ourselves. Either way, it creates in us disappointment. And we feel stuck—but since we already have found God, there is no place left to go. So we go on living, but not really.

So what happened to that promise that Jesus gave us? "*I have come that they may have life, and have it to the full*" (John 10:10). Those who are stuck in that dilemma may resonate more with the first part of that verse: "*The thief comes only to steal and kill and destroy.*" We look back at our lives, trying to make sense of it all. Yet we continue to ask ourselves the same question: "Is this the way it's supposed to be?"

I want to remind us that our perceptions of ourselves, others, and God will majorly influence our lives' outcome. We can have the same Bible, a similar upbringing, a similar "church experience," and still, the outcome will differ significantly depending on how we perceive life. This is why one sibling is a doctor, and the other is incarcerated. Our perceptions become so familiar that they become our norm.

THE STORY OF FRANK

It's amazing what someone can get used to. Frank was a client who came to see me. His main complaint was that his marriage was in danger of divorce, and his children seemed to "hate" him. Frank was miserable. He was also a Christian. In the beginning, Frank was reluctant to attribute any of his current circumstances to his past experiences. When asked about his childhood, he claimed that he had a "pretty normal" childhood, but his mother had been a little strict with him. His father wasn't around much but had provided for the family. He didn't feel particularly close to his grown siblings, but there wasn't any conflict either. Throughout our sessions, I realized that Frank's childhood was anything but normal. After some initial groundwork around safety and self-love, we could access some of the more buried (or avoided) experiences from his childhood.

Frank's mother was not "strict." She was incredibly abusive, both emotionally and physically. His mother, Marie, had grown up as an only child to mostly absent parents. Her mother never wanted to be a mother and had resented Marie being born. Numerous revolving nannies had raised Marie. At age 10, her mother ran away with another man, leaving Marie and her father alone. Marie's father blamed Marie for the abandonment. Though she was devastated by her mother's desertion, she was even more troubled by her father's blame. While still young, Marie tried to win her father's affection in every way possible, to no avail. As she became a teenager, she searched for approval from other men, eventually running away herself to marry Jerry, Frank's father. At first, Jerry seemed very different from Marie's father. Wild, carefree, and attentive, Jerry was the first man to give Marie this amount of attention. It made her feel alive, and she craved even more of his time.

Eventually, Marie got pregnant. She was not thrilled at the prospect of being a mother. She did not want to have to care for a child. Jerry seemed to be giving her less and less affection, claiming she was smothering him. Jerry felt the need to settle down after learning about Marie's pregnancy, so he got a "real job" selling insurance in the family business. After Frank was born, Jerry was dismayed by Marie's lack of interest in the baby. He pulled further and further away from Marie, diving more deeply into his work, which left little time for Marie and the baby. Marie was devastated. The old wound of her mother's physical abandonment and her father's emotional abandonment was opened wide. Frank became the focus of all her anger and resentment. She believed that "all men do is hurt women and leave them," and she wasn't about to raise another "woman-hater." So Marie attempted to dominate Frank at every opportunity. She put him down verbally, and physically abused him frequently. Jerry, as Frank's father, was dismayed by how Marie treated Frank but secretly felt grateful that her ire wasn't directed at him now. Because of his guilt and shame for feeling this way, he further distanced himself from Frank and rarely engaged in a meaningful way.

Frank, of course, internalized all this as a child. Having no awareness or ability to attribute his mother's behavior to her own shaded past, Frank received the only messages that he could: "I am bad"; "Men are bad"; "I am unworthy of love"; "I am the cause of great distress in my relationships." Though many young men in similar situations become angry and more aggressive to retain a sense of control or to finally "get the upper hand," Frank subconsciously chose a different route. He just tried harder. Frank tried to be good and tried desperately to win his mother's approval and his father's attention. One positive side effect of this coping mechanism was that Frank seemed to excel in everything he did. But even his success would turn to eventual failure. Every time he accomplished something worthwhile, hoping to gain his mother's attention, Marie would belittle Frank and point out all the ways he was a disappointment. When Frank became homecoming king of his senior class, Marie said that the school must have been honoring him because they felt sorry for him being such a failure in high school. Devastated, Frank chose not to attend the ceremonies that evening. This decision left the school and many of Frank's friends disappointed. Marie reveled in this development, using it to further "prove" her point.

Frank left for college as soon as he was able. For the first time in his life, he gained some perspective about the way others saw him. He was quite exceptionally talented and devoted to anything he set his mind to, and his professors and fellow students came to see him as a leader in his community. His contact with his parents became less and less until it was a rare occurrence. Eventually, Frank became involved in his campus Christian community. Religion was always something his mother had scoffed at and ridiculed. With some emotional and physical distance from her toxic dialogue, he found himself very drawn to the Christian message, at times feeling secretly self-satisfied to be involved in something his mother would find intolerable. After studying the Bible, Frank became enamored with the idea of Jesus, thinking that he was worthy of love. He had never felt worthy, and the stories about salvation through Jesus were very appealing. Eventually, Frank became a Christian. At first, he was elated. He finally felt free. He quickly moved into leadership roles due to his dedication and focus. He always exceeded the number of people he was called to "witness" to, gave more money during special offering collections than was asked for, and was the first to arrive and last to leave any church event. He thrived in the attention and approval he experienced.

Within a year, he met Linda, a beautiful and spunky new convert. They were a great team. Both seemed to have a strong motivation and drive to spread the gospel, and everyone around them thought it was a match made in heaven. In the early years of marriage, Frank reveled in the attention and devotion that Linda provided him. He had graduated with honors, led a campus Bible devotion, and was on track to becoming a lawyer with a great firm. Linda soon became pregnant, and though Frank was excited, he was inexplicably filled with concern and dread. Linda noticed his change of behavior and attempted to have conversations about it. Frank perceived these conversations as personal attacks on his performance, and he reacted strongly to Linda, lashing out at her lack of support and belief in him. Linda was perplexed.

Very soon, Frank began having trouble with a coworker at the firm. He was convinced that this coworker was trying to sway the firm's partners that Frank wasn't pulling his weight. Not long after the birth of his first daughter, Frank lost his job. Linda was concerned but had her hands full with the new baby. Whenever she tried to broach the subject with Frank, he would become sullen and pull away. He finally got another job at a smaller, less high-profile firm. The money was much less, but Frank seemed to be returning to his "normal self." He quickly rose through the ranks and was up for a promotion when Linda became pregnant with their second daughter. Again, Frank became increasingly distant, pulling away from Linda and their first daughter. When the second daughter was born, Frank ashamedly thought, "*Oh, great! I'm going to be surrounded by women.*" He also quit his job at the second firm, stating that the partners did not believe in him. Frank became convinced that being a lawyer was not for him. He was drawn back to the "family insurance business" with Jerry, his father. Once again, he was pulled back into the family relationships from which he had previously disengaged. Now back in his life, Frank's mother made sure to communicate her disapproval and disdain for every aspect of his life.

As the girls grew, Frank found that he did enjoy spending time with them and buying them gifts. When it came time for discipline, however, he defaulted to Linda, leaving it all up to her. Frank never wanted his daughters to be unhappy with him or to associate him with punishment. He began conspiring against Linda to provide the girls with treats and gifts. He even relaxed punishments whenever they were disciplined. Linda, exasperated, tried over and over to talk with Frank about this issue. He wouldn't hear of it. More and more, he accused Linda of not supporting him or loving him. In the meantime, mother-in-law Marie had taken to spending time with Linda in an effort to "bond." Marie would regale Linda with stories of Frank's "failures" and "misgivings" throughout childhood. Marie also spoiled Frank's children with gifts and luxuries of which Frank and Linda disapproved.

Frank hated the insurance business and sales in general. His father was distant and gave little or no feedback concerning Frank's work, aside from the occasional comment about a lack of sales and productivity. These were never aimed directly at Frank but were clear in their target. Frank continued to serve in the local congregation and was made a deacon. At church, Frank would morph into a completely different person. Full of life and energy, willing to take on any role or project, he was viewed as a "spiritual pillar" in their fellowship. At home and work, it was a different story altogether. Frank rarely engaged in meaningful dialogue with Linda, and he was becoming increasingly distant from his daughters. He began to believe that Linda, Marie, and his daughters frequently talked about him. Frank was sure that Marie had poisoned them all against him. At this time, an old college friend reached out to Frank to offer him an incredible partnership in an up-and-coming firm in another city. It was the chance of a lifetime, and Linda was hopeful that this would be the change of pace they needed.

Frank's college buddy arranged for Frank to fly in for a personal interview with the firm. The night before Frank flew out, he decided to go out to a bar with some clients from his insurance sales. Frank rarely drank outside of the occasional social gathering. But that night, he got very drunk and refused any offers to be driven home. On the way home, he was pulled over by a highway patrolman and charged with a DUI. He spent the night in jail and missed his flight for the interview. Too ashamed to face his college buddy, Frank didn't even call. He altogether avoided any further attempts at contact, and eventually, the friend stopped calling. Linda began to talk about divorce, his daughters had little respect for him, and his parents both seemed strangely satisfied by the events.

Frank found himself feeling lost and hopeless. He wasn't sleeping. Plagued with anxiety, he considered taking his own life. "*It wasn't supposed to be this way!*" Frank thought desperately. He was a Christian; he was supposed to be free and live a fruitful life. Somehow, Frank ended up right back where he started, or worse. Finally, he decided to open up with a few of his friends from church. One friend told him that he needed to pray more and get into one of the spiritual recovery groups their church was offering. Another told Frank that he seemed depressed and should probably see a doctor for some antidepressants. Another friend told him to call me. Frank tried both other options before finally reaching out to me for help through private sessions.

I wish this story were an isolated or infrequent occurrence in my practice. It is not. It is all too common. Later in this book, we will explain precisely how Frank ended up where he did. Thankfully, Frank's life is on a completely different trajectory now. His marriage is better than ever. He is more connected to his children, to his friends, and to God. He had to do a good deal of healing and changing, but it was worth it, if you ask him. Frank had to create some firm boundaries with his family of origin, but he strongly feels and knows that this is an act of love for both sides. At last report, even his relationship with his mother is improving!

SAVED FROM THE WORLD, LOST IN THE CHURCH

I heard the phrase, "saved from the world, lost in the church," from my good friend, Paolo. He couldn't remember where he had heard it, but the sentiment instantly resonated with me. One of the main attractions of a relationship with Jesus is his power to forgive us. We all want forgiveness, which means we all recognize our inability to "do it on our own" to some degree or another. We heard the stories of Jesus Christ and his ability to heal, forgive, and transform. For many of us, we begin seeing a delineation between *before* and *after* in our journey with Jesus. The *before* is described by many as "the world," and the after, "the kingdom."

Let's break down these words so that we can all be on the same page. "Kingdom" is from the Greek word βασιλεία, which is translated as *basileia*, meaning sovereign kingdom. Jesus employed the phrase "kingdom of God" or "kingdom of heaven" to indicate that perfect order of things which he was about to establish. The kingdom would encompass all those of every nation who should believe in him; they were to be gathered into one society, dedicated and intimately united to God, and made partakers of eternal salvation.[10] The kingdom of God in its totality includes everyone and everything belonging to God: our "fathers" of the faith, heaven in all its splendor, and of course the church. According to Acts 2, the kingdom is now unlocked, since the day of Pentecost when the church began. The church is the body of Christ, those who believe and have made Jesus the Lord of their lives by choosing to accept his grace through faith and in so doing, repented and were baptized for the forgiveness of sins (Colossians 1:18; John 3:16; Romans 10:9; Ephesians 2:8; Acts 2:38; James 2:17).

The church is supposed to be a place of comfort, goodness, safety, love, forgiveness, empowerment, healing, joy, peace, and many other good things. The church, the kingdom of heaven on earth, was created to be a safe haven from the world. And even though the kingdom is made up of people who sin, it is made up of people who are also continually growing and repenting to become the likeness of Christ (2 Corinthians 3:18; Ephesians 4:11–13). A taste of heaven on earth.

The "world"—κόσμος—is transliterated as *kosmos*, and the word is used in a variety of ways:

1. The *world* can refer (in a positive light) to this amazing earth that God has created for us, who are made in his image (John 1:9–10; Acts 17:24). It can also refer to the realm where one exists (John 8:23, 9:5).
2. The *world* can refer to the people who occupy the world we live in (John 3:16–17; 2 Corinthians 5:19). The love of God is unconditionally directed toward them, but the world's response to this kind of agape love is diverse (John 7:7, 12:47–50; Acts 2:41).
3. The *world* is used to represent an oppositional mindset of someone who characteristically dismisses or disregards God, Jesus, and the Word. This *kosmos* refers to those who oppose the One true God. The usage is commonly found throughout the New Testament in phrases to describe the world's character and mode of thinking; the obstacles to God's cause (John 15:19,

---

[10] Nordell, Philip Augustus. *Preparations for Christianity,* Volume 1, p232, Scribner Pub. 1910.

17:14; 1 Corinthians, 1:27, 2:12, 6:2; James 4:4; 1 John 4:5). This take on the word defines the world under the power or rule of Satan himself as the prince of this world (John 12:31, 14:30, 16:11). Therefore, anyone "of the world" is in essence under Satan's rule and in opposition to God (1 John 4:4–5, 5:18–19).

G.B. Winer puts it this way: the *kosmos*, according to the Bible, is "the ungodly multitude; the whole mass of men alienated from God, and therefore hostile to the cause of Christ."[11] This is an excellent way for us to understand what Jesus is talking about when he references the disciples being in the world but not *of* the world. Before the crucifixion, in the garden of Gethsemane, Jesus declares to God in prayer that "*[my disciples] are not of the world, even as I am not of it*" (John 17:16).

Now that we have a fuller biblical understanding of the kingdom and the world, we can better understand how people fit into one of these two categories, just like the sheep and the goats (Matthew 25:33). Those in the kingdom (*basileia*) are in God's realm, his one church, the fullness of his grace and salvation, choosing to be in full submission to him through a life of repentance and transformation. Those in the world (*kosmos*) are under the rule of the prince of darkness and are opposed to the Word and resistant to Christ's mindset.

As young students of Jesus (new Christians), we quickly and simply categorize these two sides: the world and the kingdom. The world is *bad*. The kingdom is *good*. The world is where sin is rampant and evil prevails. People hurt each other and are enslaved by every kind of iniquity. The kingdom is where people are changed, forgiven, a light to the world. The kingdom is full of love and hope. Did you have a similar view at the beginning of your journey? Was that just naïve and immature? Why would we think such a thing?

Let's consider some passages that support this paradigm.

---

[11] Winer, G. B. *A Treatise on the Grammar of New Testament Greek,* p26, Wipf & Stock Pub; 3rd edition, 1997.

It is for freedom that Christ has set us free.

Galatians 5:1

The answer is right there. Christ did not come to chain us up in his discipleship as a prison. He came to set us free! Before we surrender to his will, we think we are free, but really, we are a slave to sin, to the prince of this world (John 8:34; Romans 6:6–16). But when we claim our allegiance to Jesus, we, at the same time, choose to let him set us free (Romans 6:17–22).

Come to Me, all you who are weary and burdened, and I will give you rest.

Matthew 11:28

The word "rest" in the phrase "I will give you rest" is ἀναπαύω (*anapauó*). A clearer and more appropriate translation would be "I will *refresh* you." This further translates as giving new strength or energy; to reinvigorate, revitalize, revive, restore, fortify, enliven, rejuvenate, regenerate, renew, and breathe new life into. Isn't this exactly what God promises when he gives us his Spirit?

Continuing in Matthew 11, Jesus says, "*Take my yoke upon you and learn from me, for I am gentle and humble in heart, and you will find* ***rest*** *for your* ***souls****. For my yoke is easy, and my burden is light*" (Matthew 11:29–30, emphasis added). The word for rest in this context is different. It comes from the Greek word ἀνάπαυσις (*anapausis*), meaning to re-create. Jesus himself wants to re-create us from the inside out, not by the actions we take, but by letting him do what he does best: transform. And what does he want to transform, to re-create? Our s*oul*, which comes from the word ψυχή (*psuché*), which, in this passage, translates as the seat of feelings, desires, and affections.

Let's revisit Matthew 11:29–30 in its totality: "*Come to me, all you who are weary and burdened, and I will give you rest. Take my yoke upon you and learn from me, for I am gentle and humble in heart, and you will find rest for your souls. For my yoke is easy, and my burden is light.*"

Allow me to rephrase this with our new understanding: "*Come to me, and I will refresh you by giving you new strength, breathing true life into you, and making you fresh and new again. Follow me, and I will re-create your inmost feelings, desires, and affections from the inside out. You will be a new creation, and, just like me, nothing will weigh you down.*"

This scripture and many others tell a story of who we are, who God created us to be, and how we can be renewed, re-created, and redeemed into a life that is full and true and victorious. The questions remain: Do you believe these scriptures? Does your life reveal these passages to be trustworthy? Do you live these truths?

> *In all these things we are more than conquerors through him who loved us.*
>
> **Romans 8:37**

> *You are the light of the world.*
>
> **Matthew 5:14**

> *I pray that you may enjoy good health and that all may go well with you, even as your soul is getting along well.*
>
> **3 John 1:2**

These and many more scriptures show us what God's original intent for us is. Yet it is easy to get tripped up on life and God, considering this is often *not* what we have experienced.

At the beginning of the chapter, I said that you might feel a stronger pull toward the first part of John 10:10, that "*the thief comes only to steal and kill and destroy.*" That is often how we feel, even as Christians. How can all these scriptures above be true if what we feel is worn down, beaten down, shut down, and locked down? Something must have been missed, because when I read the Bible, I read something totally different from what many of us experience as Christians. Is this really the way it's supposed to be?

> *A thief has only one thing in mind—he wants to steal, slaughter, and destroy. But I have come to give you everything in abundance, more than you expect—life in its fullness until you overflow!*
>
> **John 10:10** TPT

Yes! That is what I want! That is what I hear Jesus offer. That is what I am after. I'm guessing you are familiar with all the passages you have read on these pages and maybe even remember being drawn to these promises. How are you feeling about them at this moment in your life? Are they still true? For you? For your fellowship?

In my 15-plus years of full-time ministry work, I began to see a trend that I could no longer ignore. I met more and more *good* people, *saved* people, whose lives looked no different from the world's (those who have an oppositional mindset toward God). They seemed trapped, ensnared, helpless, paralyzed by fear and anxiety; depressed and suicidal; or hopelessly engulfed in addiction to drugs, alcohol, sex, pornography, or food. I noticed more and more homosexual and transgender individuals who felt like they were living a lie, and countless individuals nearly incapacitated by chronic pain or illness. These people had been baptized, they prayed and read their Bible, participated in their church fellowship, and by all accounts, were part of the kingdom.

What could I say? Most of these people wanted help. They had earnestly tried everything. They prayed and fasted, did "good deeds," and tried hard to repent in whatever ways they knew how. Yet some were worse off in the kingdom than they had been in the world. Do you know what that does to someone's faith? It was easy to label these people as "sinful" or to call them to "have more faith." Sometimes the behavior would change for a while, but many would eventually circle back to the same place. The result? These individuals would just feel more miserable. They had been attracted to the forgiveness, the freedom, the redemption in Christ Jesus. Yet they now felt even worse than before. Not only were they rejected by the world, but they also seemed to be rejected by God as well. Blaming them or calling for repentance only seemed to create shame and more pain.

To make sense of all this, we turn to platitudes like, "The church is for sinners" or "This is just my 'thorn'" or "Nobody can be perfect" or "God won't give you more than you can handle." Another option seems to be that people just need to be loved and accepted for their conditions. We develop support groups and specialized ministries for these various issues. An enormous amount of resources support people in their addiction, anxiety, stress, anger, and grief. Sometimes it results in lasting change, but for the majority, it doesn't. So are we to accept that, for a large percentage of the people who come to faith in Jesus, they will never experience the freedom, joy, rest, and fullness that seems to be offered to others? Doesn't that idea negate every scripture I just mentioned above? If God does not lie, if Jesus came full of truth, and if the Bible does not contradict itself, then what is the real problem? To address this, we need to go back to the beginning.

CHAPTER 5

OUR CREATION STORY

All believers receive the power to become children of God, to be transformed and restored to our true nature, people created in the image of God.

— Charles Colson

God created us for this; to live our lives in a way that makes him look more like the greatness and the beauty and the infinite worth that he really is. This is what it means to be created in the image of God.

— John Piper

BACK TO THE BEGINNING:

Many years ago, I had a conversation with a friend. Sadly, I didn't feel equipped to confront the misconceptions I am now aware of. But I believe it is a fair example of our misunderstandings and all-too-common beliefs around God and his creation.

"I'm being punished," Lacy said.

"Really?" I replied, shocked. "What for?" I was speaking to Lacy about her battle with infertility.

"Because of my past. I was really promiscuous before I was a Christian. I'm pretty certain I am being punished by God for it now."

Perplexed, I pushed on. "But what about forgiveness?" I asked.

"Yes, I know I've been forgiven," Lacy replied, "but I still haven't learned my lesson, so I know that God is trying to teach me something through this. I don't think I have ever felt as badly about it as I needed to. I mean, what would happen if I had children and then cheated on my husband?" Lacy explained.

"Why on earth would you think that could happen?" I responded, "Have you cheated?"

"No!" Lacy defended, "But I might. What would the kids think of me? I know what it's like to grow up with infidelity in the home. It's awful. I would never wish that upon my children."

Confused, I attempted to clarify. "Lacy, have you been tempted to cheat? Are you struggling in some way?"

"No, but I know my nature. I was just created that way. I have always been unreliable and unable to stay faithful. I tried, but it's just something I need to realize that I will always have to battle."

At a loss, I continued to encourage her with scriptures that I felt were contrary to this conclusion. But it was clear to me that Lacy wouldn't be swayed. Though she said she believed in the Bible and the forgiveness of sins through Jesus, Lacy couldn't shake her "truth" that she required further consequences and that her "nature" was the culprit.

VERY GOOD

We are probably all familiar with the "creation story" in Genesis. Adam and Eve, the garden, the fruit, and the eventual fall of humankind. Whether you approach this with a literal perspective or a broader poetic mindset, it's hard to miss the overall gist: God created humankind, in his image, for the purpose of a relationship.

When God created our universe, our world, he concluded each aspect of creation by affirming that it was "good." Let's read the beginning of the account.

> *In the beginning God created the heavens and the earth. Now the earth was formless and empty, darkness was over the surface of the deep, and the Spirit of God was hovering over the waters. And God said, "Let there be light," and there was light. God saw that the light was good, and he separated the light from the darkness.*
>
> **Genesis 1:1–4**

As you continue reading Genesis 1 on your own, notice God's way of thinking. He sees a need and fills it. God is the creator of all things good, satisfying, perfect.

Everything he created, he called good. This Hebrew phrase that continues to repeat itself throughout this chapter is וזה היה טוב, which is translated "and it was good." Specifically, the word "good" is translated from *tobh*, and as in most Hebraic and Greek words in the Bible, there is much more to the context than what we filter and understand in modern-day English.

If you were to look at the five facets in which the word *tobh* can be used (practical, abstract, quality, moral, and technical), you would understand a bit more about all that God created.[12] But without digressing into a theological dissertation on this one word, I will sum up its context. When you combine the five facets of use for the word *tobh*, you will recognize the more profound feeling that God had behind each aspect of his creation. God saw all that he had made, and it was good, it was perfect, just as he intended it to be. Every detail was divinely approved. Let's continue:

> *Then God said, "Let us make mankind in our image, in our likeness, so that they may rule over the fish in the sea and the birds in the sky, over the livestock and all the wild animals, and over all the creatures that move along the ground." So God created mankind in his own image, in the image of God he created them; male and female he created them.*
>
> **Genesis 1:26–27**

A few things stick out to me in this story, The first of which is the "in our image" part. What does that mean to you? I'm sure you understand that this isn't referring to appearances. But no matter how you read this passage, God made us to be like him.

---

12 Harris, R. Laird, Gleason L. Archer, and Bruce K. Waltke. *Theological Wordbook of the Old Testament.* Chicago: Moody Press, 1980.

In Genesis 1:31 (CEB), it states: *"God saw everything he had made: it was supremely good."* However you decide to define and examine the creation story theologically, we know that after God had created everything else, he creates us, and *we* are the only creation made in his image, his likeness, his fullness; and he called us *very good, supremely good.* Humans were created profoundly perfect, just as God intended his creation to be. We are, after all, to reflect the image of the author of perfection!

So we have a purposeful, intentional, and supremely powerful Creator who provides for our every need with the intention of us having a functional and fulfilling relationship with him.

THE PROBLEM

So what's the problem? *Fear*. What was it that caused Eve to eat the fruit? Fear that God was holding her back, and in her desire for *more* (more knowledge, more power, more control), she sinned. What was the reason Satan fell? Fear that he was not enough and therefore needed to be greater than God; and in his pride, he rebelled. What caused Abraham to sleep with Sarah's handmaid? Fear that God would not come through with his promise. What was the reason Pharaoh would not relent and let the Israelites go? Fear that he would not be in control, that he would no longer be the one and only god in his life. Why did Samson tell his secret to Delilah? Fear that she wouldn't love him. How was it that even the apostles fled from Jesus when he was arrested? Fear for their lives. Even impulse decisions are from an internal fear. There are also many decisions we *don't* make for fear of what may happen. We don't feel safe. We fear what people think. We fear what will happen if we do (fill in the blank) and fear what will happen if we don't (fill in the blank). We fear facing who we really are or what we see when we look deep inside.

So what do we do? We cope, we indulge, we ignore, we bypass, we get delusional because we have to keep ourselves in alignment with that biggest fear of all: what if I am not enough? And so we stop changing, stop growing, stop transforming into the likeness of Christ. We stop being who we were created to be. We stop reflecting the image of the One who made us supremely good...out of fear.

Fear. That's the problem. Always has been, always will be. Fear will keep you down, keep you stuck, keep you away from God because God is love, and there is no fear in love (1 John 4:16–18). But when we live *in* fear, *by* fear, and *out of* fear, we will reap the fruit, the consequences, of the seeds that are sown.

ADAM AND EVE: A CASE STUDY

Here you have these two perfect beings, created in the likeness of their Creator, simply to enjoy fellowship and relationship with him. They have everything they need for health and happiness, yet, somehow, it's not enough. How did this happen? Fear, yes, but let's continue even further to add its ugly cousins into the mix: insecurity, guilt, and shame—and we get F.I.G.S. We cover our true selves in these, trying to hide. What did Adam and Eve do when they felt the *fear* of being found out, the *insecurity* of what God would think, the *guilt* from having rebelled, and the *shame* from being naked? They sewed together the leaves of figs to cover their "true" selves. As mentioned above, Eve was led into eating the fruit by the serpent, fearful that her Creator was holding her back. Eve's insecurity flared up when she felt held back. Once she believed that she wasn't enough without this, she sank her teeth into the fruit. Her guilt then peeked its head out, and she went running to Adam instead of God. Of course, shame ensued. For Adam, it was a bit of a different path leading to the same place. I'm going to take the liberty to say that he ate the fruit for fear of not measuring up to his wife, or perhaps the insecurity of being left out. His guilt was so great that, when asked about the ordeal by God, Adam felt the need to shame his wife for giving him the fruit. Neither of them took responsibility and, in failing to do so, they hid behind blame.

I believe that both Adam and Eve had other narratives in their heads that were not of God. Remember that God's narrative says, "You are supremely good. You are perfect, just as I created you to be. You are equipped and have everything you need. I will always provide for you. I believe in you, love you, and cherish you because you are *good!*" Eve, however, heard that she wasn't being provided for and listened to the voice that said she needed more: more knowledge, more experience, more equality to be "like God." The problem was that she forgot to listen to the voice of truth: She already was like God. She was already made in his image. She wanted for nothing. Adam also heard a narrative that was not of God. He heard that he needed to measure up, match up, and rule over. Even though he was already given the charge of ruling over the earth and everything in it (Genesis 1:28), he too heard the voice that said he would never be enough. And that has been the human narrative ever since: that we need knowledge, power, and some unattainable, unsatisfiable "more" that is always one bite away from satisfaction. Adam and Eve forgot the one true voice of God that would tell them, "I am more than enough."

As human beings today, we have covered ourselves with so many leaves of F.I.G.S. that it's hard to even know who we were created to be. Most of the time, we succumb to the idea that our sin is "just the way God made me." We can't even see who we truly are because we have covered up the image of God underneath sin, fear, insecurity, guilt, and shame. In the light of God, these have no place. And since God desired fellowship and relationship with us, as this was his original intent from the beginning, he sent his one and only Son, Jesus, into the world. Why? Not only to show us how to live F.I.G.S.-free, but also that his blood could cover us, cleansing all the sin and empowering us to throw off everything that hinders and so easily entangles (Hebrews 12:1).

So, what is your narrative? We all hear voices, and each one of them is groomed by our perceived experiences and resources. But which one is the voice of truth?

OUR CREATION: A WAY OUT

> *No temptation has overtaken you except what is common to mankind. And God is faithful; he will not let you be tempted beyond what you can bear. But when you are tempted, he will also* ***provide a way out*** *so that you can endure it.*
>
> **1 Corinthians 10:13**, emphasis added

I don't believe God makes mistakes. Instead, I believe that we were created *very good*. I also believe that our loving and thoughtful Creator fashioned us, mind/body/spirit, in a way that sets us up for success, even in a fallen world. If you look closely enough, you will see it everywhere in the Scriptures.

In the prologue, we focused on the Jewish Shema from Deuteronomy 6. We were created in such a fashion that the greatest command is precisely what fuels us to be who we were created to be. God made it so simple: love him with all our heart, soul, mind, and strength. Yet how easy it is to slip right back into a victim mindset, a shameful, guilt-ridden, fear-based lifestyle that drives us in circles, personally and as a church. We forget that God has always provided a way out of this redundant and despondent way of "living" for him.

The answer is in the Shema. The answer is in Jesus' teachings about the greatest commandment. We must get back into alignment with how we were created to live and thrive: to love God—mind, body, spirit.

Remember, if you will, the summation of the commandments from the Old Testament in Deuteronomy 6. Now follow this through to the New Testament, and we see Jesus carrying this central idea through to the first-century believers.

> *Love the Lord your God with all your heart and with all your soul and with all your mind and with all your strength.*
>
> **Mark 12:30**

> *To love him with all your heart, with all your understanding and with all your strength, and to love your neighbor as yourself is more important than all burnt offerings and sacrifices.*
>
> **Mark 12:33**

> *He answered, "'Love the Lord your God with all your heart and with all your soul and with all your strength and with all your mind'; and, 'Love your neighbor as yourself.'"*
>
> **Luke 10:27**

BACK TO OUR ROOTS: THE CHURCH

Going back to our roots means going back to how God created us: *very good* and *in his image*. As we age and evolve, we have a tendency to go "off-path," to deviate. We can quickly forget who we are and how we were created to live relationally with one another. God's plan for reversing this trend is the church.

The church has several analogies in the Bible: a family, a body, a banquet hall, an army, a tree or vine with branches and fruit. God created the church on purpose and for a purpose. The first church, which began on the day of Pentecost when Peter "unlocked the gates" by preaching about Jesus and reconciliation through faith, repentance, and baptism, was an incredible and countercultural force. These Jewish people, consisting of *"every nation under heaven,"* decided to lay down everything to follow Jesus (Acts 2:5). On that day, the followers of Jesus were empowered by the Holy Spirit. Peter preached to Jerusalem's crowds, and 3,000 were added to their number that day (Acts 2:41). So what is the purpose of the church? Let's go back to the first days of the church at the beginning of Acts.

> *They devoted themselves to the apostles' teaching and to fellowship, to the breaking of bread and to prayer. Everyone was filled with awe at the many wonders and signs performed by the apostles. All the believers were together and had everything in common. They sold property and possessions to give to anyone who had need. Every day they continued to meet together in the temple courts. They broke bread in their homes and ate together with glad and sincere hearts, praising God and enjoying the favor of all the people. And the Lord added to their number daily those who were being saved.*
>
> **Acts 2:42–47**

Learning, growth, community, transformation, service, prayer, worship, and outreach all took place, resulting in the church's daily growth. That's it! Does the Bible in its entirety have anything to say about how else the church should function? Absolutely. Many of the letters we find in the Bible discuss issues in the churches that need to be addressed: division (1 Corinthians 1:10, 11:18, 12:25), unrepented-of sin (1 Corinthians 5:2; 2 Timothy 3:5), orderly worship (1 Corinthians 14:40), eldership (Titus 1:5). But more often than not, these letters are dealing with specific situations, not how to "do" church. The New Testament content is mostly about how the individual can be like Christ and how to relationally interact in a Christlike manner. But let's go back to the first-century church. Ultimately, they lived full of heart, choosing to be led by the Holy Spirit and the example of Christ (either from direct interaction with Jesus or from imitating others who lived like Christ). As Paul himself said: "*Follow my example, as I follow the example of Christ.*"

So what am I trying to say? That we should not have organized religion or leadership, or that we shouldn't have any form of church as we do now, with breakout specialty ministries and other fantastic aspects of our own design? Not at all! I believe we are made in God's image, and God is a creator. I believe many creations of the way we do church are wonderful. I am saying this: we must define what the church truly is at its root. Just like we were created "very good" by God and in his image, God also created the church and purposed it for our benefit. But similarly to humans, churches can also begin to feel "broken."

All too often, I have seen the church, as a whole, be a place where people come feeling broken, purposeless, and full of sin. Then they integrate into some fellowship, seeking out a "betterment" of life or some sort of restitution. They may also try to get fed spiritually. If they get into too much sin, they stop coming around. Or perhaps they get into a specialized group to help them learn how to be a Christian while still having this constant struggle. I see many people come to church excited about a mission but soon lose that dream when they get distracted or when something more entertaining comes along. I see people arguing and complaining about the length of sermons, the topics of sermons, the dynamics of sermons, the salary models, the board members, or the location for the gathering. I see people disputing over which community event the church should focus on serving or giving to. I hear about people leaving because they don't feel comfortable or because there's too much or too little accountability. Many times, people in churches are not happy, feel guilty or overwhelmed, or are divided. Bear with me here as I share boldly and honestly what I believe church has become for many people: spiritual hospice.

Hospice is a place to send sick people so that they can die as peacefully as possible. Is that what the church has become for us? Are we really a broken mess of sinners who can't do anything right unless we go to church on Sundays and read our Bible each morning? *Who* created you? In *whose* image are you made? Was God weak? Did God create broken beings? Did he intend for us to simply live and die with perhaps less guilt than the next person and try to remember Jesus along the way? Did we forget the entirety of Jesus' dissertation on life? *Life to the full; faith that can move mountains; love overflowing; even greater things; transformed into the likeness of Christ; freedom from sin and death; more than conquerors*. Allow these passages from Romans 8 to remind us who we are as individuals in the church:

> *Therefore, there is now no condemnation for those who are in Christ Jesus, because through Christ Jesus the law of the Spirit who gives life has set you free... The Spirit you received does not make you slaves, so that you live in fear again; rather, the Spirit you received brought about your adoption to sonship... For the creation waits in eager expectation for the children of God to be revealed... And we know that in all things God works for the good of those who love him, who have been called according to his purpose... What, then, shall we say in response to these things? If God is for us, who can be against us? He who did not spare his own Son, but gave him up for us all—how will he not also, along with him, graciously give us all things? Who will bring any charge against those whom God has chosen? It is God who justifies. Who then is the one who condemns? No one. Christ Jesus who died—more than that, who was raised to life—is at the right hand of God and is also interceding for us. Who shall separate us from the love of Christ? Shall trouble or hardship or*

> *persecution or famine or nakedness or danger or sword? No, in all these things we are more than conquerors through him who loved us.*

If each church member embraced these truths and made it their personal ambition to fulfill these verses, how would this change the church? Or, has church become a spiritual hospice, where people who have nothing left in the world go and find Jesus, but still feel full of fear, insecurity, guilt, and shame? "*But thanks be to God, I have been saved*"... I challenge you with Jesus' words:

> *"Not everyone who says to me, 'Lord, Lord,' will enter the kingdom of heaven, but only the one who does the will of my Father who is in heaven. Many will say to me on that day, 'Lord, Lord, did we not prophesy in your name and in your name drive out demons and in your name perform many miracles?' Then I will tell them plainly, 'I never knew you. Away from me, you evildoers!'"*
>
> **Matthew 7:21–23**

We can do all the "right" things yet still live outside the will of the Father. Is God's will for us to be baptized slaves? No! He has set us free. What is his will? For us to embrace and live true freedom—victoriously, transformationally, relationally. Christ's bride is *not* broken. Christ's bride is *not* stunted. Instead, the bride of Christ is "*a radiant church, without stain or wrinkle or any other blemish, but holy and blameless*" (Ephesians 5:27).

I believe we connect with God through love, peace, patience, gentleness, victory, encouragement, overcoming, transformation, and holiness. And I believe this is what the church is to be. That is what it means to go back to our roots.

OUR CREATION: MIND, BODY, SPIRIT

If we are to achieve spiritual health and reconnection to our Creator, we need to give attention to our mind, body, and spirit. All deviations from our *very good* state of creation can be addressed in one or more of these areas. Since God broke it down so thoroughly, I am not inclined to do otherwise. Throughout the rest of this book, I intend to show you that any incongruency in our wellness, health, or connection to God can be traced back to some deviation from his original design in our mind, our body, or our spirit.

CHAPTER 6

THE FALL

Sin is, essentially, a departure from God.

— Martin Luther

The root of all sin is the suspicion that God is not good.

— Oswald Chambers

What is sin? Most of us would answer something to the effect of "bad" or "against God." In the New Testament, the Greek word for sin is ἁμαρτάνω, which when transliterated is *hamartánō*. It was an ancient archery term meaning to "miss the mark." An archer had their mark, their target, their bullseye, and if they missed, "*Hamartánō!*" (*sin*), would be called out. When used by Jesus or in the New Testament letters, this word was used in a few of its slightly different definitions. The reason this archery term can so seamlessly be utilized in the spiritual realm links back to the last chapter: God created us and said that we are *very good, perfect,* and *just as he intended us to be*. And yes—if Jesus is the mark to hit, missing that mark would be the sin. We were never meant to miss the mark; we were never created to go astray.

But if we decide to shoot our arrow, our life, in a direction that is not as God intended, we will bear an image that does not reflect our Creator. We have deviated from the path of our origins. This word *hamartánō* stems from the words *a* (not) and *méros* (part, share). Properly, to sin meant to have no share in something good. Spiritually, since sin is a choice, we forfeit a relationship with God (eternal loss due to missing God's mark). Every decision (thought or action) done apart from faith (outside of how we were created to think, feel, live) is sin (Romans 14:23; Hebrews 11:6).

But why is sin such a big deal? Because sin separates. A good friend of mine brought new terminology into my vocabulary regarding what sin does: *othering*.

In short, othering is to alienate someone from you. It means to push someone away due to our internal and external behaviors, thoughts, or attitudes. Isn't that what happens when we sin? Our sin pushes others away and alienates us from God. Sin isolates and causes relationships to deteriorate.

Let's go even further back to when sin was first mentioned in the Old Testament. Cain had just killed his brother, and God tells him that "*sin is crouching at your door; it desires to have you, but you must rule over it*" (Genesis 4:7). This is an indication that we have a choice. We can either choose to be in control and overcome the sin (2 Corinthians 10:5) or we can choose to let sin control us (Romans 7:5). The Hebrew word חֵטְא, transliterated as *khet*, simply means to sin or transgress. Without going into a Hebrew etymology dissertation, here's a quick rundown of how the Old Testament Jews categorized sin:

Pesha – This is an intentional sin; an action committed in deliberate defiance of God; rebellion, transgression, trespass.
Avon – This is a sin of lust or uncontrollable emotion. It is a sin done knowingly, but not done to defy God; perversity, iniquity, mischief.
Cheit – This is an unintentional sin, crime, or fault, meaning to miss, sin, or stumble.[13]

Whichever term is used, and from whichever angle we find sin mentioned in the Old or New Testament, we find an attachment of consequence to it. One of three consequences will ensue: 1) someone covers over the offense, 2) the offense is adjudicated, or 3) a natural negative consequence occurs. One of those natural consequences, and the reason sin is so harmful, is that it causes separation.

> *Surely the arm of the Lord is not too short to save*
> *nor his ear too dull to hear.*

---

[13] Strong, James. *Strong's Exhaustive Concordance of the Bible.* Abingdon Press, 1890.

But your iniquities have separated
you from your God;
your sins have hidden his face from you,
so that he will not hear.

Isaiah 59:1–2

We know this scripture, but diving into it deeper helps us understand what sin actually does. God can save anyone he wants. He brings salvation and grace and unity, and he offers this through Jesus! But it's still our choice. The word for iniquity comes from the Hebrew *avon* (עָוֹן), which means the consequences of guilt or wrongness. The scripture implies that our consequence is the separation (בָּדַל) or *badal*. The word *badal* means to be divided or severed. The passage continues, saying that God has hidden, (סָתַר) or *sathar*, his face from us, meaning that he is concealed, absent, and undetectable when we are stuck in our sin. And here's the kicker: when sin is present, it says that God does not hear—the translation is *shema* (שָׁמַע).

Let's again think back to the beginning of the book. For the Jews, the Shema was the most important command, meaning to gather together, announce, proclaim, listen, and heed to the fact that *the Lord is One*. A Jew might say something to the effect of, "I follow the one true God. He is my Lord, and he is everything to me. I understand that. I hear that. I adhere to that."

Sin means God does not hear, and the Jews knew that they no longer held to the Shema if they remained stuck in sin. The connection was lost. So are there consequences to sin? Absolutely. But I believe that the way we view sin leads to how we deal with it.

Several years ago, my wife and I went on a walk soon after moving to our new neighborhood. We like to talk about our plans and our dreams and our marriage and our kids on our walks. But we also enjoy being outside, looking at God's creation. We love the mountains, the ocean, and the beauty of the trees. As it just so happens, we also are DIY house project junkies. No matter where we move, we seem to choose houses that need some fixing up. So we look at other homes for inspiration. As we were walking and talking, I noticed, out of the corner of my eye, something that I thought must have been my imagination. So I did a double take. I stopped, jaw dropped, eyes in disbelief. There was a house with a tree growing out of the roof. I'm not talking about those million-dollar custom homes built architecturally around a beautiful tree. I'm talking about a 4-foot monkey-pod tree that was literally growing in the middle of the roof! I then looked at the rest of the house—cars parked outside, yard maintained, lights on. It was as if nobody even acknowledged that there was a problem. *Hello!* There's a tree growing out of your roof, people!

When a stable and sound house is built, turn-key, it's perfect. What if it was built on a couple of acres with beautiful trees and fields surrounding it? It would still need maintenance, because if you don't clean the gutters, replace the roof every 20 years, repaint, and keep the pests out, then it will deviate from the house's original sound structure. It will move away from how it was built, made, created. It will modify itself into something with holes, bugs, faulty wiring from mice, and a tree growing out of it! So if that were your house, and you realized that it was breaking down, what would you do? Leave it? Hope for the best? Just be happy you had some semblance of a house? *No!* You'd clean it up, clean it out, fix it, care for it, and get rid of those pests, and take that rooftop tree out, saying, "Those don't belong here!" And then you'd maintain the home so that nothing surrounding it could infiltrate.

Sin is the same. So often, we treat sin as this *bad* thing someone does. And it can be, but we have created a culture of tending the sin rather than uprooting it. We would rather build around it because "that's just who that person is" or "well, they are just..." (fill in the blank). People walk by that person, that house, knowing there is a big fat tree growing out of it.

You see, the roof began to evolve into something it was never created to be because it was left unchecked and not dealt with. But ultimately, sin does not have to be this taboo thing that we hide and sneak and feel guilty about. Fear and shame and guilt only produce more of the same. Instead, let's remember that sin (in all its nastiness) is simply any deviation from what we were created to be. Sin is a natural result of what happens when we are surrounded by it in this sinful world. That becomes the norm.

People used to think our brains were hardwired—"this is just the way I was born." Science shows that we can change anything in our brain, and we now know that the brain is actually "plastic." Scientists use this term to refer to the brain's malleability. Neuroplasticity, or brain plasticity, refers to the brain's ability to change throughout a person's life. Isn't that what God says when he tells us that we can renew our minds? Science calls this neuroplasticity—God calls it metanoia. So what about something you were born with, predisposed to, or something that is "just the way you are"? Did God create you with flaws? According to Genesis 1, we are created in God's image, or at least Adam and Eve were. Ever since rebellion against God entered the world, we, as humans, have been deviating from the image of God that is inside us. God calls this sin.

When we choose to steer away from who God intended us to be (his likeness), we are deviating spiritually. And although we were created perfect, just as we were supposed to be, beautiful brain and all, we are born into a world that deviated a long time ago, which has lasting impact, or what the Bible would call consequences of sin. And we are surrounded by that. But what if you were born with the power of transformation inside you already? What if you had the power to create, heal, and function in alignment with what you were created to be? But over time, the choices we make to deviate from our perfect alignment with God cause more and more issues, problems, and filters of perception.

GOD'S CREATION: THE BRAIN

When you were in utero, as a fetus, you began to "download" some of your basic operating systems, and in doing so, your brain began to grow. Where did that information come from? Yes, your DNA. From your parents, but also the hundreds of thousands of years of brain evolution in humankind. Barring any genetic or environmental disruptions, you were born with some fundamental abilities that were "hardwired" into your brain—breathing, for instance. In the time it took for you to read the first few sentences of this paragraph, you took an average of six breaths. Did you think about it? Nope! Breathing, thank goodness, is a skill with which you are very familiar. You got a jump-start on that skill with some of your initial programming. Are you with me so far?

While these seemingly hardwired programs of breathing, digesting, cell production, and many other vital operations are essential (and thankfully automatic for most of us), even they are not fixed and permanent. Have you ever gone swimming? If so, you have likely held your breath for an extended time. If you are a good swimmer or swim at a competition level, you have fundamentally changed a skill that seemed to be hardwired. You now possess the skill to override and control your breathing system. Many people have mastered the art of lowering their blood pressure by simply bringing awareness to their breath. Wow! We can literally change the rate at which our heart pumps blood through our bodies. And this is accomplished with our basic operating systems for our survival! What does this mean for you? Enter metanoia.

REPENTANCE: GOD'S PLAN FOR OUR BRAIN

> *Do not conform to the pattern of this world, but be transformed by the renewing of your mind. Then you will be able to test and approve what God's will is—his good, pleasing and perfect will.*
>
> **Romans 12:2**

We get the word "repentance" from the Greek word μετάνοια or *metanoia*, which means mind change, or changing the inner self. Even from the creation of humankind, the plan of God has always been to give us a way out of sin, a way to grow, a way to evolve, a way to change, a way to overcome, a way to be victorious. I want to share some Scripture with you to enhance your view of how God created our amazing brains to accomplish metanoia, to repent, to undergo a mind change. "*Therefore, if anyone is in Christ, the new creation has come: The old has gone, the new is here!*" (2 Corinthians 5:17).

We are a *new* creation in Christ, right? But what does that involve? Metanoia, repentance. Putting to death (carrying your cross daily) the "old" and renewing your mind every day—living a transformed life, now! To live new, you have to let go of the old, completely.

So I find this law at work: Although I want to do good, evil is right there with me. For in my inner being I delight in God's law; but I see another law at work in me, waging war against the law of my mind and making me a prisoner of the law of sin at work within me. What a wretched man I am! Who will rescue me from this body that is subject to death? Thanks be to God, who delivers me through Jesus Christ our Lord! So then, I myself in my mind am a slave to God's law, but in my sinful nature a slave to the law of sin.

Romans 7:21–25

How many of us can relate to Paul here? I want to do good, but evil is right there. How many of us have felt like *Satan* is right there with us? But does the scripture actually say that? Let's take a closer look. There is a war going on in our mind. The Greek word for evil here is *kakos* (κᾰκός)—it's a mode of thinking, feeling, or acting wrong *inside*. The guilt, the shame, the baggage, the wrong mode of thinking is the evil in our mind, and if we allow it, it holds us down as a slave, depriving us of our freedom. Jesus offers us a new way of thinking. Yes, there is a spiritual war out there, but our way of thinking is the battle within us. Many people have misused this passage under the guise of "the devil made me do it" while others have simply misunderstood it, believing they (as Christians) are under the control of the sinful nature and cannot escape it. This is not what Paul meant! Instead, Paul is making the point that "it doesn't have to be like that" because of what Jesus has done for us. Romans 7 is what happens when we try to simply "do the right thing" but are still stuck in human-invented Christianity (righteousness by the law). Romans 8, however, goes on to talk about how living by the spirit frees us from the raging war inside, from repeatedly being taken captive by sin. Jesus gives us a way to rewire our mind, our brain, our spiritual GPS.

But solid food is for the mature, who by constant use have trained themselves to distinguish good from evil (Hebrews 5:14). The recipe here is the retraining of our mind so that we can distinguish a God-thought from one of our own modes of thinking. We all have been subconsciously trained by the world's way of thinking in some form or fashion. Therefore, we need to continually train ourselves to distinguish the good in our mind from the *kakos*, the mode of thinking and feeling wrong on the inside that leads to wrong actions on the outside. Do we have that old way of thinking: "*I'm so evil and bad and guilty and...*"? Or are we constantly being renewed in our thinking? How does God want us to feel, to think, to see ourselves?

> *Finally, brothers and sisters, whatever is true, whatever is noble, whatever is right, whatever is pure, whatever is lovely, whatever is admirable—if anything is excellent or praiseworthy—think about such things.*
>
> **Philippians 4:8**

Thinking this way is a skill developed through our mind's wiring system. And what's crazy is how God designed us perfectly, and his "law" is set to help us thrive on every level. Science has shown for a long time that stress/anxiety/worry can kill you and that a life of peace and connection and satisfaction brings about a more enjoyable life. That's the secular world telling us to follow the commands and principles of the Bible!

So what if you *only* thought about such things? How would your take on life be shifted? How would your life be different?

Paul speaks about two outcomes of the way we think and therefore live: "*Godly sorrow brings repentance that leads to salvation and leaves no regret, but worldly sorrow brings death*" (2 Corinthians 7:10). Metanoia (repentance/mind change) leaves no regret in our life. The term "godly sorrow" is formed from three different Greek words:

Thehos – θεός – God, the Creator and owner of all things
Kata – κατά – by way of
Lupé – λύπη – pain, grief, affliction, distress in the body and mind

We could rewrite *Godly sorrow* as: "Pain and distress, the way God would have us handle and learn." The word "produces" (ἔργον), *ergazomai*, is derived from the root word *ergon*, meaning to "labor into existence." It takes work and effort to produce something. Metanoia won't just happen because we want it to.

However, when godly sorrow is produced, it paves the way for *repentance* or *metanoia* (change of mind, change of inner self). And that kind of mind change leaves "no regret" (ἀμεταμέλητος), *amétamélétos*, defined as something irrevocable, about which no change of mind can take place.

It's this kind of irrevocable mind change that leads to salvation—σωτηρία—*sótéria*, which is God's rescue into his safety and deliverance. Your subconscious may be trying to keep you safe, but God is trying to show us that in him, we already are safe (more on the subconscious mind in the next chapter). Here are a few versions of 2 Corinthians 7:10 in different translations to give you a broader understanding:

> *For the sorrow that is according to the will of God produces a repentance without regret, leading to salvation, but the sorrow of the world produces death.* (NASB)
>
> *In fact, to be distressed in a godly way causes people to change the way they think and act and leads them to be saved. But the distress that the world causes brings only death.* (NOG)
>
> *Pain handled in God's way produces a turning from sin to God which leads to salvation, and there is nothing to regret in that! But pain handled in the world's way produces only death.* (CJB)

Now that we have dug out the Greek and various versions of the passage, let me put all these together to give you a fuller translation of my own rendition:

> *Trauma, handled in a worldly way, deals only death. But pain and distress, the way God would have us handle and learn from*

these labors, produce a transformed mind that changes the inner self so irrevocably that nothing could reverse this mind change. This is what keeps us safe now and forever with God.

Real change *can* be produced in us that will transform us forever. On a side note, I will use the word "trauma" frequently in these pages. When I speak of trauma, I simply mean *anything* that could be perceived as a traumatic event. What one person finds to be traumatic may not register for another person, but this does not negate the fact that a trauma occurred. I've heard it referenced as "big T" trauma, and "little t" trauma. Clear-cut events that most would consider "big T" traumas are things like physical abuse, sexual abuse, death of a parent, loss of a limb, a divorce, rape, etc. "Little t" trauma is anything else that the body registers as a traumatic event.

THE MIND: HOW WE CREATE PROBLEMS

Science has shown that the mind is the brain at work. To handle the absolutely incredible task of being your brain, it splits the load. Dr. Joe Dispenza, DC (best-selling author and neuroscience researcher) breaks the brain down into three parts: the *thinking brain*, the *emotional brain*, and the *reptilian brain*. The thinking brain is the neocortex, the most evolved part of the human brain. New neurons are formed in this part of the brain with every new thought. It's the part of your brain you are using right now! Next is the limbic brain, also known as the emotional brain or the mammalian brain. This part of your brain produces and regulates chemicals responsible for our feelings and emotions. Finally, the reptilian brain is the area in which your cerebellum lies. I often refer to this as the primal brain. Those of you who are not particularly fascinated by brain research or factoids, don't leave me just yet! Though I have been probing into the recent discoveries in neuroscience, epigenetics, and psychoneuroimmunology, that is not what this book is about. Think of this book as sort of the "Cliffs Notes" to your brain.

These three brains and their relevant counterparts (the hippocampus, amygdala, and cerebellum) are critical to what makes you, you. But luckily, you don't need to go to medical school to understand and harness their power! I will address some of the brain's individual systems as we progress, but for now, I want to focus on *how* the mind works. Let's further clarify this by breaking the mind into two categories, or operating systems if you will—the conscious mind and the subconscious/unconscious mind.

To illustrate this further, we need to touch on a small part of brain anatomy and function. For those who would like to investigate this subject further, there are extensive resources on neurobiology and brain function listed in the back of this book. I wrote about this previously in my book, *Mind Change*, and will repeat those thoughts here to give us a small insight into the amazing brain with which God has blessed us.

For many years, scientists have been comparing our brain to a computer. And just like the incredible advances that we have seen in technology, our understanding of the brain and mind has also grown. For a moment, I want you to imagine the human brain like a computer. Personally, I prefer Mac over PC. Even if you are a diehard PC lover, stick with me for analogy's sake! First, a disclaimer: I am one of the least tech-savvy people I know. So for those of you who are knowledgeable in this area, bear with my rudimentary comparisons!

My MacBook Air came to me preprogrammed with a particular operating system. It was already "hardwired," so to speak, with specific programs. There are things it does by itself without my knowledge or effort. One thing it does is to provide the ability to create file folders so that I can organize all the extra stuff I put into it. Though my husband and I each have a Mac, and they are basically the same model, they have unique content based on what we individually decided to add. For instance, my husband is an incredible creator and editor of videos. To fulfill this hobby, he decided to download Final Cut Pro, which is an advanced video editing software program. This program came with countless files full of data that, once downloaded, allowed his Mac to run the program and install the software to create and edit videos. Our brain has a similar "filing system." Let's call this the subconscious mind.

Dr. Joe Dispenza, in his book *You Are the Placebo*, states that the brain processes 400 billion bits of information a second. Yep, 400 billion, with a B!! It is generally accepted that the conscious mind can handle seven chunks of information (plus or minus 2) at a time, or about 50 bits per second. Our subconscious mind must find a way of reducing millions and millions of sensory messages every second, down to a level where it can process the messages and make sense of them.

If your conscious mind had to deal with the absolute barrage of information that we take in every second, it would melt down. So the subconscious mind comes to the rescue. Your internal programmer, the subconscious mind, filters through all this information and decides what's important, and then files this information into the proper files. So your brain is filled with all these "file folders" that are chock full of information that you have been collecting since birth! Incredible, huh? If we were to do an MRI of your brain, these "folders" would show up as bright little clusters. These are your neurons. And they are all connected to form a neuro-net highway in your brain. This conglomeration of bright little clusters holds the data that makes you who you are!

To illustrate this further, I would like to give you an example. Assuming you are over the age of 18 and one of the 87 percent of the US population who can legally operate a motor vehicle, you have a skill we call driving. At what age did you learn to drive? Likely, the answer you provided to this question would hover somewhere around ages 14 to 16. What if I told you that you were wrong? That you actually started to learn to drive the very first time you were cognitively aware of a car. Otherwise, driver education would have been a *much* longer course! How did you know how to get into the car? Which seat did you sit in to drive? How did you know what the steering wheel was for? All the knowledge that you have been accumulating concerning driving has been stored in a "file," or neurocluster, in your brain. The nanosecond that your brain receives the message that you are going to need the relevant information, it pulls up the associated "file" and begins to produce the "skill" associated with this event. Though you may not be consciously aware of it, your subconscious mind has sorted through the file and will now send the messages to the body to "do driving." You don't even have to think about it. And at this point, this skill is so rehearsed, so often utilized and practiced, that it becomes second nature. Haven't you ever arrived at work or the store and realized you don't even remember driving there? Yes? Now let's continue with this example to show how whatever data that file folder holds will be the outcome of how we operate.

Let's say that in your particular "file" labeled "Driving," your mind finds a few negative resources. For instance, when you were 16, you and some friends were messing around, and you took a corner on a dirt road a little too fast, and your car flipped over. Then, at 19, you were involved in a traffic accident that resulted in a fracture to your leg. And tragically, when you were in college, a group of friends you were supposed to be riding with was involved in a head-on collision, and one of your friends was killed. Let me ask you, do you think that you might have a different reaction to getting behind the wheel than someone who hadn't had these experiences?

Your subconscious mind has one primary objective when sorting through the millions and millions of bits of sensory input every day: to keep you safe. That's it. That is why it regulates your breathing, blood flow, digestion, and many other primal features to keep you alive daily. The subconscious mind does not distinguish the difference between the danger of meeting a bear in the woods or getting up in front of a group of strangers to do a speech. It only recognizes something as "dangerous" if we have prior knowledge that it is. Most of us know from movies or stories that bears are not good company alone in the woods, but some people have equally terrifying experiences in front of crowds. Though consciously, we would deem the bear encounter more dangerous, the subconscious mind might disagree, having far more references regarding the fears and dangers of public speaking.

So, back to the driving example. The person with the numerous references that driving is a potentially lethal activity will produce some different things than the person without those experiences. Let's say it's Susie that has the negative experiences that I referenced before, and Lisa does not. When Lisa gets behind the wheel to drive to work, her "file" is pulled up, and she automatically produces the skill of driving and can go about her driving normally. When Susie gets behind the wheel, a whole different outcome occurs. Susie's subconscious mind pulls up the file and notices that it has been "flagged." Her subconscious mind has flagged this file as a potential threat or danger because of her previous adverse experiences. It did this because it needs to get the conscious mind's attention so that every system is on high alert for possible danger.

The subconscious mind and the conscious mind do not speak the same language. It's a good thing they don't. This is why: consciously, we are able to handle only a small fraction of the data that we receive on a daily basis. The subconscious mind is tasked with the responsibility of dealing with all the rest. The conscious mind controls our awareness during our waking hours. But like an iceberg, we are only seeing the tip of the bigger picture. The mass of the iceberg beneath the surface (what you cannot see) is what is driving the trajectory of the iceberg. Likewise, it is widely accepted that nearly 95 percent of our day-to-day thoughts/feelings/emotions are controlled by our subconscious mind. The conscious mind is analytical and must try to create order and make sense of every experience. It is constantly asking "why" and relies on our intellect to make decisions and solve problems. For the most part, that sounds like a good plan. The unfortunate part of this process is that what we deem logical actually comes from the filters we use to perceive our world. The filters we use are created by what we hold within our subconscious mind.

How are these filters created? Our subconscious mind uses our earliest memories and experiences to develop the core beliefs and values that form our personal identity. So all of our conscious thought is actually being filtered through the lens, or "reality," that our subconscious mind has created. This explains why we can be triggered by something that has happened around us and end up feeling angry, anxious, or scared, yet have no real, "logical" reason for those emotions. The conscious mind looks for the "why" of the trigger and tries to make sense of it logically. The subconscious mind doesn't care if it's logical or not. It sees the trigger as a reminder of something that felt bad in the past, and therefore deems it a potential threat to the system. It simply "outputs" feelings of anxiety, fear, or anger in response to the triggered memory, without us even having to be conscious of the memory itself. It simply tries to protect. Our conscious mind is ever-changing, depending on how we perceive or make sense of any given situation. If we feel it, it's real. If we think it, it must be right. If we see it, it's absolute. It's a fickle thing. If our conscious mind were responsible for our breathing, let's say, most of us would forget to breathe within the first minute! Our subconscious mind is responsible for all our physiological functions. Therefore, it cannot possibly involve the conscious mind in that process because the conscious mind would be too analytical to handle those tasks that need to come so automatically.

When we sleep, our subconscious mind does the majority of its sorting and filing of the data we received during the day. That's a good reason to get a good night's sleep! It doesn't spend time "analyzing." It simply files. When it recognizes that an event from our day resulted in a negative reaction, it flags this memory and keeps an eye out for similar circumstances that might cause discomfort. The flagging process is the work of a little cluster of neurons in the lower part of our brain called the amygdala. Its primary function is to regulate our fight, flight, or freeze response. If, at any time during our day, we feel that we might be in danger, that little neuron cluster kicks in to assist in the solution. The subconscious mind makes a note of the event and files it as "potentially dangerous." It remains there unless another, similar event comes through with an equal or elevated response, at which time, the subconscious mind files the events as "known to be dangerous." Dr. Freidman Schaub holds a PhD in molecular biology and an MD in cardiology and is the award-winning author of *The Fear and Anxiety Solution*. Listen to what he has to say about this process:

> *Considering its vast responsibilities, it makes sense that the root causes of many emotional and physical problems reside in the subconscious mind. For example, unexpressed and unresolved memories and emotions that are stored within the subconscious mind can function as negative, limiting filters and lead to chronic anxiety, phobias, depression, addictions, and low-self-esteem. Limiting core beliefs, such as "I am not good enough" or "I am not safe" are imprinted on subconscious levels and can keep us stuck and prevent us from seeing who we really are and accessing our true potential.*

> *Once the subconscious storage capacity is exhausted, negative emotions begin to accumulate in the physical body, which can weaken our immune system and lead to chronic pain, inflammation of the joints, and auto-immune diseases. This transference of emotions from the subconscious mind to the body may not only be about creating additional storage room, but also function as a form of subconscious communication, letting us know that it is time to address these unresolved emotional issues . Discomfort as a form of wake-up call.*[14]

The fact that there are such complex processes involved in the storage and retrieval of these files (memories) and the fact that they are able to provide us with amazing communication and insight into the way we operate points to a Creator.

I am acutely aware of how I have overly simplified some very complex systems. Though these individual systems and how they function independently and together are fascinating, that information would take up numerous books. My purpose is to show you the results of this process and how it relates to changing our minds and, therefore, our lives. To give another illustration, I will provide you with an example of how an individual could develop a common but crippling phobia: fear of public speaking.

Justin, a well-kept man in his late 20s, walks into my office with quite a problem. Since before he can remember, he has been terrified of getting up in front of a crowd to speak. Though he cannot remember when it started, he feels that it has become worse the older he gets. Justin is up for a promotion at work that will involve presenting his team's ideas to upper management.

Though he is highly qualified, he has turned down the promotion in the past due to his fear of speaking publicly. He is now faced with a decision to stay in his current role and watch younger colleagues pass him by, or to take advantage of the higher salary and further promotions in his career. Not only is his professional

---

[14] Schaub, F., Dr. (2019, October 31). What is the subconscious mind? https://drfriedemann.com/empowerment-tools/written-resources/what-is-the-subconscious-mind/

life affected, but his personal life is on hold as well. At his current rate of pay, he isn't able to save enough money to buy an engagement ring he has wanted and has put off proposing to the girl of his dreams for much longer than anticipated. Yep, quite a predicament!

To pull all our previously mentioned information together in a practical example, let's look into Justin's mind, shall we? First, let's pull up the little neurocluster tucked nicely into his hippocampus that is labeled "Public Speaking." This file is populated with every experience he has heard about, seen, perceived, felt, or watched on TV. The key is to travel back to the first known adverse experience that was flagged in this file. We find the jackpot! It's something we call the primary imprint. This is the first known adverse experience we find within the file. As a side note, Justin is entirely oblivious to this particular memory. It has been stored in his subconscious mind and replayed countless times, but his conscious mind has remained unaware of it. Here is how this folder in the file is labeled: "Kindergarten Show and Tell."

In kindergarten, Justin is a well-liked and well-adjusted boy. He feels comfortable and safe with his teacher and classmates. On this particular Friday, they have show and tell. Justin has been anticipating this all week and can't wait to introduce his classmates to his favorite stuffed animal, Teddy. As Justin approaches the front of the class, he very much hopes they will like Teddy too. Justin stands in front of the teacher's desk at the front of the room. He begins to tell the class about Teddy and how they came to be friends. In the middle of his explanation, the entire class suddenly bursts into raucous laughter. Justin stands in horror as the class laughs at him. He is mortified. Not only do they not like Teddy, but they also do not like him! Justin thought these were his friends. Now Billy is laughing so hard that he has fallen out of his chair. Justin's face flushes red, and he bursts into tears, running out of the room.

The brain is receiving all this information and finds the appropriate response. It creates feelings of shame, embarrassment, hurt, and even anger. Because of the intense emotions being created, the amygdala has been activated and has decided that Justin should run to avoid any further harm. To prevent any possible recurrence of this horrific event, the amygdala flags this memory by attaching undesirable physiological responses to it. Now, any time the subconscious mind opens this folder and replays the memory, the body will produce the attached physiological responses.

Justin now has a "proof" or a "reference" in his file that public speaking can be a dangerous and painful event. Just one or two adverse experiences in a file full of good experiences usually will not result in an adverse reaction. But if enough folders in the file contain these negative associations, the subconscious mind will automatically produce behavior in alignment with the negative. But guess what? What if what happened to Justin wasn't the whole story? As Justin was facing the class, he observed them from only one perspective: what he sees. In reality, as Justin was talking, his teacher was attempting to take her seat at her desk behind the place where Justin was speaking. Because it's a rolling chair, and Ms. Brown was distracted by Justin's story, she completely missed her chair and fell flat on the ground! So, what were the kids really laughing at? Ms. Brown!

But do you think Justin knew that? Nope. Even after it was explained to him, his memory (the file folder) still shows the class laughing at him. Though the explanation of what really happened made Justin consciously feel a little better, his subconscious mind still holds the memory the same way he saw it, and the initial responses are still attached.

So guess what happens in third grade when Justin has to get up in front of the class to give a book report? He has no conscious memory of the kindergarten event. But remember, everything we do is a skill.

So when Justin's mind scans his folders for the skills he needs for this task, his mind pulls up (subconsciously) the kindergarten event, and for reasons he cannot explain, he begins to feel nervous. He knows the book and has written a good report. He feels comfortable with his friends and teachers and has no reason he can (consciously) think of that he would be nervous, but he is. Thanks to the activation of the amygdala, the body goes into a survival state. Granted, it's a low-grade danger. But the mind still warns the body by elevating the senses to have a heightened awareness of danger. For Justin, his body is on alert: pulse raised, palms sweating, heart racing. Primally, he is ready for possible danger, which makes him more susceptible to finding it!

As he gets up to do his book report, Justin finds that it's easier to keep his eyes glued to the paper to keep from looking up. His body, unbeknownst to him, is ready to catch even the slightest form of danger. Angie passes a private note to Susie at the back of the class, but Bobby intercepts it. As Bobby teases the horrified Angie by revealing the note's content, the last few rows break out into laughter. Immediately, Justin reacts: *"They are laughing at me!"* his mind screams. And the flood of current emotions mixes with the emotions from the previous event. Justin is shattered.

As his subconscious mind goes to file this information, it now has a stronger flag for the situation. Each time Justin is required to speak in front of others, he is prepared for the worst. By the time he must present his final paper his senior year, Justin is nearly paralyzed with anxiety. This is a bold attempt by his subconscious mind to protect him. The level of danger is now at high alert, and the result is the mind communicating very strongly to the body.

Along with the anxiety, Justin experiences an increased heart rate, lightheadedness, sweaty palms, and now he is extremely nauseous. This is the body's way of communicating what the subconscious mind is saying: *This is dangerous!* With the final paper being half his grade, Justin tries to push through the physical warnings only to vomit on the entire first row and then pass out.

Now Justin is sitting in my office with a full-blown case of glossophobia, or fear of public speaking. I will say it again: our behavior in any given situation is simply the output of previously "uploaded" data to our drive. If there are more adverse experiences found in the file folder compared to the positive experiences, what do you think the outcome will be?

So is Justin a failure? *No!* He is successfully producing this outcome. Every time he goes to speak, he successfully produces the skill of glossophobia. He doesn't *have* glossophobia. He *does* it. Every time. Without fail. Good job, Justin! The problem is, Justin wants to be successful at something different. Right now, he has a well-practiced skill that produces a public speaking phobia, but he wants to be successful at getting up in front of people without the fear of passing out or vomiting on his audience.

I'm going to say something now that cannot be overstated. Are you listening? Good, here it goes: *we will always produce from what we hold within*. Did you catch that? Let me say it another way: An orange tree cannot produce apples. Not even if it really, really wants to. As much as Justin would like to effortlessly stand in front of his peers and give a presentation, his mind and body literally won't let him. It's too dangerous.

How do we apply this to our lives? If we become aware that everything we think or do is in fact a skill, then it should change our perception of everything. Remember, our brain is the wheelhouse for our entire body. The body cannot do anything without the approval of the brain. This leads us to an essential understanding that I will repeat again: *everything we do is a skill*.[15]

HOW WE VIEW THE WORLD

> *"Neuro-Linguistic Programming (NLP) teaches that we all operate from our own unique Model of the World. No two human beings have the same exact experiences. The model that we create to guide us in the world is based in part upon our experiences. Each of us may, then, create a different model of the world we share and thus come to live in a somewhat different reality."*[16]

Let's take an example to illustrate this.

External Event: Encountering a dog at the park

Observe the behavior of Subject A, whom we will call Steve, and Subject B, whom we will call Jeff. Both men are parents and have taken their child to a park to play. They are familiar with the park and are each soon engrossed in tossing a ball back and forth to their child. Soon, a large dog comes out of nowhere,

[15] McKean, Heather. *Mind Change: Changing the World One Mind at a Time*. KDP, 2019.

[16] Bandler, Richard; Grinder, John. *The Structure of Magic I: A Book about Language and Therapy*. Science and Behavior Books Inc, 1975.

barreling toward them. Let's observe these parents' individual reactions and, using the model above, try to guess the resulting behavior.

STEVE: Steve is presented with the external event of the dog arriving. Within seconds, his subconscious mind has analyzed all relevant data stored in the mind concerning dogs. He deletes, distorts, and generalizes the countless bits of information that are occurring so that he can decide a course of action (behavior). In his mind, he is brought back to his own childhood pet and the joy and comfort his dog brought him. The images of countless backyard adventures with his trusty companion flood his mind, and he can almost feel the soft fur under his fingers. The approaching dog reminds him of his old friend Scout, with its goofy grin and clumsy paws. He is flooded with love as he hears the playful bark. Even as he stands here 20 years later, he experiences the same feelings of loyalty and friendship that Scout provided him for so many years in his youth. He grabs up his daughter, eager for her to run her fingers through the fur of this welcomed guest! He laughs out loud as he prepares for the inevitable tongue bath they will receive. He kneels down and calls the dog closer, happy to share this moment with his daughter. The dog instantly rolls over for a good belly scratch.

JEFF: Jeff is presented with the same external event. In an instant, he uses his subconscious mind to analyze all relevant data stored in his mind concerning dogs. Without even thinking about it, Jeff begins yelling at the dog, "Get away!" His sudden shift in behavior startles his young son, and the boy becomes frightened, though he has not noticed the dog yet. He is overcome with adrenaline and feels near panic. Jeff runs over and roughly grabs his son up, all the while shouting at the dog. The young boy begins to cry, and Jeff assumes that the boy is terrified of the dog. Jeff braces for the dog to attack and starts kicking wildly at it, screaming for help. The dog, responding to the threat that it now feels, stops its advance and begins barking at Jeff and his son. The boy is hysterical, and Jeff holds him tighter as he chases the dog away. Though he can't exactly explain why, Jeff has always gone out of his way to avoid dogs. He could never quite understand people's fascination with the animals. Instinctively, Jeff feels that dogs are dangerous, especially around children. What Jeff doesn't know is that he has a very good reason for this reaction. As the subconscious mind scanned all the files, it found an extremely strong memory from early childhood. Jeff and a childhood friend had been secretly playing in an abandoned farmhouse they had previously been forbidden to enter. Hearing noises from under the house, they crawled under to investigate. There they found an old dog that was likely injured or dying. As they crept closer to get a better look, the dog turned and snapped at the boys, biting Jeff's friend in the face. Terrified, Jeff ran home, leaving his friend behind. Jeff's friend required stitches and developed a scar. He also needed a round of painful injections in case the dog had been infected with rabies. Jeff never told a soul, afraid that he would be punished. The guilt, shame, and fear associated with this memory created a powerful imprint. In an effort to keep him safe, Jeff's mind buried it deep into his core belief system and quickly erased any conscious awareness of it. Though he cannot consciously recall this event, it has shaped every experience he has had with dogs. Later that evening, safe at home, he goes into great detail with his son about the dangers of dogs and how they should never be trusted.

Which scenario is reality? Who is right? Is the dog dangerous and scary, or a joyful opportunity? Why does a dog bring joy to some and strike fear in the hearts of others? I have always loved dogs and thought of them as loyal and trusted companions, but after watching *Cujo* at a young age, I can definitely say that I shied away from a few St. Bernards in my life! Welcome to how you develop your model of the world!

In the next chapter, we will explore how our own personal model of the world can shape the way we see everything…even our view of God.

CHAPTER 7

OUR VIEW OF GOD

The way you view God will eventually show up in the way you live your life.

— A.W. Tozer

You see, when I was little I tried to be a perfect little girl for Jesus. I loved him, I wrote to him in my diary, I wrote songs to him. Then I realized that he was demanding and wanted to see me go to Hell and that is when everything changed. I knew I could never be good enough, I could never please him. I felt when I was created God must have made a mistake. I just couldn't be like everyone else. I was told that I was rebellious etc. I was so tired of being told that I was bad, not good enough. I think back, I was a pretty good kid that had a little OCD and just wanted to be perfect and excel in everything.

— *Constance*[17]

My whole life from my first memories of God was a vision of him as an angry, full of retribution God. I had fear of disappointing him and paying dire consequences. "Be careful little eyes, ears, mouth, etc. Because there's a Father up above." (We got the looking down but the love part wasn't emphasized and didn't register).

— *Nancy*[18]

My main obsession was that I was not saved eternally because of some unconscious sin that I'd not repented of. Or because of the intrusive thoughts that accused me of things like "do you really love God in your heart? Maybe you just intellectually love him?" The intrusive thoughts were destructive and always

[17] Spiritual Abuse Blogs. *Constance's United Pentecostal Church Experience.* http://blogs.spiritualabuse.org. December 19, 2018.

[18] Spiritual Abuse Blogs. *God Is Love.* http://blogs.spiritualabuse.org. July 19, 2016.

accusing me of being the worst and most disgusting sinner—unworthy of love and grace because I wasn't perfect. (Caused by hearing a perverted version of the Gospel). It caused me to repeat the sinner's prayer obsessively; question whether God was truly a God of love; fear praying to God because he was so big and scary and had the ability to banish me to hell for eternity so I didn't get warm and fuzzy thinking about him. I also secretly questioned his existence for most of my adult life.

— *ThereIsLife*[19]

My childhood church emphasized God's willingness to inflict massive amounts of pain and suffering on Jesus as the ultimate example of God's love. Jesus was abused and shattered because humanity is so evil and wretched, that only blood and death can lead to the forgiveness of a broken and selfish human race. In fact, God's love is such that Jesus became a substitute for the divine and human abuse that each and every one of us as individuals deserves to experience. In other words, the God of this tradition was portrayed as expressing "his" love (because God was always referred to using the pronoun "he"), through the infliction of violence. This God is a vindictive being that not only sanctions but actively engages in divine child abuse.

— *Naiomi*[20]

OUR VIEW OF GOD: SEEING THROUGH THE LENS OF OUR PAST

"Being sexually abused as a child was a gift from God," my client said confidently. "Without it, I would never have been able to reach as many women as I have reached. It's my ministry. I couldn't possibly heal the hurt; it's what keeps me going. Who would I be without it? I wouldn't be able to relate to any of

[19] Spiritual Abuse Blogs. *Scrupulosity – Obsessive fear of sinning – You Are Not Crazy!* http://blogs.spiritualabuse.org. October 30, 2017.

[20] Gonzalez, Naiomi. *God Abusing Jesus, Helped My Family Justify Abusing Me.* The Salt Collective, http://thesaltcollective.org, June 5, 2018.

the other women who have been through it. Now I can share with them what a gift their abuse was."

I shuddered. Partly because of the compassion I felt for this woman and partly in shame. Shame that I used to believe a similar narrative about myself, and worse, about God.

It is my opinion, from personal experience and my work within the ministry and professionally with clients, that many of us have a very distorted view of God. As we discussed, our belief systems start in early childhood and become solidified throughout our lives. The way we view God is distinctly shaped not only by our upbringing, but also by our religious affiliations. That is neither "bad" nor "good." It just is.

Human beings are learning machines! From the moment we are born (and even before that), we are gaining skills. Some of those skills are a little more basic and start to be practiced even in the womb. Breathing, eating, hearing; these skills (though done differently inside the womb) are being developed even prior to our being born. The "skill" of eating, which we all possess and use regularly, has had quite an evolution! After birth, the skills that we had been developing and practicing in the womb (sucking, digesting, etc.) now face new learning. Depending on whether they are breastfed or bottle fed, each child needs to add new layers to the "skill" of eating. As we get older, depending on our influences and environment, this skill develops and changes until it becomes second nature and we don't have to think about it at all (at least consciously).

Remember the computer analogy? We need to be programmed, all of us. Most of us come with similar basic hardware when we enter the world. But after that, our "programming" is highly variable, given our environment and upbringing. For instance, with the eating example, if you were brought up in China, you may have learned to eat with chopsticks rather than a fork or spoon. This has become second nature to you. Later, if you encounter more Western influences, you may have to become accustomed to using unfamiliar tools. We are *all* programmed. We have to be. From driving a car to walking to coping with stress, almost everything we do is a learned behavior.

There are about 100 billion neurons (folders in the files) in a human brain, which is about the same as the number of stars in the Milky Way Galaxy. Our unconscious mind has a bunch of filters that delete, distort, and generalize external events that we see, hear, feel, or read about. These filters have been programmed by our experiences in life and thus distort, delete, and generalize according to our previous programming. This is what some refer to as our reality. The interesting part of this is that what equals "reality" comes from our own personal programming, which makes it subjective! This is *so* huge. We can argue it all we want, but research shows that what we *think* is real is only an outward projection of what we hold within.[21]

Each of us is unique regarding what we hold. This leads us back to the issue of "problems." To understand why we have problems, we need to look again at how we create our problems. For another illustration, I would like to share a story from Gilda Radner's book, *It's Always Something*.

> *When I was little, Dibby told me a story about her cousin who had a dog—just a mutt—and the dog was pregnant. I don't know how long dogs are pregnant, but she was due to have her puppies in about a week. She was out in the yard one day and got in the way of the lawnmower and her two back legs got cut off. They rushed her to the vet, who said, "I can sew her up, or you can put her to sleep if you want. But the puppies are OK—she'll be able to deliver the puppies.'" Dibby's cousin said, "Keep her alive." So the vet sewed up her backside and over the next week that dog learned how to walk. She didn't spend any time worrying; she just learned to walk by taking two steps in the front and flipping up her backside and then taking two more steps and flipping up her backside again. She gave birth to six little puppies, all in*

[21] Wilson, Andrew D. and Golonka, Sabrina. *Embodied cognition is not what you think it is.* Frontiers in Psychology, https://www.frontiersin.org/, February 12, 2013.

perfect health. She nursed them and then weaned them. And when they learned to walk, they all walked like her.[22]

"They all walked like her." Powerful illustration, right? You see, the puppies had perfectly functioning back legs, but because of their earliest "programming," they didn't use those legs as they were intended. As those puppies grow and begin interacting with other dogs, we could see several possible scenarios. Let's say that half of the puppies decide that they can get around much more quickly if they use those back legs. They have places to go and shoes to chew up! Their little brains scan all the available files to make sure this is not a "dangerous" option, and if no flags are found, this becomes a possibility. So by choosing this option, they use their mind to tell their brain, "*Hey, we would actually like to use these other two legs as well.*" The brain responds by telling the body to increase blood flow to the back legs, and with a little practice, voilà, the puppies are walking normally.

The other half of the litter decides that they don't really need their back legs. "Mom seems to manage fine. Those tall human folks seem to always bring the food to us and even pick us up and carry us." For these puppies, the mind communicates to the brain that the back legs are not needed, and the brain responds by reducing blood flow. This leads to muscle atrophy and eventual paralysis of the hind legs. The brain (computer) can run either program, "need back legs" or "don't need back legs." The mind needs to decide which. To do so, it performs a basic cost/benefit analysis to see which decision has the biggest "payoff" and is the safest option. Again, this will be different for each puppy, depending on how they process the world.

As easy as it would seem to just blame all our problems on our parents or our upbringing, it's not that simple. You have seen proof. Two children grow up in the same abusive and alcoholic home. One grows up to be seemingly well adjusted, and the other becomes an addict. I want to show you that our upbringing and surroundings as a child have an undeniable effect on how we process the world. Still, we cannot necessarily blame those circumstances for our current behavior.

---

[22] Radner, Gilda. *It's Always Something.* Simon & Schuster Pub. 2009.

From infancy, as we begin to use our eyes for the first time, we construct internal visual images of those around us. The experiences we have with our early caregivers, in addition to our internal images, become a lens through which we see others. Through this unique filter and way that we have learned to see the world, we begin to project this ideal onto other people. This is how we initially learn to process the world around us and, in turn, decide how to interact with that world. This learning especially shapes the way we view authority figures in our lives. Inevitably, it also shapes our view of God.

From the moment we are born, we begin building our unique and individual model of the world. As human beings, we are born almost entirely helpless. We are entirely dependent on the care of others to be alive. That sets the stage for a "dependent-driven" model of the world. This serves a baby and child well. Our brains are a virtual blank slate, and we need to learn *everything*. We must learn to walk, talk, feed ourselves, go to the bathroom—everything. Though we are incredibly complex as humans, we are born with very few survival skills and mechanisms. Babies are not only entirely dependent on their caregivers to meet their basic needs, but they also rely solely on them to develop their social/emotional skills and construct of spiritual beliefs. The child's very survival depends on the attachment with primary caregivers. Attachment is one of the first fundamental needs for survival. The capacity to move beyond survival and begin to mature and relate to the world develops out of this attachment bond. In other words, the child needs to adopt the beliefs and functions of their primary caregivers to gain the necessary skills to survive.

These attachments are central to developing the child's concept of self, others, and God. Ideally, attachments are safe, nurturing, and attentive experiences where the child is seen, heard, known, and loved. We are all aware that attachments can also be enmeshed, punishing, rejecting, or abusive. In these cases, the child will need to develop beliefs about themselves to allow continued attachments to their caregivers. A child simply does not yet possess the required prefrontal development to understand that the caregiver is acting out of their own experiences and learning and that it has little or nothing to do with the child. These children will make adaptations in their beliefs, bodies, and minds to maintain attachment and survive. These adaptations are a survival mechanism of the child, and therefore, are learned ways to "keep them safe."

We all come innately equipped with the ability to adapt for survival. This serves us well in childhood. Unfortunately, over time, these adaptations often become core belief structures that ultimately limit a person's capacity to see truth and develop safe and nurturing views of others.

Many children who experience negative attachments in their formative years develop the belief that they are unlovable or unworthy of love. Their coping skill often develops into one that is built around "doing enough" to feel worthy or lovable. But the more they work at doing better and being better, the farther away the finish line seems to be. As a way to continue in this belief, they subconsciously view *others* as unloving, including God. This "protects" them from having to suffer the dangers of developing true intimacy or attachment to others, God included.

As the child grows and continues any form of religious education, they are exposed to many and varied ways of conceptualizing God. With every new learning or observation, the child's brain revises its "God definition and view."

When this person becomes an adult and hears that they should trust God as a loving and nurturing Father, they may find they are unable to truly understand what this means. There is an inability for this individual to make that kind of intimate connection to God, not by conscious choice, but by the primal drive to remain "safe." As they keep God at a distance on a subconscious level, consciously, this only confirms that they are inherently unlovable, even by God. Intellectually they may read the Bible and hear otherwise, but their internal programming keeps playing the old records and revisiting the foundational beliefs. And that programming, unless changed, will always win. Dr. Bruce Lipton of Stanford University Medical Center, an expert on the subconscious mind, explains how this is true: "Most people don't even acknowledge that their subconscious mind is at play when the fact is it is a million times more powerful than the conscious mind and that we operate 95 to 99 percent of our lives from subconscious programs." This makes sense, considering that all our involuntary/ automatic actions (breathing, digestion, temperature regulation) happen without us being consciously aware of it. The subconscious mind does not have the ability to reason, be logical, or rationalize. It simply "outputs" whatever has been stored within.[23]

OUR BRAIN ON GOD

A special research team at the University of Pennsylvania has dedicated its resources to studying the human brain in relation to God. Headed up by Andrew Newberg, MD and Mark Robert Waldman, this team's findings were the subject of the book, *How God Changes Your Brain*. Though secular in its development, this book gives incredible insight into the neurological development of our "God construct."

I believe it is essential to understand that when someone says "God" or "the Bible" or speaks about Jesus, those things will mean drastically different things for each person. Ideally, certain sects or denominations strive for unity in doctrine and life application, but realistically, this is nearly impossible. Each one of us has a unique "God construct" that we reference subconsciously whenever we engage in spiritual thought or conversation. Our individual upbringings and life experiences inevitably influence this construct.

It is fascinating to realize that different religious activities, like praying or going to church, have different impacts on distinct regions of our brain. For the purpose of this book, I will not be deeply diving into the neuroscience of belief. But suffice it to say, it is out there. It is my belief and experience that when we acknowledge the fact that our upbringing has a direct effect on the way we conceptualize God and discern Scripture, we will be willing to observe our views from a higher perspective. Consider this quote from Newberg and Waldman from *How God Changes Your Brain*:

> *Many people use the word "God" to express what they feel is a universally understood concept, but when you look more closely, the definition of God becomes extraordinarily diverse. According*

---

[23] Bau, Annette. *The Power of Your Subconscious Mind.* https://www.iris.xyz. December 17, 2020

to the Baylor research, some see God as kind and loving, but twice as many Americans see God as punitive and stern. Some see God as distant and unconcerned, but many experience God as being actively involved in their lives. In fact, 20 percent even believe that God favors a specific political party.[24]

VICTIM VS. VICTOR

Children are almost always the "victim" of anything outside their control. Infants and young children require another human being to provide for their very survival, and this is responsible for this "victimhood." For example, if a baby is born to a mother addicted to methamphetamines, we simply cannot ascribe fault to that baby if it dies of starvation or neglect. The infant couldn't get away, reason with the mother, call for help, or feed itself. This child would unequivocally be a "victim." I think we can all agree on that. This dependent-driven model of thinking lasts into our early adolescent to late teen years and corresponds directly to our brain development. The problem is that a good percentage of the population never graduates out of this model of thinking. This facilitates an unwillingness to mature at the most basic of levels.

Though other versions of models of thinking exist, I have chosen to narrow it down to two primary mindsets and call them the *victim* and the *victor.*

The word "victim" has an interesting beginning. The root *vict* comes from Latin, where it has the meaning "conquer." The words "victor" and "victim" come from the same origin—the victor being the conqueror, and the victim being the one conquered. First recorded in 1490–1500, we see the Latin word *victima*, which described a sacrificial animal. "Victim" is now defined in the *Random House Unabridged Dictionary* as:

1. A person who suffers from a destructive or injurious action or agency: a victim of an automobile accident.

---

[24] Newberg, A. B., and Waldman, M. R. *How God changes your brain: Breakthrough findings from a leading neuroscientist.* New York: Ballantine Books, 2010.

2. A person who is deceived or cheated, as by his or her own emotions or ignorance, by the dishonesty of others, or by some impersonal agency: a victim of misplaced confidence; the victim of a swindler; a victim of an optical illusion.
3. A person or animal sacrificed or regarded as sacrificed: war victims.

I have personally struggled with this word and being labeled with it. Growing up in a home and family wrought with drug/alcohol addiction and sexual/physical abuse, I certainly felt like a victim! I definitely relate to definition #2 from *Random House*. Deceived? Uh-huh. Cheated? Yup. The problem was, I began to feel *more* victimized as I grew older. Though I was no longer in danger, abused, or neglected by my family members, I still felt like I was being deceived/cheated/neglected in many areas of my life.

It is true, bad things happen. While we are alive on this planet, I don't foresee an end to that. There will always be perpetrators, and there will always be victims of those perpetrations. So what is the difference between being a victim of a perpetration and having a victim mindset? I think a key to this lies in the second definition listed above. Notice #2, "a person who is deceived or cheated, as by his or her own emotions or ignorance."

In my personal life and my field of work, it has become important to differentiate between being a victim of a perpetration and having a victim mindset. We need to be very careful not to "blame the victim." I believe that a deeper understanding of the two mindsets, victim and victor, will help us acknowledge and respect the difference.

In the Gospel of John, Jesus interacts with a man at Bethesda. This was the home of many sick and diseased people. But whoever was the first to get into the pool after the angel would "stir the waters" would be healed. As Jesus walks through this supernatural site, he finds a man who has had an ailment for many decades.

> *Some time later, Jesus went up to Jerusalem for one of the Jewish festivals. Now there is in Jerusalem near the Sheep Gate*

> *a pool, which in Aramaic is called Bethesda and which is surrounded by five covered colonnades. Here a great number of disabled people used to lie—the blind, the lame, the paralyzed. One who was there had been an invalid for thirty-eight years. When Jesus saw him lying there and learned that he had been in this condition for a long time, he asked him, "Do you want to get well?" "Sir," the invalid replied, "I have no one to help me into the pool when the water is stirred. While I am trying to get in, someone else goes down ahead of me." Then Jesus said to him, "Get up! Pick up your mat and walk." At once the man was cured; he picked up his mat and walked.*
>
> **John 5:1–9**

At first glance, it is evident that Jesus knew this man was not new to his ailments. He understood that the man had been living with this issue for most of his life. Jesus also knew that people who have handicaps and diseases of sorts for an extended period often wrap their identity up with the disease. Whatever comes against us, many times, can end up being part of who we believe we are deep down.

But I love the question that Jesus asks the man. It confronts the victim mindset head on. To the typical modern reader, it would be easy to assume that Jesus was being a bit uncaring and insensitive, at least by the standards of our modern "tolerant" and "politically correct" world. Jesus doesn't ask for the story behind how tragedy fell upon this innocent man. He does no intake surrounding the factors that perhaps got him to his current state of being. His one single question is directed at the crux of the man's core desire and motivation: "*Do you want to get well?*" Jesus slices through the fluff and searches the heart: Do you really and truly long to be healed? To the average reader, this seems like the dumbest question in the world! Who would want to stay sick? But isn't that the same question Jesus poses to each of us, asking us to follow him? We have to *want* it and *do* something about it. Jesus didn't come to earth, wave his hand and say, "You are all healed and you're all saved because I want you to be. Yay!" Instead, Jesus takes our choice into account.

Now you'd think this guy would be like, "Oh yes, Jesus! That's why I'm here. I'll do anything! Please help me get well!" This is not what we read. Instead, we hear victimization as this man tells Jesus a story about the reasons he has problems and how everyone else is getting in his way, and no one is helping him. But Jesus did not ask for the story or the excuses or the reasons for why he was not well. He was simply asking a yes-or-no question.

Someone who is stuck in their victim mindset doesn't answer yes or no because that would draw the inevitable line in the sand, forcing a new way of living from that day forward. If the man were to reply with an enthusiastic "Yes!" then he would have to take personal responsibility from then on, living a new life as a healed man. If he were to say "No," when he has been sitting by this pool waiting for years to be healed, then he would look foolish and hypocritical in the eyes of everyone around. So then, how does he respond? He gives a list of reasons (excuses) why he hasn't been able to get his turn in the healing pool.

If this guy really wanted to heal, and if he really believed that this pool could do the job, then he would have convinced someone to help him out in all those years. He could have bribed someone by pledging his servitude or the bulk of his future earnings. He could have said, "Get me into that pool when the angel stirs the waters next month, and I will give you anything you want, do anything you want. Whatever it takes to repay you, I will do it if you just knock everyone else out of the way and give me the help I need to get well!"

Unfortunately, like many cases today, this was not the response we hear in the scripture. This man was so anchored to his story that his answer was the story. And if we are not careful, we, too, can all carry a story inside us that is different from the free life God would have us live. Our story that we many times carry around even after we find God and "give everything over to him" can often be flooded with chapters containing disappointment, regret, hurt, shame, guilt, insecurity, fear, pain, distorted perspectives, and thoughts that are limited to our own proofs and references. And then we live a new life in Christ, still carrying that old story in many different situations, projecting them into our future encounters.

The man by the pool was given an incredible opportunity to face his story and change it, replace it with the new life, the *new* story that Jesus was offering him. This new story was full of healing, wholeness, and transformation. And that is the same story that God is offering to each of us today. We must ask ourselves the same question that Jesus asked: do I truly want to be healed, changed, transformed?

I've sat down with many people who were looking for help in various settings: discipling or counseling or private sessions. They come to me to see if I can help them get out of whatever issue they are stuck in. I like to ask this question: "What are you willing to do or give up if this could be totally rectified, changed, and completely turned around?" They usually look back at me like I am crazy and reply with, "Anything!" But that's not always the case. I was on a phone call with a desperate woman last year who was going to leave her husband, children, and current life situation so she could live a "free life" away from the abuse and neglect.

I asked her (since she reached out and called me) if she really wanted things to change. Of course, the answer was an emphatic, "Yes!" (this had become a pattern of hers: leaving spouses, family, and churches to get her needs met and to stop what she felt was hurting her). She said she was willing to do anything to make this situation disappear. I then asked her if she wanted my perspective. She, again, replied, "Yes." I began to ask her questions that caused her to question her own history of choices and thoughts. I told her that she would have to stop abandoning and hurting others if she wanted to change being hurt and abandoned. I told her she would have to start to see people as helpful even when it didn't align with her staying a victim, that she would have to change, reach out to others, and see her part in the abuse and how she created her situation in the first place. Obviously, there was a lot more to the story and conversation, but you get the idea that there was a pattern, and she was always the victim. This was not the first or 10th conversation like this I had with her as the church minister. But she needed that question: "Are you willing to do anything to find the change?"

Healing always accompanies a new lifestyle and a whole new way of thinking, being, and living. Most people want the healing but are not willing to embrace what a healed life is all about. When Jesus tells the man to get up and walk, the Scriptures follow by saying that the man was "cured." The word here in Greek is ὑγιής (*hugiḗs*), which means sound or whole. Jesus healed the man, but the scripture does not say that he only healed him. The Scriptures reveal that Jesus makes him whole. God's interest is in our all-around wholeness. At this point, we tend to think the story is over. Jesus came. Jesus healed. Jesus left. But if we keep on reading, a few passages later, we see that Jesus again finds this same man inside the temple and gives him specific direction for his post-healed life.

> *Later Jesus found him at the temple and said to him, "See, you are well again. Stop sinning or something worse may happen to you.*
>
> **John 5:14**

Jesus wanted to make sure that this newly healed man understood that he was healed despite his sin issues. But Jesus also expressed that if this man was careless or irresponsible with this newfound gift of wholeness, a sin issue could rise up again, and he could be worse off than before. Jesus instructed the man to carefully guard and protect this wellness he had been gifted. He needed to watch his thought patterns and processes so as to not fall into the old ones that kept him sick, stuck, and stalemated. Jesus has a plan for us to claim victory over anything in our lives! Are you ready and willing to take hold of it? Let's continue exploring the *victim versus victor* mindsets.

THE VICTIM MINDSET

The power is *outside* us

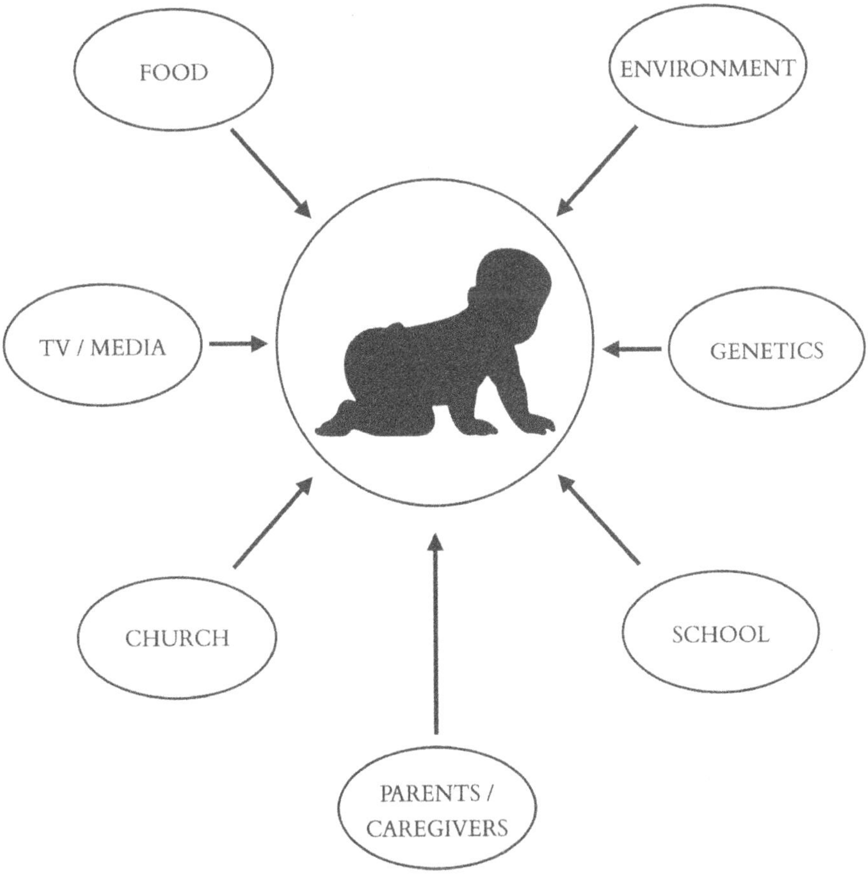

"*They*" are doing it to me

THE VICTIM MODEL OR MINDSET

The victim model of thinking is the one with which we come into the world. The child in the middle of the illustration is literally a victim of the necessary influencers. Though many of these "outside forces" or "influencers" may vary per child, the principle remains the same. We are undeniably influenced by our caregivers (parents, grandparents, other family members). In the "Victim Mindset" graphic, you see that the individual is surrounded by, or trapped by, the world around them. When someone remains in this model of thinking as an adult, their common mantra is, "*They* are doing it to me." Of course, the "they" and the "it" can be any number of things and people.

"*The food is making me fat.*"
"*My illness is the only thing that keeps me humble and close to God.*"
"*My parents abandoned me, so I can't trust people.*"
"*My pastor isn't really helping me, so I'm weak spiritually.*"
"*My coworkers make me feel bad.*"
"*I wouldn't get so angry if my husband would just listen to me.*"
"*Nobody understands my situation.*"
"*Purity will always be my struggle. That's why I can't give up pornography.*"
"*I'm depressed because nobody will love me.*"
"*I can't do it because of my ADHD/fibromyalgia/depression/(fill in diagnosis).*"
"*Aren't we all sinful by nature? I can never really be free from this sin.*"
"*My whole family loses their temper. We're just angry people.*"
"*I carry the gene for addiction, so that's why I abuse alcohol.*"
"*You shouldn't get your hopes up. Someone will always let you down.*"

The list goes on. In many ways, we are taught to continue in this model of thinking. Everywhere we look, people are searching for the reason why we are the way we are. Our society and culture promote the idea that we all need something or someone else to fulfill us. We have given the responsibility for our health and wellness to doctors. We have handed over the responsibility for our spirituality to churches and preachers. We have transferred the responsibility for our financial health to the government or economy. The list continues. We feel helpless until "they" tell us what to do, believe, eat, wear. When it doesn't work out, we blame those to whom we gave that responsibility.

But it's not all bad! The victim model of thinking comes with perks. Being a victim gives you power: power to avoid personal responsibility. This power allows you to feel "righteously" sad and persecuted, avoid uncomfortable emotions, and manipulate other people. People neglect to realize that the *power* they desperately seek is being handed over to others. This model of thinking puts the power of how to think/act/feel outside themselves. Because they have relinquished any responsibility for self, they now must find their value in the opinion of others. The saddest part about this model of thinking is just how much time and energy are spent on continuing to feel this way. Though people get better and better at what they practice, and the victim model comes naturally, they are spending a tremendous amount of effort on feeling terrible!

Though our caregivers are likely our biggest influencers, other people or entities have a significant effect too. Teachers, ministers, and friends are early influencers. TV, social media, politicians, doctors, and many other influences contribute to the way we shape and view our world.

DIANNE AND SHERRI

Let's take two examples of people with whom I have worked. Sherri was raised in the Midwest in a devoutly Christian home. Her parents were strict and dogmatic, but she never doubted their love or approval. Sherri's family shunned politics and media and allowed little contact with people they felt were "lost." Sherri sensed her parents' harrowing experiences surrounding childrearing. Sin and danger lurked around every corner. She felt oppressed at times and went through seasons of rebellion. Though her parents never forced her to follow their belief system and encouraged her to think for herself, Sherri sometimes felt responsible for keeping herself "in line." Despite this, Sherri believed she had a strong support system in her family and church and felt confident in her own identity.

Dianne, on the other hand, was raised in a "nontraditional" home. Dianne's parents were lesbians. Both her moms were liberal and very involved in activism and politics. While both were self-professed feminists, they encouraged Dianne to explore her own feelings and beliefs around being a woman. Dianne often struggled with the "nonparental" role that her mothers took. Essentially allowing Dianne to make her own rules, they believed they were empowering Dianne to be the "strong woman" she was intended to be. They did not believe in discipline and allowed Dianne to conveniently learn her lessons from her mistakes. Although this approach was envied by many of her friends, most of the time, Dianne wished she had a "normal" life and longed for structure.

Interestingly, both these women came to me as clients, struggling with the exact same "problem." Both women were battling infertility. Though both women had grown up feeling loved and supported, their individual environments led to feelings of fear and inadequacy when it came to the role of being a mother.

Infertility can often result from a subconscious fear or intimidation at the idea of being a parent. It can also signify deep, unresolved issues with one's own mother. Though not necessarily "traumatized," a person who has struggled with too many responsibilities as a child can have a deep fear that having a child will be overwhelming and may take up the little bit of free time or energy there is. Again, these are usually deep-seated and subconscious programs. They were input as a child through a child's understanding.

Both Dianne and Sherri had "good" childhoods. Upon further inspection, however, both also had a good deal of unresolved anger with their mothers. This deep internal conflict kept their bodies from fulfilling a natural and desired outcome—pregnancy. In both women, we had to go back and deal with the "victimized" child within. Individually and through different approaches, both women perceived that motherhood was a fearsome and challenging task. For Sherri, this played out through control and fear-based parenting. For Dianne, this manifested as "unparenting." Though they were both now adults, they were still manifesting their childhood confusion in their bodies. When the inner relationship with their mothers and their childhoods were healed, both women ended up conceiving and having an easy labor and delivery.

Neither one of these women would have said they felt like victims, but they were operating from a belief that said otherwise. When they took back their power and realized that they had filtered much of what their parents had been trying to do, they found compassion and forgiveness. Through this, they took responsibility and made peace within. As a result, both women became pregnant. The feeling of empowerment was much more conducive to childrearing than was victimization.

The victim mindset says, "*They* are doing it to *me*." Who is "they"? "They" is whoever is being held responsible for the discomfort. The problem is the way we perceive power.

The main problem with the victim mindset is where we place the power. In this mindset, the power is outside us. We give "them" the power to "make us" feel or do something. But it's actually *our* power to *give* power. Does that make sense? No person, place, or thing can make you feel a certain way. Only *you* have the power to determine how you will react to the things that happen around you. This is part of God's amazing gift of free will. We often think people are "taking away our power." And yes, when you were a child, that was possible. But as adults, what we do in our minds is far more powerful than what someone is trying to do to us.

Viktor E. Frankl, an Austrian neurologist, psychiatrist, and Holocaust survivor, said this: "*Everything can be taken from a man but one thing: the last of the human freedoms—to choose one's attitude in any given set of circumstances, to choose one's own way.*" [25]

Unspeakable atrocities have been perpetrated upon countless individuals over the time of human existence. I am not, in any way, trying to minimize that. Being victimized is rarely our choice; staying a victim is. We must take 100 percent responsibility for who we are being right now. That often means that we acknowledge some of the contributing factors in our life that helped us get where we are, good and bad. We can only change to the degree to which we are willing to take responsibility.

---

[25] Victor Frankel, *Man's Search for Meaning*, Beacon Press, June 1, 2006.

The Victor Mindset

The power is *inside* us

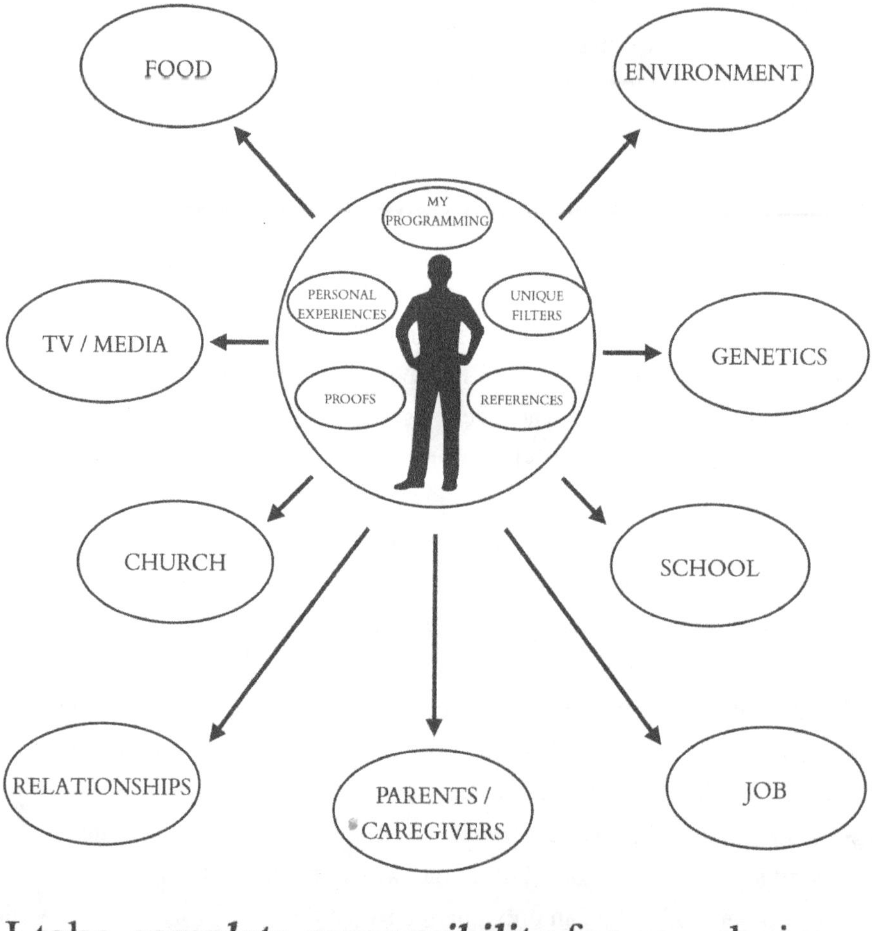

I take ***complete responsibility*** for my choices, actions, reactions, feelings, and emotions

THE VICTOR MODEL OR MINDSET

Now let's look at the victor model. The word "victor" comes from the Latin word meaning "to conquer."

This is some of what *Merriam-Webster Dictionary* has to say:

vic·tor (noun)
- a person who defeats an enemy or opponent in a battle, game, or other competition; "congratulations to the victors"
Synonyms: winner, champion, conqueror, vanquisher, conquering hero, prize winner, medalist, cup winner, champ, top dog, number one

Remember I mentioned power? While the victim model puts the power outside you, the victor model puts the power back where it really is: within! Living from this model of thinking shifts the power and responsibility back to you. Here we recognize that, though our family of origin and personal experiences in this world have shaped us, WE are in control over the way we feel about a situation and, as a result, the choices we make. Each one of us contains a unique set of experiences, filters, and perceptions. When we realize it is through those things that we evaluate the world around us, the power comes back to us.

We realize and understand that we are creators of the world that surrounds us. Though we cannot always control what people do around us or to us, we can have complete authority over the way we feel about it and what we do with it. Instead of giving others the power over how we feel, we take responsibility and realize the choice is ours. So rather than saying and believing, "You made me angry when you did that!" we can say, "I am angry about this." Better still, we don't have to choose to be angry, even if it's what we have always done in the past. If we feel angry, we realize it is by choice. This empowers us the way God always intended for us to be empowered. If I can choose to be angry, I can also choose to be something else instead. It doesn't mean that the situation didn't happen. It just means that we are taking control of the outcome.

Let's take traffic as an example. Likely, all of us are familiar with the unpleasant experience of being stuck in traffic or dealing with road rage. Say that you are driving to work one morning and somebody cuts you off. The victim model says, "I cannot believe that guy did that to me!" Because you now perceive that you were personally affected and targeted, you must retaliate. You may honk loudly and gesture wildly to convey the near-death experience that the person just caused. Or perhaps you yell loudly and proceed to give them a detailed account of what a terrible driver they are. Of course, they can't hear you, but still! Or you could wait until the next light and strategically place yourself in the next lane so that you can turn slowly and give an epic stink eye. All this, in response to "what they did to you." The victor model says, "I can choose to be angry, or I can choose to be at peace." If you typically choose the lower, victimized model, your first inclination will be to anger. That is your go-to response. You likely practice this daily and, therefore, are very good at it. But when you recognize that it's your choice how to feel and react, the power is back inside you. Again, this is how God intended and made us to work!

GOD'S ROLE IN THE VICTOR MINDSET

If you are reading this book, you may likely have some religious affiliation. Some of the resistance or pushback we have received on this subject matter is that it seems as if we are leaving God out of the equation when it comes to self-empowerment. So I want to clarify our stance. To address this, we will look at the longstanding religious debate around free will versus determinism.

Far be it from me to try to solve this debate or even explain it fully in the following text. If hundreds of theological scholars haven't been able to briefly summarize it, I seriously doubt I can.

Theological determinism says that free will does not actually exist because God has inevitable and absolute power and dominion over the earth and its people.[26]

If I asked you whether you believed in free will, my guess is that you would say yes. It is essential to understand that much of who we are and how we process life comes from the way we were raised, in and around our early

[26] Wikipedia. *Theological determinism*. https://en.wikipedia.org, August 31, 2020.

influences. But we must also realize how our current religious beliefs have been shaped and influenced by Christian history.

Historically, the concept of theological determinism has its roots within a significant theological dispute during the 16th century. This argument between two highly respected thinkers would help create two distinct divisions. Desiderius Erasmus held to the belief that God created man and woman with free will. Martin Luther, a leading Protestant Reformer, attacked this idea, believing that a person can *know* what is morally right but cannot attain it. For Luther, this meant that humans must, therefore, give up trying to do good since they are basically unable to do so.[27] There are a few widely held variations within the extremes:

Determinism: Fate with No Freedom
Compatibilism: Freedom within Fate
Concurrence: Fate within Freedom
Libertarianism: Freedom with No Fate[28]

Again, the goal here is not to tackle this theological debate. My goal is to remind us that our beliefs around this concept will inevitably change how we see our relationship with God. At some point in your life, I'm sure you have heard (or said) something to the effect of, "It's only because of God that __________ happened." Here are a few modern examples you may encounter:

"This job is totally from God."
"God brought me to this city."
"God brought this man/woman into my life."
"God got me into this school."
"God healed me."
"God said no to my healing."
"This is a test from God."

---

[27] Wikipedia. *Theological determinism*. https://en.wikipedia.org, August 31, 2020.

[28] Chilton, B. *4 Views of Free Will*. https://www.christianpost.com, December 1, 2018.

Of course, "*we know that in all things God works for the good of those who love him*" (Romans 8:28). Overall, none of the above statements are "bad." But are they true? We need to think about what they ultimately communicate. How do you *know* that it was God? (Or is this just lip service?) This general line of thinking has one pivotal pitfall: what happens when things don't go our way? We almost immediately place blame on the "other guy." Yep—Satan.

If you have spent any time with me in the last few years, you have likely heard me say this: I think we give Satan way too much credit. I think we talk about him too much, involve him too much, and use him as a scapegoat for all types of issues. Consider James 1:14, which teaches us that "*each person is tempted when they are dragged away* ***by their own evil desire***" (emphasis added).

I know what happens to things we give attention to: they grow. I have no desire to be in the "Satan-growing" business. But just like I think we give too much credit to Satan, I think we also need to check in with how we view God within the realm of our own choices. We must understand that our definitions of "good" and "bad" are highly personal and uniquely shaped.

As 17th-century theologian John Bramhall dramatically words it:

> *It were better to be an atheist, to believe no God; or to be a Manichee, to believe two Gods, a God of good and a God of evil; or with the heathens, to believe thirty thousand Gods; than thus to charge the true God to be the proper cause and the true author of all the sins and evils which are in the world.* (*Vindication of True Liberty*, 1655, 1.11)[29]

Mr. Bramhall is saying that it would be better to be a pagan than to place responsibility for a human being's choices, actions, or consequences on God. In case you are unfamiliar with what a Manichee is, "Manichaeism was a major religion founded in the third century CE by the Persian prophet Mani. It was

[29] Fieser, J. *Great Issues in Philosophy*. https://www.utm.edu, January 1, 2021.

briefly the main rival to Christianity before the spread of Islam in the competition to replace classical paganism."[30]

Sometimes we make dumb choices. This often results in uncomfortable consequences. This is usually not spiritual warfare; this is how we grow as humans. We are meant to learn from our mistakes and celebrate our victories. Our religious obsession with scapegoating God or Satan for our every move keeps us immature in our spiritual growth. Since Adam and Eve participated in the fruit debacle, we have struggled with our ability to use the gift of free will. When I speak about self-empowerment, self-esteem, self-love, or any other "self" related teaching, I am inevitably including God, because our will comes from God. Our ability to decide, make choices, and discern "good" from "evil"; and our subsequent role in accepting the consequences of those decisions is what we mean when we say empowerment. We simply cannot leave God out of something that is his design in the first place. Because of my inherent default to this belief, I do not feel the need to qualify every mention of our own power with credit being given to God. It's already there. God is in the victor model because victory was his will for us. When we take back our power or transform with the renewing of our mind, God is right there, cheering us on to victory! You may have noticed that I have not mentioned the role of the Holy Spirit in this equation. One of the greatest gifts God has given to those who turn to him is the indwelling of the Holy Spirit. I believe the counsel and help provided by the Holy Spirit are a marvelous mystery, and an integral part of what allows us to change. I think the Holy Spirit is instrumental in helping us reveal the places inside us that need healing. Ultimately, this book is not about how the Holy Spirit works. I don't think that knowledge is in my wheelhouse! It is about God enabling us to inherently transform—mind, body, and soul.

DANGERS OF THE VICTIM MODEL

Remember I said earlier that the victor model shifts the power and responsibility back to you? We like the idea of power being ours, but

---

[30] Wikipedia. *Manichaeism*. https://en.wikipedia.org/, January 16, 2021

responsibility...not so much. I will be the first to admit that blame-shifting is *much* easier than taking responsibility. At least at first glance. If "they" made me do it, then I am not technically responsible for my actions. Of course, this is seldom true. You know the saying, "With great power comes great responsibility."

Many decades ago, there was a famous black-and-white TV series entitled *The Twilight Zone*. The opening sequence is narrated with a monologue that I think is well fitting for the scriptures I am about to share.

> *You unlock this door with the key of imagination. Beyond it is another dimension: a dimension of sound, a dimension of sight, a dimension of mind. You're moving into a land of both shadow and substance, of things and ideas. You've just crossed over into...the* [Victim] *Zone*.[31]

You see, playing the victim is a rather slippery slope. It may start with an imagined thought of the mind, but that thought becomes more and more real. No longer a shadow, it turns to substance. This victimization is felt, seen, heard, and shortly after that, fully believed. This idea of fear is now a thing to blame. No more are you responsible because you have a reason, an excuse, and a scapegoat to blame. Welcome to the *Victim Zone*.

This mentality is seen throughout the Bible. It's there when Adam blames Eve for giving him the fruit and Eve blames the serpent for tricking her. It's evident when Abraham sleeps with Hagar, blaming Sarah, who then blames God for not coming through in a timely fashion. The victimization is seen in David when he, in fear, gets Uriah killed so that he can keep Bathsheba's pregnancy under wraps. Many times when we feel threatened, we find a way to victimize others, like the Pharisees and the sinful woman in John 8. But even when Jesus was persecuted, lied about, spit on, put on trial for no wrongdoings of his own,

[31] Sterling, Rod, creator. *The Twilight Zone*. Cayuga Productions, 1962. CBS Television Network.

Here we have fear, followed by blame, sinking Saul right into the *Victim* *one*, followed up with consequences. Now hear me out: consequences can have ɔsitive outcomes or negative ones. It depends on the decision made. For ıstance, if someone eats fast food for five years with little or no exercise and an ıhappy lifestyle, the consequence will be an overweight, unhealthy body and ind. On the flip side, if someone chooses to eat a whole-foods organic diet hile exercising regularly and living a joy-filled lifestyle, the consequence will a fit, healthy, and happy body and mind. It's simply a matter of choice. Saul ose to play the victim, which, in the end, will always lead to adverse outcomes mind, body, and spirit).

Unfortunately, Saul continues in the victim model. In 1 Samuel 15:3, God, rough his prophet, tells his anointed King Saul to "*totally destroy all that longs to them.*" This word "destroy" comes from the Hebrew וְהַֽחֲרַמְתֶּם, which en transliterated is *vehucharumiem*. In its totality, this word refers to the evocable giving over of things or persons to the Lord, usually by utterly stroying them. This is very strong and direct language spoken to Saul. Here is other God-given chance to make wise choices out of trust, love, patience, joy, l peace. God goes on to further instruct in detail, with specific guidelines, what do with the plunder. So what does Saul do?

> *But Saul and the army spared Agag and the best of the sheep and cattle, the fat calves and lambs—everything that was good. These they were unwilling to destroy completely, but everything that was despised and weak they totally destroyed... When Samuel reached him, Saul said, "The Lord bless you! I have carried out the Lord's instructions." But Samuel said, "What then is this bleating of sheep in my ears? What is this lowing of cattle that I hear?" Saul answered, "The soldiers brought them from the Amalekites; they spared the best of the sheep and cattle to sacrifice to the Lord your God, but we totally destroyed the rest... I went on the mission the Lord assigned me. I completely destroyed the Amalekites and brought back Agag their king. The*

flogged, and crucified to death, he never succumbed to the *Victim Z* gives birth to blame. Jesus held on to neither of these.

Now let's dive deeper. In 1 Samuel we have many stories about the God acting out of fear and then blaming their faults on someone or s else. Saul, for example, continuously jumped into the *Victim Zone*. Al reigned for about 40 years and was given chance after chance to learn, overcome his major shortcomings, he still chose to fear, to blame, a sorry for himself. So much so that, in the end, he even took his own life

In chapter 13 in the book of 1 Samuel, God has instructed the I wait for the Lord's timing. At just the right time, Samuel would make to the Lord, which would then allow for Saul and his army to fight w their side. Instead, Saul, driven by fear, sacrificed in his own time in hi

> *Saul remained at Gilgal, and all the troops with him w quaking with fear. He waited seven days, the time set by Sam but Samuel did not come to Gilgal, and Saul's men begar scatter. So he said, "Bring me the burnt offering and fellowship offerings." And Saul offered up the burnt offering. as he finished making the offering, Samuel arrived, and went out to greet him. "What have you done?" asked San Saul replied, "When I saw that the men were scattering, and you did not come at the set time, and that the Philistines assembling at Mikmash, I thought, 'Now the Philistines come down against me at Gilgal, and I have not sough Lord's favor.' So I felt compelled to offer the burnt offer "You have done a foolish thing," Samuel said. "You have not the command the Lord your God gave you; if you had, he v have established your kingdom over Israel for all time. But your kingdom will not endure; the Lord has sought out a after his own heart and appointed him ruler of his pe because you have not kept the Lord's command."*
>
> **1 Samuel 13**

> *soldiers took sheep and cattle from the plunder, the best of what was devoted to God, in order to sacrifice them to the Lord your God at Gilgal." But Samuel replied: "Does the Lord delight in burnt offerings and sacrifices as much as in obeying the Lord? To obey is better than sacrifice, and to heed is better than the fat of rams. For rebellion is like the sin of divination, and arrogance like the evil of idolatry. Because you have rejected the word of the Lord, he has rejected you as king." Then Saul said to Samuel, "I have sinned. I violated the Lord's command and your instructions. I was afraid of the men and so I gave in to them.*
>
> **1 Samuel 15:9, 13–15, 20–24**

A different story with a different situation on a different day within a different year—but with the same outcome. Why? You guessed it! The *Victim Zone*. Saul, holding onto the fear of losing his kingdom (from 1 Samuel 13), now adds more fear to this battle and, in so doing, makes more poor choices.

I know for me, when I am fearful of what my wife is thinking or feeling, or perhaps that I am not doing right in her eyes, the victim cycle begins. When I so desperately want to do right by her, I envision and guess at what she might be thinking or feeling about me. This causes me to pull back, and I start to act according to what she *might* be feeling. My attempts to walk on eggshells cause me to mess things up even more! When I am extra careful (really, because I am driven by fear), I am not present, not fully attentive, and will default to my way of doing things. I make terrible decisions driven by fear, followed by excuses and blame-shifting in order not to make her more angry or disappointed with me (my own filtered assumptions). Guilt and shame follow. Congratulations, Kent. You have just crossed over into the *Victim Zone*. I take on the role of the victim when I react with or live out of fear and insecurity. And there are always consequences. But not punitive ones. The consequence is needing to rebuild trust within myself; strength, confidence, attentiveness, and truthfulness within myself. Although Heather may have her own emotions from this situation, the more considerable consequence is that I now must work at climbing out of my victimhood hole. I must come back into the light, into the truth, and take off the filters I have covered myself with. Because this is *not* the way God created me. I have covered myself with the leaves of F.I.G.S. and have let that sin (fear, insecurity, guilt, shame) show up. The choice from here is mine: be the victim by blaming, or be the victor by showing up, growing up, and getting up.

Saul made the mistake of making poor decisions driven by fear and then trying to cover those up by "giving" and "sacrificing" to the Lord. And Samuel tells us that God doesn't want even the best sacrifices. He wants obedience. And what is the bigger picture here? God made us to *be like him*. He made us *very good*! Obedience to God is not just about "doing the right things," but about living in accordance with the truth of who we really are. And we were not created for fear, insecurity, guilt, or shame. We were created to bear his image. We were created to be victorious. He created our bodies and our brains with the capability to overcome anything: "*I can do anything through him who gives me strength*" (Philippians 4:13). God made us with the ability to be continuously "*transformed by the renewing of* [our] *mind*" (Romans 12:2).

OUR VIEW OF GOD: LIVING AS A REFLECTION OF OUR PERSPECTIVE

How we see God and what kind of God we worship has a massive impact on how we live and feel. Take the parable of the talents (bags of gold) in Matthew 25. Three men were given three differing amounts of money to handle. How they took responsibility for this borrowed wealth was completely up to each of them. Two of them, although having very different amounts, took what they were given and multiplied it. This would have been in response to a twofold view of their master: 1) they believed that just as greatness was bestowed upon them, so too, greatness was expected of them, and 2) these men took pride in their master and joy in their work. In so doing, they were able to take part in their master's joy: "*Come and share in your master's happiness*" (Matthew 25:23). The third man, however, had a contrary view of his master and therefore created a very different outcome. He was so fearful of his master (God), that he froze and did nothing (Matthew 25:25). He even made excuses, accusing the master of being "*a hard man, harvesting where* [he had] *not sown and gathering where* [he had] *not scattered seed*" (Matthew 25:24). The response was interesting. The master did not argue with the man, telling him that he was wrong. Instead, he simply asked him why, if this was the man's view of him, did he not make different choices. The man's misconception of his master, as well as his poor decision-making following from this wrongful view, created quite a different outcome for him. Did the master *want* to throw this man out? No. This man created his own reality by reflecting his own perception.

We can do the same thing in our relationship with God. If we see God as a Zeus archetype, we may just follow him out of fear, missing out on the power and wonder he wants to bring in our lives. If we view God as evasive and distant, we may disregard him completely, missing out on the safety, grace, fellowship, and purpose he offers. Our lives, in one way or another, will reflect our perspective of the amazing Master. Do you ever feel like God is against you or that life is just too hard? Is it possible that your victim-model beliefs are paving the way for this reality? After all, you, like God, are a creator.

We tend to think that the USA is becoming more and more secular. But the government's recent General Social Survey shows that only 11 percent of people in the country do not associate with any sort of religion. At the Baylor Institute for Studies on Religion, a detailed survey was taken that proved some very interesting connections between beliefs in God and the outcome of people's lives.

One specific part of the survey questioned people's perspectives on God's engagement and emotional disposition. Researchers found that the type of god people believe in can predict their political and moral attitudes, more so than just looking at their religious tradition.[32]

31% believe in an Authoritarian God, who is very judgmental and engaged.
25% believe in a Benevolent God, who is not judgmental but engaged.
23% believe in a Distant God, who is completely removed.
16% believe in a Critical God, who is judgmental but not engaged.
The other 5% were scattered.

---

32 Baylor University News. *Losing My Religion? No, Says Baylor Religion Survey.* https://www.baylor.edu/mediacommunications/, September 11, 2006.

Dr. Andrew Newberg (mentioned earlier) is a doctor of neurotheology—this research applies science and the scientific method to spirituality through brain-imaging studies. These scans have shown how religious practices such as meditation, prayer, or even how we view God can help shape a brain.

Dr. Newberg's research has shown that worshiping a god whom we deem as punitive and distant causes anxiety, depression, and stress. His research also indicates that a fundamentalist form of Christianity (reading the Bible in a strict, legalistic way with a similarly rigid and judgmental mode of practice) damages the brain in ways that are hard to heal. On the flipside, worshiping a loving, compassionate, and engaging God increases feelings of security, compassion, and love. And the results show that brain function is higher with faster thinking and processing.[33]

The clearer our view of who God is, the perfect God of agape, the more our neuro-circuitry will flow with security and love and compassion, thinking and feeling clearer than ever before. When we have that kind of God-spirit in us, transformation continues to flow.

> *Now the Lord is the Spirit, and where the Spirit of the Lord is, there is liberty, emancipation from bondage, true freedom. And we all, with unveiled face, continually seeing as in a mirror the glory of the Lord, are progressively being transformed into his image from one degree of glory to even more glory, which comes from the Lord, who is the Spirit.*
>
> **2 Corinthians 3:17–18** AMP

Let me close this chapter with this question: what is your view of God? When you let go of the filters from your past, you will begin to recognize that your view of God is freer, bigger, broader, truer. God made you in his image to be a victor in every sense of the word. The choice is yours. He has given you that amazing power. *With great power comes great responsibility.*

---

[33] Newberg, A. B., and Waldman, M. R. *How God changes your brain: Breakthrough findings from a leading neuroscientist.* New York: Ballantine Books, 2010.

CHAPTER 8

POWERFUL CREATORS

"Creator" is the first characteristic God reveals to us about himself in Scripture. In the first chapter and verse of Genesis, we are shown who our God is. He is the *Creator*. Not *a* creator or someone who simply "creates." He is *the* Creator.

> *Through him all things were made; without him nothing was made that has been made.*
>
> **John 1:3**

> *By the word of the Lord the heavens were made,*
> *their starry host by the breath of his mouth.*
>
> **Psalm 33:6**

God brought to life all things out of nothing. That is how powerful he is, and we are created in his image. We were created to *be* creators. Notice how God invited Adam to "get creative" in his naming of the animals (Genesis 2:19–20). God also allows Adam to create the name "woman." I believe God relishes our ability to create.

I love to see my children's creations—early misshapen drawings, unidentifiable structures built of popsicle sticks, glue, and construction paper, and notes of love with words like "speshal." I love their creations. Even now, as their fabrications are much more refined and intricate, it is a joy to watch them create. Sometimes, they ask what they can give me for a birthday present, and I simply reply for them to make me a card. It's not the card itself or the drawings or the words even. I love when they create something from their own mind and heart. That's what makes it so special.

In Genesis, we also notice that God endowed Adam and Eve with dominion or rule over the fish, birds, wild animals, and all creatures. We also see an important development in Genesis 2: the recognition of free will. God created us to create, and our free will is the essential component of that ability. This was a risky but necessary endowment to his creation. But it was the only way to enable his children to choose a relationship with him. God fearfully and wonderfully created us to be powerful creators. We have the ability to create our own personal experience with our surroundings. Adam and Eve did not choose what they were born into, but after that, they were able to choose *what they did with it*. I love this quote from Marianne Williamson:

> *Our deepest fear is not that we are inadequate. Our deepest fear is that we are powerful beyond measure. It is our light, not our darkness that most frightens us. We ask ourselves, "Who am I to be brilliant, gorgeous, talented, fabulous?" Actually, who are you not to be? You are a child of God. Your playing small does not serve the world. There is nothing enlightened about shrinking so that other people won't feel insecure around you. We are all meant to shine, as children do. We were born to make manifest the glory of God that is within us. It's not just in some of us; it's in everyone. And as we let our own light shine, we unconsciously give other people permission to do the same. As we are liberated from our own fear, our presence automatically liberates others.*[34]

I find that many people "do" their Christianity with a rather backward mindset. The contemporary Christian world says that we, as humans, are powerless, broken sinners. When you search for a "Christian" song on the radio, more times than not, you will find lyrics containing one of two categories: either the magnificence of God or the brokenness that is us. I believe most songwriters are composing from their heart and soul, but our feelings and thoughts do not

---

[34] Williamson, Marianne. Quoted in the *Inaugural Speech of Nelson Mandela.* https://uh.edu/~hwagan/pnl/mandela.pdf. 1994

always make what we write true. Yes, God is magnificent, majestic, merciful, mighty, marvelous. God is sovereign, sacred, and our savior. He is powerful, and he is holy. How great is our God! But where in the Bible does God call us broken or powerless? Romans 5:6 may come to mind: "*You see, at just the right time, when we were still powerless, Christ died for the ungodly.*" Yes, the word "powerless" is used in English, but the Greek word here is ἀσθενής (*asthenés*), meaning without vigor, living in a state of weakness, sluggish in doing right. And the scripture is true: we needed Jesus to save us, to die for us. But it is still within our power to respond and *take* the help. Many people associate powerlessness with having no choice in the matter. On the contrary, the power of choice is exactly what God has bestowed upon all of humanity. Where in the whole text of God's word does he deem us naturally limited or instinctively powerless? When did God start creating us as weak? Never! I challenge you to find any truth that God created humans with these "less-than" attributes. Yes, you can find all the scriptures about the Spirit helping us in our weakness (like Romans 8:26). But that weakness is only there due to our choices to stray from the strength God instills in and offers all of us.

Let's cut to the chase regarding our current Christian society's definition of "strength in weakness." I believe that accurately defining any misconceptions will clear many other ill-attachments to the idea of us as powerless or weak. First of all, we must remember who we are and who God created us to be (very good, divinely created, perfectly made). Then we need to recall what sin is (a deviation from the way we were originally created) and how this will influence and distort our lives, beliefs, and truths. Remember that the thief (whether that be sin or Satan) comes "*to steal and kill and destroy*" (John 10:10). So yes, sin does have an effect on us, but is this who we are? Are we sin? Are we weak? Are we powerless? Even Paul says that his sin is not him, but rather "*it is sin living in me*" (Romans 7:17). In a moment, I will share several scriptures that we will examine to understand the context fully so we can truly comprehend God's standpoint of weakness versus power. Although we cannot go into all the scriptures that present this idea, I believe looking closely at a few will help shed light on the whole.

Let me start by saying that I do not believe we are made weak, nor are we inherently weak. Instead, we *do* weakness. If weakness is not who we are or how we were created, then weakness is simply a filter/burden/sin that we put on or hold onto. So weakness comes as a result of believing what the world says about us, rather than God. The closer we are to God, the more power we come into contact with. True weakness is believing that we need something *outside* us to make us strong. However, when we choose God, we can choose to transform. We can take off the old self, the filtered self, the deviated self and, instead, shine brightly from the strength God already planted inside us.

Think about it this way—you have a bright shining lamp and decide to cover it with a thick blanket. Does that mean that the lamp is no longer bright? Do we just need to force more wattage and try to shine through? Of course not! All we have to do is take off the blanket (the filter) and let it shine, let it shine, let it shine. I'm pretty sure Jesus told us that no one lights a lamp and puts it "*under a bowl. Instead, they put it on its stand, and it gives light to everyone in the house*" (Matthew 5:15). You see, the issue is never the lamp. The predicament is never God's creation (you and me). The dilemma is simply the filters, the sin, the deviations from who we really are. That is what Jesus came to set us free from.

I find it interesting that with all the wonderful scriptures that speak about our strength, power, holiness, and righteousness, Christians still seem to gravitate toward the verses that appear to contradict that sentiment. Paul goes into great detail in Romans 8, explaining that we are justified, chosen, and no longer condemned when we are in Christ. He reminds us that Jesus is interceding for us and that nothing can separate us from God's love. He reminds us that we are more than conquerors. Even after all this, many of us relate more strongly to what we *think* Paul is saying in 2 Corinthians 12:7–10 regarding his "thorn." We must always remember to consider the context when looking for biblical truths or precepts for Christian living. In my experience, the thorn scripture is one of the most often quoted to argue for our "weakness." But we need to consider the entire context of what Paul is trying to communicate.

> *Therefore, in order to keep me from becoming conceited, I was given a thorn in my flesh, a messenger of Satan, to torment me. Three times I pleaded with the Lord to take it away from me. But he said to me, "My grace is sufficient for you, for my power is made perfect in weakness." Therefore I will boast all the more gladly about my weaknesses, so that Christ's power may rest on me. That is why, for Christ's sake, I delight in weaknesses, in insults, in hardships, in persecutions, in difficulties. For when I am weak, then I am strong.*
>
> **2 Corinthians 12:7–10**

I can't tell you how many times I have heard people reference this scripture to explain an illness, hardship, or unrepented-of sin in their lives. I have even heard people say, "God has given me this thorn."

Let's start by remembering that Paul was not only Jewish but also a Pharisee, deeply indoctrinated in Jewish culture and scriptural symbolism. We can all agree that this "thorn" was not a literal thorn in Paul's side. Some people have said that the thorn was a physical ailment, but that is unlikely, as Paul has candidly spoken about his physical hardships in other letters without the use of symbolism. The first time the Bible ever uses the phrase "thorns in your sides" is in Numbers 33:55. The reference to thorns in this verse refers to the harassment and persecution that Israel received from the surrounding nations at that time. We see this same context used in Joshua 23:13 and Ezekiel 28:24. Interestingly enough, in the two chapters before 2 Corinthians 12, we find Paul speaking about being persecuted by the religious leaders, political authorities, and false prophets surrounding him.

Remember that Paul says this "thorn" is a messenger of Satan. What do we know about the language of Satan? The native tongue of Satan is lies, usually pertaining to the way God feels about us. Paul was being persecuted by the very people he used to pander to, and it might be tempting to feel weak about his status with God. Foreign nations were often deemed enemies because of their power to pull people away from God-worship.

"Three times I pleaded." Why three times? Have you ever wondered why he only prayed three times, or why that is mentioned? For the Jews, the number three signifies completeness and stability. We see this also in the number of times Jesus prays to God at Gethsemane, looking for clarity of will. Paul intended to let us know that he had prayed, pleaded, and spoken with the Lord precisely the right number of times until everything was divinely fulfilled. What was the "divine answer" Paul received? Most people say that God said no. I invite you to reread the verse. God did not say no. He said that his grace was sufficient and that his power was made perfect in weakness.

The Greek word for "grace" used here is χάρις (*charis*). Properly, this word is defined as leaning toward someone to share a benefit. It is used when speaking of "the Lord's favor." God is always "leaning toward his people." In other words, God is telling Paul that "I am already leaning toward you. I already have given you everything you need for life and godliness. I have created you *powerfully*. Don't *think* you are; *know* you are." God goes on to talk about how this *leaning in toward Paul* is "sufficient" for him. Could this "thorn" be how Paul was tempted to feel about himself after the persecution from the religious and political leaders that were formerly allies—the same men who commissioned Paul to kill the very Christians he is now counseling? I'm sure Satan had a field day with that reminder. I can imagine these statements stabbing right into his side, trying to penetrate his heart.

What if God was saying, "Paul, this weakness that you are feeling is fear, insecurity, guilt, and shame. This is what weakens you. But this is where I shine. This is where I get to stand in for you and disagree. This is where I get to say that *you* are powerful because you belong to *me*. And I am powerful enough to overcome the persecution. When you realize that I am powerfully leaning toward you and that I am enough, you, in turn, can lean toward me and realize that you are powerful—that you are enough."

God does not need our weakness to make his power perfect. Think about that. What kind of God requires his people to be weak so he can be strong? I don't believe that is what this scripture is saying. Thankfully, we can find the truth through context! Paul closes his thoughts on this matter as he states that he will "boast all the more gladly" about weaknesses (opportunities to lean in to God). He remembers that he already has the power to "*demolish arguments and every pretension that sets itself up against the knowledge of God*" (2 Corinthians 10:5). Paul now delights in the opportunities he has to remember his strength from God's love. He closes with a powerful statement that is imperative for us to understand correctly: "*For when I am weak, then I am strong*" (1 Corinthians 12:10).

As we consider the deeper context of these verses, we can see our weaknesses for what they are: deviations from the goodness that God created in us. Like Paul, our thorns are the mental roadblocks, the emotional strongholds, the condemnation that Satan tries to ensnare us in. Our weakness is an opportunity to *lean in* and remember who we are—and *whose* we are.

To further help you understand Paul's true perspective, I want to talk about acorns. Acorns are small seeds that, if you're not careful while strolling around the woods in the Northeast, will bounce off your head in the autumn breeze. When I was a kid, I would find them on the ground and see how far I could throw them. Sometimes I would take a few of them home. Other times I would try to open them up carefully and set them out for squirrels to find. But the thing about acorns is that they are relatively small compared to the giant oak trees they produce. But how do they grow? God instilled a power of growth and transformation inside that tiny little acorn. That power can allow that small seed to become a giant oak tree that can live for centuries! Do you think that God comes down each year and zaps each individual acorn as they are planted with the power of life and unlimited growth potential? No! God has already placed all that potential power inside each and every acorn from the very start. But what if I planted the acorn in a sealed plastic box to "protect" it? The seed would die, because that is not how it was created to live. God gives us the same instilled power. Since he made humans in his image, in his likeness, there is no special "zapping" that needs to be done. It's already there if we will only take the "protective" layers and filters off and let that power grow!

I hope this brings clarity to the fact that God did not make us weak, but instead that we are strong because we are made in his image, in his power. David Carr says it this way when he explains the creation story of us:

> *God's climactic creative act is to stamp humans with divine form so that they may access a royal authority over what God had created. Every bit of Genesis 1 up to the creation of the humans has underlined God's own king-like ability to order creation. Then God makes humans, [and] the human body, rather than being a sign of human limitation, is actually a mark of our connection to God. Contrary to ancient Western presuppositions, the human body is not a mark of slavery to the earth. Instead, Genesis 1 asserts that the human body, male or female, is a mark of awesome, free authority over creations for which we as humans were created to "be fruitful and multiply," a reflection of God's power to give life.*[35]

I love that God has even given us the amazing power to create, not only who we are and what we do, but even the power to create other human beings! When I first held my daughter in my arms after my wife gave birth, I felt the power of responsibility. But somewhere deep down, when the world was still and quiet, I knew, as I held my little girl, that I was able, capable, and that God trusted me with that power.

We, like God, can call into creation what is not. He has given us everything we need!

> *For his divine power has bestowed upon us all things that are requisite and suited to life and godliness, through the full, personal knowledge of him who called us by and to his own glory and excellent virtue.*
>
> **2 Peter 1:3** AMPC

---

[35] Carr, David M. *The Erotic Word: Sexuality, Spirituality, and the Bible.* Oxford University Press, 2005.

To illustrate our own relation to our creation and to our personal power, I'd like to explain a little bit about the power of our thoughts.

THOUGHTS = THINGS

Have you ever felt controlled by a thought? You can be going along, minding your own business, and then a random but powerful thought enters your mind and takes over. "*I wonder if my coworker is mad at me.*" You weren't even thinking about work, but now this seemingly random thought enters your mind, and you can't shake it. You were just driving home, listening to the radio, and thinking of what you were going to make for dinner. Now you are engaged in a full-on mental investigation into your day to see if you can figure out why your coworker may have been mad at you. "*Did I say something that offended her?*" You rack your brain and replay the conversations from earlier in the day to see where the possible offense may have been. "*Maybe someone told her I said something about her.*" Now you are going through a list of possible suspects in your mind. If someone were to be a casual observer of your mind and body, they would notice that your mood and body language dramatically changed, even though the outside environment remained the same.

See, thoughts are things. Actual things. In my first book, *Mind Change*, I discuss the chemical make-up of a thought in more detail. For now, just know that thoughts produce feelings and emotions, and those feelings and emotions create our mood and perceived reality.

When we think, the physical nature of our brain changes. Prentice Mulford, who wrote *Thoughts Are Things* in 1889, states that "we think in matter," meaning that when we produce a thought, matter is produced. This seems congruent with God's method of creation. God *thought* of what he wanted and consequently *spoke* those thoughts into matter and substance. Consider some of the biblical references to our thoughts:

> *How long must I wrestle with my thoughts*
> *and day after day have sorrow in my heart?*

How long will my enemy triumph over me?

Psalm 13:2

Hear me and answer me.
My thoughts trouble me and I am distraught.

Psalm 55:2

Search me, God, and know my heart;
test me and know my anxious thoughts.

Psalm 139:23

In your thoughts you will ponder the former terror.

Isaiah 33:18

Jerusalem, wash the evil from your heart and be saved.
How long will you harbor wicked thoughts?

Jeremiah 4:14

Yet you know me, Lord;
you see me and test my thoughts about you.

Jeremiah 12:3

This is what the Sovereign Lord says: On that day thoughts will come into your mind and you will devise an evil scheme.

Ezekiel 38:10

Knowing their thoughts, Jesus said, "Why do you entertain evil thoughts in your hearts?"

Matthew 9:4

For out of the heart come evil thoughts—murder, adultery, sexual immorality, theft, false testimony, slander.

Matthew 15:19

For it is from within, out of a person's heart, that evil thoughts come—sexual immorality, theft, murder.

Mark 7:21

They show that the requirements of the law are written on their hearts, their consciences also bearing witness, and their thoughts sometimes accusing them and at other times even defending them.

Romans 2:15

All of us also lived among them at one time, gratifying the cravings of our flesh and following its desires and thoughts.

Ephesians 2:3

Therefore, holy brothers and sisters, who share in the heavenly calling, fix your thoughts on Jesus, whom we acknowledge as our apostle and high priest.

Hebrews 3:1

It is well known among the scientific community that our thoughts can control and create matter. Again, I go into more detail in my book *Mind Change*, but I also encourage you to do the study and research yourself. I include a substantial additional reading list at the end of *Mind Change* that references the scientific research. I will ask that you accept my humble "layman's" version of these truths for all intents and purposes for this book.

EMOTIONS AREN'T REAL

The heart is deceitful above all things
and beyond cure.
Who can understand it?

Jeremiah 17:9

Emotions aren't *real,* at least not in the way you probably think. The classical view of this topic is that emotions are things that happen to you. We are taught, incorrectly, that emotions are hardwired "feelings" that we should control, suppress, accept, or release. A buzz phrase today is to "be triggered." For example, someone or something does or says something, and it triggers an emotion and a stress response in us. We wrongly believe that we have little or no control over the trigger and are therefore powerless to deal with it. This still implies that something outside us is causing a reaction inside us (victim model).

When you think a thought, you have just created matter. To figure out what to do with this newly created matter, the brain must make meaning of this sensory input to prepare for what the body needs to do next. As you now know, the way it does this is by scanning all our internal files to find the closest previous experience to relate to. The brain prepares the body to respond physiologically (through our nervous, cardiovascular, immune, endocrine, and musculoskeletal systems).

Emotions are the nearly instantaneous meanings the brain gives to external and internal sensory input (bodily sensations). Lisa Feldman Barrett, a neuroscientist at Northeastern University and author of *How Emotions Are Made*, puts it best: "In other words, emotions are your brain's best guess of how you should feel in the moment. Emotions aren't wired into your brain like little circuits; they're made on demand. As a result, you have more control over your emotions than you might think."[36]

So emotions are our own personal creation! Taking the victor mindset, that means if we acknowledge that it is our creation, we can also decide to create something different. This places responsibility right back where it belongs—inside us. At this point, you may be feeling a little uncomfortable. A great many people have spent the last decade or two trying to "get in touch" with their emotions, only to find out that they are simply making a "best guess" at what they are feeling. The implications of understanding this perfectly designed

[36] Strong's Greek Lexicon (NIV). Blue Letter Bible. https://www.blueletterbible.org/. 2020.

engineering achievement are huge! If we are the creators of our emotions, then it stands to reason that we could create an emotionally fulfilling life.

Am I saying that emotions are useless or should be avoided? By no means! Emotions provide incredible insight into our internal wiring.

DAISY AND WILMA

Let me offer another practical example: a Sunday morning church service with Daisy and Wilma. The stage is set with two different women of basically the same age, social status, and life stage. Daisy and Wilma have been part of the same large fellowship for some time. Each woman loves God and feels that church is an important part of her personal walk with God.

Daisy arrives about 30 minutes before the service begins. With a big smile on her face, she greets the members that she sees. She is excited to catch up with some close friends and meet as many new faces as possible. Daisy feels strongly that she comes to the fellowship to give and, through that belief, her experiences reciprocate that fulfillment. She makes sure to get a seat up front where she can be fully engaged.

As she makes her rounds, Daisy notices a couple of women in a corner seemingly in deep conversation. One of them looks distressed and visibly upset. This same woman briefly meets Daisy's gaze and quickly looks away. Daisy decides to go over and offer support. As Daisy approaches, the woman talking to the distressed individual notices Daisy's arrival and quickly shakes her head at her.

Daisy understands that this must be a private conversation and quickly retreats. "*I sure hope she's okay,*" Daisy comments to herself, and says a quick prayer in her mind for each woman, making a mental note to check in with them after the fellowship. Just then, she spots a family she doesn't recognize arriving and happily goes over to introduce herself and invite them to sit with her up front.

Wilma arrives about 20 minutes after Daisy. She is already feeling a little self-conscious, as she had been feeling guilty lately about arriving later than what she felt was acceptable. Wilma walks in, hoping nobody notices her, and quickly moves to grab a seat in the back. As she reaches the back row, she notices the minister's wife talking with a group of women. "*Oh no!*" she thinks, "*She probably noticed me coming in late and is judging me already.*" Wilma fixes her eyes on the ground and moves farther down the aisle.

In an effort to avoid the minister's wife, Wilma makes a beeline for the coffee. On her way, she notices two women in a corner having a conversation. One of the women looks upset. "*She's probably getting rebuked for something!*" Wilma decides. At that moment, the upset woman meets Wilma's eyes and quickly looks away. "*Oh, great!*" Wilma fumes, "*Clearly she is talking about me. Does she think I didn't notice that look? So rude!*" This reminds her that she has unresolved feelings with another sister in the congregation. Wilma felt sure that she heard this sister talking about her on the previous Sunday, and she has been thinking about it all week. Forgetting the coffee, she looks around to find the sister so that she can give her a piece of her mind.

Soon, she sees the sister in question chatting with an unfamiliar family. Wilma walks up briskly and stands quietly behind the group, waiting for an opportunity to get the sister's attention. As she stands there, the minister's wife approaches her. Noticing the look on Wilma's face and her body language, the minister's wife is concerned for her and asks to speak to her. "Really?!" Wilma nearly shouts, "You seriously want to confront me now?" Genuinely taken aback and confused, the minister's wife says that it can wait.

Just then, the singing begins, and the people are asked to find their seats. Wilma storms off, thinking, "*Argh! This always happens to me. I am not appreciated here.*" She grudgingly moves to her seat in the back, feeling angry and hurt. As she listens to the sermon, she sincerely believes that the minister's wife spoke to her husband before he got up there, and now he is using this public platform to speak directly about her and her sin. Humiliated and incensed, Wilma leaves right after the sermon. "*These people are just a bunch of hypocrites! The leaders only care about the people who put large donations in the tray anyway. I'm going somewhere that I can get a little respect,*" she thinks, and she storms out the door. Same event. Same circumstances. Two *very* different emotional reactions. To explain this event, I'd like to introduce you to something that you use every day but have probably never heard of: the reticular activating system (RAS).

THE RETICULAR ACTIVATING SYSTEM: SETTING OUR MINDS

The Bible instructs numerous times to *set* your mind, heart, face, hope, eyes, and desires. Colossians 3:2 says, "*Set your minds on things above, not on earthly things.*" The word for "set" is *phroneō* (φϱήν), which literally means to direct one's mind to a thing, to seek and strive for. It is to exercise the mind intensively, like a laser focus.[37]

> *Those who live according to the flesh have their minds set on what the flesh desires; but those who live in accordance with the Spirit have their minds set on what the Spirit desires.*
>
> **Romans 8:5**

I'll explain the *how*, *why*, *when*, and *where* of the system in a minute, but for now, let me show you its result. Linda and Tom are in the market for a new car. They drive to the sales lot and look around. An eager salesman takes them to the "Sale of the Day," a blue Jeep Wrangler. Linda and Tom were not really in the market for a Jeep but decide to take it for a test drive. Both have a good time envisioning all the 4WD adventures they could have, and it suddenly becomes a real option. They decide to go home and think about it. If they still want it in a week, they will come back and buy it. A funny thing happens over that week—they see Jeep Wranglers *everywhere*. They can't believe how many people drive them. Maybe all the dealerships in the area were having a sale on Jeeps, and a bunch of people decided to buy them! After the end of the week, Tom and Linda take all the Jeep sightings "as a sign" and decided to purchase the Jeep.

Were all the dealerships randomly selling Jeeps that week? Maybe, but not likely. Does this scenario sound familiar? A friend brings up a particular topic at

---

[37] Lisa Feldman Barrett, *How Emotions Are Made.* Mariner Books; March 7, 2017.

lunch, and then for days following, it seems like everyone is talking about it! This well-known phenomenon is simply a bundle of nerves at our brainstem that acts as a filter. It "tunes out" unnecessary information so the important stuff gets through. What is the "important" stuff? Whatever you have been focusing on (thoughts). This system is at work when you can easily tune out a crowd full of loud noise, yet immediately snap to attention when someone calls out your name. Your RAS takes what you focus on and creates a filter for it. It then sifts through the filing system and presents only the pieces that are relevant and important to you. Of course, all this happens without you being aware of it.

Okay, this is big! This is where our thoughts end up dictating what we get more of. Whatever we focus on, we get *more* of. Our brain is engineered to see/feel/know *more* of what we have already deemed important. The RAS seeks information that validates our beliefs. It filters the world through the parameters you give it, and your beliefs shape those parameters. If you believe that you are bad at math, you probably will be. If you believe you are a good friend, you most likely will be. The RAS helps you see what you want to see, and in so doing, influences your actions.[38]

DAISY AND WILMA REVISITED

Let's revisit Daisy and Wilma to see the RAS at work. Wilma arrives at church, having already "planned" what she expects to find. Her mind sorted and filtered data from the billions of files held within her subconscious mind to access the "skills" to navigate this event. It goes through all the various "church" experiences but also pulls up every associated memory from her past. It finds a hardline and perfectionistic father who used shame and guilt as a motivating factor to "better his children." Wilma's files also contain experiences watching her mother be put down and ridiculed by her husband. Wilma's mother, feeling inadequate and belittled herself, would often sharply criticize her children. This set Wilma's RAS toward negativity and criticism, especially in authority figures. In school, she finds that she is "singled out" and "picked on" by teachers. She is

[38] Van Schneider, Tobias. *If you want it, you might get it. The Reticular Activating System explained.* https://medium.com, June 22, 2017.

always feeling like the teachers are looking for what she is doing wrong. As an adult, Wilma finds it hard to connect with others in a positive way. Most of her close friends are people she gossips with or who have similar feelings of negativity. These friendships often devolve into eventual conflict.

Wilma finds it very difficult to take personal responsibility for things. This was never modeled for her as a child, and she subconsciously feels that it is unsafe to admit that she may have made a mistake. Therefore, she projects her difficulties and feelings of inadequacy onto others. When Wilma became a Christian, she was unconsciously drawn to the familiarity of feeling "not good enough." From her experience with her parents, try as she might, she would never actually be able to live up to the expectations they had for her. Through this filter, she experienced God as an "ever watchful but never pleased" authority in her life. Though she intellectually understood that she could never "earn her salvation," it didn't stop the belief that she needed to try. For Wilma, the church was not the safe and family-like environment it was meant to be. Wilma had never experienced the safety to be "herself" in her own family of origin, so she operated in the fellowship with the skills she learned from her physical family.

Wilma desperately tried to find approval through serving or trying to be involved in everything. But she was difficult and argumentative in most situations, and because this was her norm, she was unable to hear feedback about the way others experienced her. Wilma had very strong opinions about how things should be done, and this resulted in negativity and criticalness when her opinions were not instituted. After a while, more and more people in the fellowship distanced themselves from the negativity that Wilma produced. Of course, Wilma took this as confirmation that she was always "left out" or "picked on," pulling up subconscious memories of her childhood and school experiences. Church leadership would eventually be involved in similar situations, and Wilma used this as an opportunity to feel further misunderstood and attacked. Wilma's view of authority was already damaged, and she would attend these meetings with her emotional "dukes up." Wilma is stuck in a survival feedback loop, and her go-to mechanism for this is the "fight" response. Every part of her body language, physical posture, and emotional default is set to fight mode. This happens without her conscious awareness. It is the automatic response of her autonomic nervous system to a perceived threat.

As expected, Wilma initially feels better after "giving everyone a piece of her mind" and launching a character attack on the leadership and any other involved party. But later, she is left with the deep loneliness and sadness that comes from being chronically disconnected from those around her. Wilma may indeed decide to find another fellowship, believing that the "real problem" is the people around her. And while she might find peace for a time in her attempts to serve and show her worth in the new fellowship, she will eventually find the same situations repeating themselves over and over again.

Wherever you go, there you are.

Daisy, on the other hand, has an entirely different experience from Wilma's. Daisy's mind also did the obligatory scan of the held data to assess the appropriate behavior for this experience. Without her awareness, her mind travels back to her childhood and finds that she was part of a soccer team as a little girl. Though the girls were far from being skilled in soccer, the coach made an intentional effort to help them work as a team, understanding that they were only as strong as their weakest link. This cultivated a group mentality of wanting to work together and be better together. They were open to feedback and correction, knowing that each improvement in their ability helped build a better team. Though the team didn't often win a game, Daisy cherished those times together with her teammates. And she felt sure that her coach believed in her and always had her best interest in mind. Throughout school, Daisy was always known to be a team player and was a coveted partner for projects and friendship all through school.

Without even trying, Daisy believes that she comes to the fellowship to give and be powerfully used by God. Her RAS is set to look for ways to encourage, build up, and spread joy. Her mind finds no significant "danger" in a crowd of people gathered together. In fact, to Daisy, this signals safety and family. Her RAS is attuned to opportunity, and she finds it wherever she goes. It does not occur to her that she would be the object of criticism or focus. A pair of women huddled in a corner conversing does not register as a personal threat to her. Her zero-threat observation of this event allows her to accurately assess the situation, unfiltered. She then acts in accordance with what is objectively observed. Her default is set toward the good, and she is able to assume the best of others in most situations. Daisy feels that church fellowship is a place of safety and a gathering of like-minded people who support and encourage each other. She brings joy to many of the members of the fellowship and is genuinely missed if she has cause to be absent. The leadership is grateful for her steadfast and reliable contribution to anything she is a part of.

Daisy was initially drawn to Christianity because she knew that she was part of something bigger in this world. She wanted to "give back" from the overflow of what she had been given. She felt consistently in awe that she could connect with her Creator. Ironically, Daisy did not grow up in an idyllic home. Raised by a single mother, her father had left early on in life, and she had no recollection of knowing him. Daisy's mother did what she could to provide for the family but worked long hours and left Daisy to help raise the younger siblings. Daisy's grandmother lived close by and provided incredible emotional support for Daisy. Through her grandmother's wisdom and unfailing love, Daisy had a safe place to process emotions. She was taught to notice her emotions and that she was ultimately in control of how long they stayed or how quickly they left. At a relatively young age, Daisy became aware of the outcome of holding onto bitterness, anger, and pain. Through her grandmother's love and safety, she learned to let go of emotions that no longer served her. She now does this naturally and with little or no conscious effort. Daisy got ready for church that morning having already created what she wanted to find there, based on her past experiences. When she arrived, she found just what she was "looking for."

This is not just a Law of Attraction idea. This neuroscience has been laid out in the Bible more than once. Take, for instance, Job 3:25 in various translations:

> *For the terror of which I meditated has come upon me, and that which I had feared has befallen me.* (Brenton Septuagint Translation)
>
> *What I always feared has happened to me. What I dreaded has come true.* (NLT)
>
> *For what I fear comes upon me, And what I dread befalls me.* (NASB)

In his book, *Breaking the Habit of Being Yourself*, Dr. Joe Dispenza mentions, "We just love the rush of energy from our troubles! In time, we unconsciously become addicted to our problems, our unfavorable circumstances, or our unhealthy relationships."[39]

These automatic reactions are based on emotions resulting from chemicals interacting with your cells, and we can become addicted to the sensations. Yes, even if the sensations are "negative." We become so familiar with our addictive emotions that they start seeming normal.

Let's consider for a minute that what I am saying is true. Doesn't it change *everything*? It should. This is true metanoia. We need to change our minds about what we think about our minds.

PERCEPTION

I've mentioned the word "perception" numerous times, so I think it is worth digging into a bit. What is perception? It is the way the body "takes in" the information from the outside world. According to the *Oxford English Dictionary*, perception is "the process of becoming aware or conscious of a thing or things in general; the state of being aware; consciousness; understanding." This requires the use of one or more of the senses to process data. To be perceivable, the object must be understood by the mind through sight, sound, taste, touch, or smell. To

---

[39] Dispenza, Joe. *Breaking the Habit of Being Yourself.* Hay House Inc, 2013.

interpret that sensation is what is known as perception. The perceivable is that which can be interpreted by the body. I'm particularly fond of the word's original Latin meaning as "the action of taking possession; apprehension with the mind or senses." Perception is what allows us to make sense of the world through the experience of our senses and the collection of data.[40]

Simply put, perception is how we view the world based on our experience with it. Sound familiar? It goes back to how we form our particular model of the world. Perception is how we create our personal reality. For example, let's take a bottle of Tabasco sauce. A person will view this bottle and instantly have a perception of its meaning. If you are someone who likes spice and heat (how do you know? You will search your files and find previous experiences to draw from), then you will have feelings of satisfaction. Your mouth may even salivate when you think of the smell or taste. If, on the other hand, you are someone who has a negative association with Tabasco sauce, your perception of this bottle will be very different. You may scrunch up your face and even put a hand on your stomach as memories of heartburn arise from your files.

See, Tabasco sauce isn't good or bad. It just is. The meaning we give it comes from our own personal experience with it. And our perception becomes our reality. What if someone has never had an experience with Tabasco sauce? What will their perception be? The first thing they would do is search their files to see if they have any similar references that will help them establish a meaning. They will likely use their visual capabilities to assess the look, color, and shape of the bottle. Do they find a familiar shape, look, or color? If nothing is definitive, they may decide to smell it. This will likely create a response as they search through their filing system (memory) to see if a similar smell can be found. If they find something that seems familiar, they will use that event to perceive the current situation. Let's say that this person finds a similar bottle color and smell in a memory of visiting Mexico with family. It was a great trip, and they used a similar bottle to season some tacos. The tacos were spicy, but it was an enjoyable experience shared with friends and family. The tacos were washed down with

[40] University of Chicago Theories of Media. *Keywords Glossary:* Perception. https://csmt.uchicago.edu, 2004.

horchata (a cinnamon rice drink), and it was an overall pleasant experience. This person will perceive the bottle of Tabasco sauce as a possible pleasant experience and will likely try it out.

Let's say another person who is unfamiliar with Tabasco sauce searches their memory bank to find an associated experience. This person finds a memory of a time when their older sibling and some older cousins pulled a prank on him involving a "special" ice cream topping. The older kids made a big fuss over this "delicious" new topping and convinced the younger boy to try it. Saying it was a fruit topping, they dumped the hot sauce from a bottle onto a bite of vanilla ice cream. Asking the boy to "open wide," the older boys shoved the spoonful of hot-sauce-covered ice cream down his throat. Instantly, the boy realized that he had made a grave mistake in trusting these older boys. As he remembers, he can still feel the burn of his throat and tongue. What is his likely conclusion about Tabasco sauce by just seeing the bottle? What if he smells it as well? Clearly, these sensations are powerful indicators for us. Even more than that, they are the building blocks of what we call memories, which we will now discuss in the next chapter.

CHAPTER 9

THE CALL TO REMEMBER

MEMORIES

God has a lot to say about what we do with our memory. He knows that what we populate our mind's memories (file folders) with will directly influence the choices we make down the line. God wants his people to remember what he has done for them. Why? Is it because he is an egomaniac and needs our constant approval or admiration? *No*! Our Creator is aware of the workings of his creation. Neuroscience tells us that what we practice and focus on will become the filters through which we see the world. So it is no surprise to realize the importance God placed on using mandated ceremonies to help the Israelites remember his grace. The overall takeaway from the events of the Passover in Egypt was that God loves his people and will always provide a way out. Truly getting this concept would provide his people with the faith to move forward toward the promised land, so it seems worthy of remembering! The Israelites were commanded to conduct a ceremony of remembrance annually, without fail, to reinforce the memory of God's love, rescue, and mercy.

Many other feasts and festivals were commanded throughout the Old Testament. Each was designed to remember a collective experience that illustrated God's character and his relationship to his people.

In the New Testament, Jesus instituted a new commemoration "in remembrance of me." Every time we participate in the Lord's Supper, we are being asked to remember a message of victory and freedom; victory over death and freedom from sin.

God wants us to focus our minds and hearts on "*things above*" (Colossians 3:2). He wants our minds to be filled with excellent and praiseworthy things (Philippians 4:8). What we think and hold in our minds will inevitably bring about the "fruit" that we produce. As modern-day Christians, we no longer observe many of the former rites, rituals, or festivals that defined the early Jews. Is it possible that we have neglected to realize their true purpose? These ceremonial practices were textbook cases of how to create and store long-term, foundational memory. The more senses we involve in the creation of a memory, the more powerful and permanent it becomes: visual, kinesthetic, auditory, olfactory, and gustatory (I will further explain these terms later in this chapter). These are also known as the five senses. Many of these ceremonies involve a physical act, something we are directed to feel, a mantra that is spoken, or a remembrance that is highlighted, as well as specific tastes and smells. If we practice that memory, again and again, year after year, it becomes a skill that we use to approach all other areas of our lives. In his infinite wisdom, God had specific and life-altering reasons for instituting these rituals.

Consider the following scriptures in the context of what we know about memory creation and the importance of what we remember:

Let love and faithfulness never leave you;
bind them around your neck,
write them on the tablet of your heart.

Proverbs 3:3

Bind them on your fingers;
write them on the tablet of your heart.

Proverbs 7:3

"This is the covenant I will make with the people of Israel
after that time," declares the Lord.
"I will put my law in their minds
and write it on their hearts.
I will be their God,
and they will be my people."

Jeremiah 31:33

"This is the covenant I will establish with the people of Israel
after that time, declares the Lord.
I will put my laws in their minds
and write them on their hearts.
I will be their God,
and they will be my people."

Hebrews 8:10

"This is the covenant I will make with them
after that time, says the Lord.
I will put my laws in their hearts,
and I will write them on their minds."

Hebrews 10:16

Why was it emphasized in the Old Testament to write God's law on the heart and mind? These figurative expressions stressed always keeping (storing) the Law (God's heart and will for humankind) in the most inner and secure place, from which everything else flows. The Book of Psalms is replete with examples of this concept. In many of the psalms, the authors are in some sort of agony, pouring out their hearts in the midst of trouble. Yet somewhere near the middle of the psalm, they remember God and what he has done and how they have been rescued before. They remember the great deeds of their Redeemer, and they change! They are rescued by their memory.

Consider this psalm. Here we find Asaph in desperation as he begins his lament.

Will the Lord reject forever?
Will he never show his favor again?
Has his unfailing love vanished forever?
Has his promise failed for all time?
Has God forgotten to be merciful?
Has he in anger withheld his compassion?

Psalm 77:7–9

The Call To Remember

Asaph is feeling pretty lousy. He is doing an outstanding job of staying in his funk! But notice what happens as soon as he begins to remember, pulling from some of his previous experiences with God:

> *"I will remember the deeds of the Lord;*
> *yes, I will remember your miracles of long ago.*
> *I will consider all your works*
> *and meditate on all your mighty deeds."*
> *Your ways, God, are holy.*
> *What god is as great as our God?*
> *You are the God who performs miracles;*
> *you display your power among the peoples.*
> *With your mighty arm you redeemed your people,*
> *the descendants of Jacob and Joseph.*
> *The waters saw you, God,*
> *the waters saw you and writhed;*
> *the very depths were convulsed.*
> *The clouds poured down water,*
> *the heavens resounded with thunder;*
> *your arrows flashed back and forth.*
> *Your thunder was heard in the whirlwind,*
> *your lightning lit up the world;*
> *the earth trembled and quaked.*
> *Your path led through the sea,*
> *your way through the mighty waters,*
> *though your footprints were not seen.*
> *You led your people like a flock*
> *by the hand of Moses and Aaron.*

Psalm 77:11–20

Well, that certainly took a turn, didn't it? Something tells me that these were not new revelations for Asaph. I would be willing to bet that he was intensely familiar with the events he spoke of and "remembered." Was he actually there, at the parting of the Red Sea, standing with Moses and Aaron? No, not physically. But this was no less real to him than if he had been. He knows this story. It is *his* story. God's redemption and rescue of his people were part of what defined Asaph. By it, he was rescued out of his captivity too.

WHAT IS MEMORY?

Memory is extremely powerful and important to us as humans. It is continuously shaping and reshaping our brain, our life, and our identity. The study of memory and the neurobiology associated with creating, storing, and retrieving our memories is a relatively new science. With the creation of brain-imaging devices, researchers are gaining new insights into human memory every day.

As much as I would love to share all the incredible research associated with memory in the following pages, it would take up too much space. For those of you interested in learning more, please feel free to review the research papers that I reference in the bibliography from this chapter and many of the books listed in the recommended reading section at the end of the book.

But briefly, let me explain how we encode, store, and retrieve memory as a vital part of learning to change our lives by changing our minds. The brain's main parts involved with memory are the amygdala, the hippocampus, the cerebellum, and the prefrontal cortex. The amygdala is involved in fear and fear-filled memories; it is responsible for regulating our fight/flight/freeze response. The amygdala plays a part in how memories are stored because stress hormones influence that storage. The hippocampus is associated with declarative and episodic memory as well as recognition memory. The hippocampus's main job is to project information to cortical regions that give memories meaning and connect them with other interconnected memories. It also plays a part in memory consolidation: the process of transferring new learning into long-term memory.

The cerebellum plays a role in processing procedural memories, such as how to play the piano. The prefrontal cortex appears to be involved in remembering semantic tasks. There also appear to be specific neurotransmitters involved in the process of memory, such as epinephrine, dopamine, serotonin, glutamate, and acetylcholine.[41]

I find it interesting that these areas of the brain (amygdala, hippocampus, cerebellum, prefrontal cortex, and related neurotransmitters) are the exact mechanisms responsible for creating our overall well-being. If you are diagnosed with depression, that is a direct outcome of an imbalance or incongruency somewhere within these systems. It is hard to miss the direct correlation between our memories and our well-being overall.

What if our memories and the information they contain could be the answer to unlocking complete wellness and healing in our mind, body, and spirit?

THE "HOW" OF MEMORY

You were probably introduced to the idea of the five senses in school : sight, feeling (touch), hearing, smell, and taste. For our purposes, we are going to explore these a little more closely. I learned most of what I'm about to describe to you by studying NLP. Dr. Matt James of NLP.com defines it like this: "NLP stands for Neuro-Linguistic Programming. Neuro refers to your neurology; Linguistic refers to language; Programming refers to how that neural language functions. In other words, learning NLP is like learning the language of your own mind!"

NLP refers to the five senses as the representational systems and uses the terms visual (what we see), auditory (what we hear), kinesthetic (what we feel), audio-digital (words that we say to ourselves/knowings), olfactory (smell), and gustatory (taste). As we take in information from any of these senses, the brain uniquely encodes that information. The term "representational systems" comes from the observation that we will *re*-present our memories from one of these

---

[41] Myhrer T. *Neurotransmitter systems involved in learning and memory in the rat: a meta-analysis based on studies of four behavioral tasks.* Brain Res Rev, 2003.

modes. Studies have shown that humans primarily use the visual, auditory, and kinesthetic systems. In the USA, approximately 20 percent of people process strongly auditorily, 20 percent do so kinesthetically, and 60 percent do so visually. Because a large percentage of the population primarily uses the visual system, many people think of memory as a picture in your head. That is not always the case.

For instance, if I were to tell you to close your eyes and remember your childhood home, some of you would produce a *picture* of that home in your mind. That is the visual representation of that memory. Someone else might get a warm and safe *feeling*, remembering what it *felt* like in the home. This is a kinesthetic representation. Yet another person may *hear* the familiar sounds of dishes being washed, the symphony of voices at the dinner table, or even the neighborhood kids playing outside. This is an auditory representation. They are all "memory."

Different memories may have been encoded in different ways. The memory of your childhood best friend may be a picture in your mind, but your first bike may be remembered with the feeling of the wind going through your hair. It is also possible to have multiple senses represented in one memory. Perhaps you remember your childhood pet with a picture or movie inside your head, the feeling of his fur under your hand, and the warm, loving feeling you got from being with him. This is all memory! (See diagram on next page.)

EXTERNAL EVENT

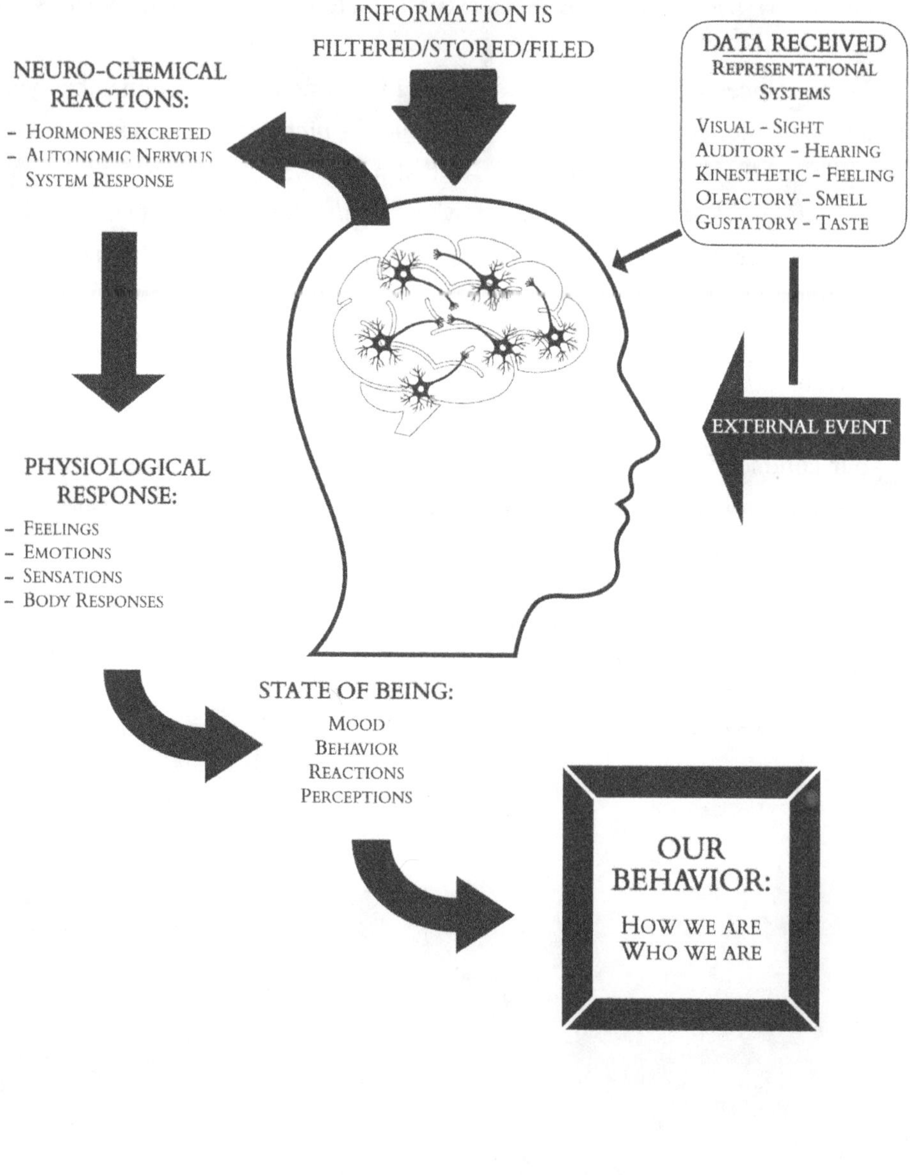
INFORMATION IS
FILTERED/STORED/FILED
NEURO-CHEMICAL
REACTIONS:
- HORMONES EXCRETED
- AUTONOMIC NERVOUS
SYSTEM RESPONSE
DATA RECEIVED
REPRESENTATIONAL
SYSTEMS
VISUAL - SIGHT
AUDITORY - HEARING
KINESTHETIC - FEELING
OLFACTORY - SMELL
GUSTATORY - TASTE
EXTERNAL EVENT
PHYSIOLOGICAL
RESPONSE:
- FEELINGS
- EMOTIONS
- SENSATIONS
- BODY RESPONSES
STATE OF BEING:
MOOD
BEHAVIOR
REACTIONS
PERCEPTIONS
OUR
BEHAVIOR:
HOW WE ARE
WHO WE ARE

Why is this important? Because it's helpful to understand that by simply pulling up a picture, feeling, or sound from our head, we can feel those same sensations *now*, just as if the event were happening to us at this very moment. This can be a good thing, but also a terrifying and horrible thing. Why? Because we can see something or experience *sensations* and *feelings* by recalling something from our past, so we feel that our memories are "real." This common misunderstanding about the way we perceive reality can definitely shape the way we see memories. Most of us assume that our memory serves us well enough, and therefore whatever we do remember is accurate. And we have learned that events are recorded and encoded into our brains using one or more of our five senses. But our mistake is in believing that those memories, as we recall them, are shown exactly as they were encoded.

MEMORIES ARE NOT REAL

Most of us are familiar with the fact that our ancestors believed the world to be flat. As science and thought evolved, this widely held belief became antiquated. Much of what the world at large believes about memory is similarly outdated. Whether we can articulate it or not, most people believe that our memory works much like a video recorder. We believe that whatever we experienced is exactly how it was recorded in the mind. And that "video" gets stored in our memory banks until we need to retrieve it. If that were the case, it would be natural to think that when we went back and accessed that stored memory, it would play back *exactly* what happened. So "remembering" is basically accessing and replaying those old video recordings. That seems reasonable, right?

It might seem reasonable, but it is wrong. Elizabeth Loftus is an American cognitive psychologist. She is one of the world's foremost experts on human memory. She has conducted research on the malleability of human memory, ground-breaking work on the misinformation effect, eyewitness memory, and the creation of false memories. I highly recommend viewing her infamous TED Talk, *How Reliable Is Your Memory*? In it, she explains:

Many people believe that memory works like a recording device. You just record the information, then you call it up and play it back when you want to answer questions or identify images. But decades of work in psychology have shown that this just isn't true. Our memories are constructive. They're reconstructive. Memory works a little bit more like a Wikipedia page. You can go in there and change it, but so can other people.[42]

In an NPR interview, psychologist and memory researcher Ayanna Thomas says this about memory: "A paleontologist uncovers a fossil, just as we have to uncover a memory...but that paleontologist doesn't have all the pieces," she says. "And what that individual has to do is fill in the gaps with best guesses and prior experience."[43]

The reason it is so difficult for us to consider that our memories are "more like a Wikipedia page" is that many people believe we are "just born a certain way." But an abundance of scientific research shows that the memories we choose to hold onto are the ones that go on to shape our identity. Individuals with certain brain traumas or forms of amnesia have been known to lose all sense of personal identity.[44]

Memory research reveals that we don't access and utilize *all* our stored memories when creating personal narratives. Without realizing it consciously, we pick and choose what we remember, filtering out anything that does not align with the current idea that we have of ourselves. For instance, if we believe that we are "unlucky," we filter out any memories that might contradict that belief.

I did this personally, as I have referenced before. To help explain the confusion I felt about my childhood and make sense of certain behaviors within me, I created the narrative that I had a "really rough childhood." But reality is a

---

[42] TED Talk. Loftus, Elizabeth. *How Reliable is your memory.* 2013.

[43] Thomas, Ayanna. NPR Interview. *Did That Really Happen? How Our Memories Betray Us.* December 17, 2019.

[44] Conway MA, Pleydell-Pearce CW. *The construction of autobiographical memories in the self-memory system.* Psychol Rev. 2000.

matter of perception. What I deemed "rough" could be seen as a cakewalk to certain people and a hell on earth to others. Regardless, it was a narrative that I subconsciously chose. To stay in alignment with this belief (personal reality), my brain had to filter out anything that was incongruent with that narrative. As a result, I had very few memories of my actual childhood. I was shocked to find out that my brain had filtered so effectively that I could not cognitively remember anything but negative and traumatic events from my past. In reality, although there were some arguably difficult traumas in my memory bank, there were far more positive references stored. To "keep me safe," my subconscious mind had blocked off most of my positive childhood moments. How did that keep me "safe"? Great question. Many of my family members were still engaged in addictive, destructive, and unsafe behaviors. In my mind, the way to keep me safe was to be as far away from my family as possible. This was done subconsciously, of course. Consciously, I loved my family and felt enormous guilt about leaving home and not wanting to be around them. To support my "safety," my subconscious mind began sorting, editing, and blocking memories that would make it more difficult to keep my distance. If I could believe, and have remembered "proof," that I had a horrible childhood at the hands of my parents or stepparents, then I could feel a lot better about not wanting to be around them. See how that works? Not convinced?

Memory is subjective, pliable, malleable. Stored files of our past experiences can be edited and distorted rather easily. Lab research shows that by suggestion and imagination, we can actually *create* memories. These "memories" can be very elaborate and filled with emotion, even though they are completely false.[45] Within days of the 9/11 terrorist attack on New York City, a group of psychologists created a consortium of researchers from some of the top universities in the nation. In-depth surveys were distributed to thousands of individuals, asking them to recall details about their experiences with the 9/11 attack. Over the course of three years, the researchers reinterviewed the participants yearly to track the accuracy of their memories in relation to the

[45] Mazzoni, G, Loftus, E, Seitz, A. and Lynn, S. *Changing beliefs and memories through dream interpretation.* 1999.

event. The result was a clear decline in accuracy over time. By the end of the three-year study, nearly 50 percent of participants had drastically changed the events they reported. New York University psychologist Elizabeth A. Phelps, a lead investigator of the survey, explained the results by stating:

> *Emotion kind of focuses you on a few details but lets you ignore other details. And if you are highly aroused by fear, that emotion helps you store things in your memory better, in a storage process called consolidation that depends on the interaction of the amygdala and hippocampus. But what we've known for a while is that emotion gives you a stronger confidence in your memory than it does necessarily in the accuracy. Usually, when a memory has highly vivid details and you're confident in those details, that means you're likely to be right. Confidence often goes hand in hand with accuracy. But when something is highly emotional, they often get separated.*[46]

Melanie Mignucci, the Health & Wellness editor at *Bustle* (an online magazine), recounts her own inaccurate memories around 9/11. She does not remember being picked up from school or watching the TV footage with her family. Her most profound memory is looking out her classroom window and seeing the black smoke from the attack rising over the water. She also distinctly remembers feeling afraid because her mother was working in New York City at the time of the attack. The problem is, both these "memories" are completely inaccurate and quite literally impossible. Melanie was living in Connecticut at the time, not New York, and her school classroom did not look out over the water. Although her mother had commuted into New York for most of Melanie's life, she worked in Connecticut from 2000 to 2002. On 9/11, her mother was in

[46] Scientific American. Chen, Ingfei. *How Accurate Are Memories of 9/11?* https://www.scientificamerican.com, September 6, 2011.

Easton, PA for a meeting. Melanie explains, "I have these two memories of the day, both rock solid in their accuracy in my head, neither of which are real."[47]

Jean Piaget, a famous Swiss developmental psychologist, describes a classic case of false memory from his own life:

> *I was sitting in my pram, which my nurse was pushing in the Champs Élysées, when a man tried to kidnap me. I was held in by the strap fastened around me while my nurse bravely tried to stand between me and the thief. She received various scratches, and I can still see vaguely those on her face. Then a crowd gathered, a policeman with a short cloak and a white baton came up, and the man took to his heels. I can still see the whole scene, and can even place it near the tube station. When I was about fifteen, my parents received a letter from my former nurse saying that she had been converted to the Salvation Army. She wanted to confess past faults, and in particular to return the watch she had been given on this occasion. She had made up the whole story, faking the scratches. I, therefore, must have heard, as a child, the account of the story, which my parents believed, and projected it into the past in the form of a visual memory.*[48]

Examples of this type of memory editing or fabricating are abundant. But rather than focus on what might seem to be the negative repercussions of this, it's good to realize that this mechanism works both ways. There are incredible benefits in our malleable memory. Picking and choosing memories to support our beliefs is the natural application of our memory.

---

[47] Mignucci, Melanie. *If You Can't Remember 9/11, You're Not Alone.* http://www.bustle.com, September 11, 2017.

[48] Oxford Reference. *Piaget kidnapping memory.* https://www.oxfordreference.com/

This ability empowers us to rewrite our past, so it resembles what we feel and believe now. In Philippians, Paul admonishes us to release our "confidence in the flesh." He then gives us step-by-step instructions.

> *Brothers and sisters, I do not consider myself yet to have taken hold of it. But one thing I do: Forgetting what is behind and straining toward what is ahead, I press on toward the goal to win the prize for which God has called me heavenward in Christ Jesus.*
>
> **Philippians 3:13–14**

So what does it mean—forgetting what is behind? "Forgetting the past" (ἐπιλανθάνομαι) is an interesting statement. It means to forget, to overlook, to neglect. Specifically it means to overlook the effects by failing to notice. Nowhere does it say ignore or just try to stop thinking about it. This extended version of the Greek word for "forget" (*epylanthanomahee*) is a super-powered version. In other words, it's like completely eradicating the perceived negative memory of the past. What does this really mean, practically? It means that when we look into the past, we neglect to see anything negative, out of place. We overlook the effects of any problem. Do we just "forget" by not thinking about it? You can't *not* think about something subconsciously if it's still in there. A better question is: are we letting the good things in our past affect us, or the bad stuff?

I mentioned the idea of neglect as a possible part of the definition. What does it mean to neglect? Abandon, desert, forsake. Therefore, we let go of, completely, our past negative experiences by failing to notice them. Now listen, I know that our past negative experiences can become our precious stories. Most of the time, we don't want anyone to take away this identity of sickness or sin or past abuse or trauma or hurt because it "makes us who we are." Do you recall Gollum from *The Lord of the Rings*? He, at one point, was a Stoor Hobbit of the River-folk. He was pleasant and happy and festive, as are all hobbits. He lived near the Gladden Fields and was originally known as Sméagol. But his insecurity and perceived notions about himself caused him to hold on to the One Ring. And the longer he held on to his "precious," the more distorted his past and present reality became. Even his body made it clear that something was way off. Although he *knew* it was the ring that distorted his mind and his life, he wasn't willing to let go of his "precious." It became who he was, and without it, he saw no hope. Holding onto something you are not supposed to hold onto makes you look and act like that! "Don't take my sickness/trauma/past away from me. It's *precious* to me! This makes me *who I am!*" But is that what makes you who God created you to be?

WHY WE REMEMBER THE "BAD" SO WELL

Have you ever felt like it's easier to remember negative events in your life as opposed to positive ones? I had a close friend who was like this. It was almost impressive, the degree to which he could recall what went *wrong* in any given situation. Maybe you know someone like this (or are someone like this). I do believe this is attributed partly to disposition and also to the way each of us individually views the world. But an incredible amount of science and research on memory consolidation and retrieval might also shed some light on this phenomenon.

From our days in formal education, we have all heard the admonition to "focus!" "Sit still, Billy, and put your eyes on the board!" "Stop talking, Sally, and pay attention." "Turn off that TV, Jane, so that you can focus on your homework." What is the general message here? We will learn better and retain more if we focus on the information that is important or that we are trying to learn. That is generally accepted and experienced as truth. This is the power of our conscious mind: to focus in on what we deem important and make an effort to store the information away for eventual recall. But remember, our subconscious mind is taking in *billions* of bits of information every day. It is busy storing all the excess data that we might not be focusing on. This is how we function day to day. But when stress of any kind is introduced into this scenario, things get a little funky!

Research has shown that when there is elevated emotional stress during an event, this leads to an impairment in the way we store and eventually recall memories associated with that event. Hence, details of unpleasant emotional events are remembered less accurately than details of neutral or everyday events. A common assumption behind this view is that a decrease in available processing capacity occurs at states of high emotional arousal, which, therefore, leads to less efficient memory processing.[49]

On a most basic level, if a student at school is in a heightened state of stress for any reason (being bullied, being yelled at by a teacher, a dangerous home environment), they may sit and "focus" on the information being given, but retain little to none of it. Also, when our body is in a constant state of stress, we begin *looking for more* possible stressors in our environment. This is because we have dropped down into a lower brain function, our emotional brain, which is a more animalistic function of our thinking. When experiencing an emotional event, our attention is focused primarily on the *arousing* details of the stimulus, resulting in better encoding of *those* details and impaired encoding of less relevant ones, such as what the teacher is wanting the student to focus on.[50]

What does this mean? When we experience trauma, our brain becomes laser focused on the stressful or traumatic details of that experience. *But*…because of the stress and influence of the various neurotransmitters being released, we will store the memory with less accuracy than how we experienced it. So when these memories are brought up for recall, they highlight only the most troubling aspects of the event, *and* we produce the stress hormones that were associated with it, essentially causing a state of stress just by remembering. Ironically, this further strengthens and flags this memory. The more we practice it, the stronger it gets. So it stands to reason that our most traumatic memories are likely the most inaccurate.

---

[49] Cahill, L., Prins, B., Weber, M., and McGaugh, J. L. *Beta-adrenergic activation and memory for emotional events,* 1994.

[50] Loftus, E. F., Loftus, G. R., and Messo, J. *Some facts about weapon focus.* Law and Human Behavior, 1987.

RECALLING MEMORIES CHANGES THEM

Another fact that was instrumental for me in understanding the connection between my memories and my identity was learning that *every time you revisit a memory, the memory changes*. A study conducted at Northwestern University concluded that every time you remember an event from the past, your brain's networks change in ways that can alter the later recall of the event, meaning the next time you remember it, you might not recall the original event but rather what you remembered the previous time.[51] In a landmark 2010 paper in *Nature*, Daniela Schiller (then a postdoc at New York University) and her NYU colleagues published the results of human experiments indicating that memories are reshaped and rewritten every time we recall an event.[52]

So, it turns out that our memory's recall process is a lot like playing the Telephone game with ourselves. Do you know the old game? You start with one sentence, whispering it quietly into the ear of the person sitting next to you. This goes on until the sentence has been passed from person to person in a circle. When it comes back to the originator of the sentence, that person says aloud what they heard. More often than not, the sentence at the end barely resembles the original sentence. The more people you have, the sillier the game gets.

If we fundamentally (and unknowingly) change our memories every time we revisit them, what does that mean about our memories? They cannot be relied upon to portray the "truth" of any situation. Research shows that memory is elastic and malleable. If you think about it, it makes sense to realize that we cannot access information from our past and recall it with the exact same thoughts, feelings, and ideas that we encoded it with—simply because we are not the same person from one day to the next!

For example, I worked with a client who was revisiting a memory of childhood trauma. This event took place when she was three years old, but she had vivid pictures and feelings surrounding it. As I asked more questions, it was

---

[51] Paul, Marla. *Your Memory is like the Telephone Game: Each time you recall an event, your brain distorts it.* Northwestern Now. https://news.northwestern.edu/, September 19, 2012.

[52] Schiller, D., Monfils, M., Raio, C. *Preventing the return of fear in humans using reconsolidation update mechanisms.* Nature 463, https://doi.org/ 2010.

clear that this memory was one that had been accessed and revisited countless times over a 30-year period. She had done extensive talk therapy around this trauma and was well versed in every aspect of this memory. At one point, I asked her to go back and feel the feelings of that little three-year-old girl. When I asked what she believed the little girl had been feeling, she quickly gave me a few complex and articulate feelings: violated, manipulated, and worthless.

I don't doubt for one second that my client was experiencing feelings of violation, manipulation, and worthlessness as she sat in my office recalling the memory. But I also know that a typical three-year-old simply wouldn't and couldn't possess the emotional wherewithal to express such complex feelings and emotions. See, she was recalling that memory and changing it every time it was recalled. A three-year-old child cannot understand or feel the emotion of "manipulation" because they have absolutely no context for it. But a 33-year-old woman would and did. Over the years, this individual had used these memories to define her and therefore was very skilled in the language of a sexual abuse victim. She didn't do this purposely or even knowingly. Over the years, she developed the vocabulary and the emotional intelligence (EQ) to project those complex emotions onto that three-year-old girl.

Our brain automatically rewrites the details of our memories to support our current view of ourselves and our life story now. It's been said that our memories are like Swiss cheese, with "holes" that we try to fill each time they are recalled.[53] We try to fill those holes up with related information or new insights into our learning. It may be more accurate to say they are like processed cheese or —full of synthetic and other fillers so that you get something that resembles cheese but isn't really. Since what we remember changes each time we recall the event, the slightly changed memory is now embedded as "real," only to be reconstructed all over again with the next recall. We are completely unaware of this happening.

So if memory is like a file in our brain, we need to be aware that the file data is edited every time it is accessed. At each retelling or revisiting, there are

---

[53] Kennon, Tammy. *Why forgetting is actually good for you.* The Week, https://theweek.com/ August 31, 2016.

attached emotional or visual details. When the data is altered, the output or behavior that is produced is also reshaped.

Since 2013, I have witnessed this phenomenon of memory rewriting in myself and my clients. In Part 2, I'll explain in more detail how we do this. But for now, just wrap your head around the fact that it's possible. Memory is subjective and pliable. In the TED Talk, *A Mouse. A Laser Beam. A Manipulated Memory,* MIT graduates Steve Ramirez and Xu Liu explain their experience with memory manipulation in the brains of mice. The conclusion states that memories, and more specifically, the details of memories, can be purposely manipulated to produce a chosen behavior.[54] As the world attempts to "life-hack" their way to health and happiness, this information allows us to go right to the source of our current problems (how they were created) and redecorate! Can you imagine the implications? For us, this simply means that no matter what was put into the filing system of the mind that goes on to dictate our thoughts, feelings, and behaviors, we can go in and intentionally remove or change any information that doesn't serve or support what we want to be, feel, and think—*now*. We are "mind architects," if we choose to be. We get to "let go" of what is not working in our lives and "put in" the skills and outcomes we do want. We have the power to design and build an emotionally fulfilling life by the experiences we choose to have and memories we encode in our brains. This is why I believe this information and knowledge needs to be spread to the world—that God has given us the remarkable ability to transform by the renewing of our minds in order to live life to the full!

A CASE STUDY

A client whom we will call Jan came to see me because she was having problems in her marriage. At the time of her first session, Jan had consulted a lawyer and was ready to move on to the next stage and file for divorce from her husband of 15 years. In our first session, Jan did not seem very hopeful. She wanted things to work out with her husband, Bill, but she didn't think she could

[54] TED Talk. Ramirez, Steve, and Xu Liu. *A Mouse. A Laser Beam. A Manipulated Memory.* www.ted.com, June 2013.

move past her feelings of fear and suspicion in the marriage. After a bit of conversation, I asked Jan to identify the "problem" from her perspective. "I don't trust Bill," she said decidedly. Assuming that Jan had tangible evidence to support this belief, I asked her how she knew that Bill was untrustworthy. "I can't say exactly," Jan stated, "It's just a feeling I have. He is very suspicious, and I feel like he is keeping things from me and not telling me the truth." Again, I probed for more internal references that Jan was using to support this claim. Jan found that she could not come up with any "real" proof that Bill was untrustworthy, but she believed it strongly nonetheless.

From what I gathered, Bill was equally perplexed by the conclusion that Jan had come to. As I reviewed some of the preparatory work that I ask clients to do, I came across an incident from her childhood that had similar emotional outcomes. Jan explained that she was very distant from her father from a very young age. Though she could not really "remember" any particular incident that caused her to feel this way, she described her father as being unreliable, secretive, and untrustworthy. Because she had used similar words to describe her husband at one point in the conversation, I made a mental note of the connection.

As is my usual practice, we began working through perceived traumas in Jan's early life while also inviting her subconscious mind to give us any possible connections to her current "problem." Rather quickly, Jan found a memory that had a good deal of emotional charge to it. Even though she claimed to have "just remembered" this event, I had a suspicion that it was something she was using as a strong subconscious resource for her life and identity. Jan went on to tell me that she had had a beloved dog named Trixie. Trixie had been a stray that Jan's family had taken in. To Jan's recollection, Trixie had been with the family since she was very small and was her "best friend." One summer, when she was seven, Jan broke her leg by falling from a tree. She was devastated at the prospect of being relegated to a cast while all her friends and siblings enjoyed riding bikes all day and going to the local swimming pool. Jan remembers that Trixie was a welcomed companion during that time and helped her cope with the disappointment.

Within a week of having the cast removed, Jan's father sat her down to explain that Trixie needed to go back to the farm she came from. Jan was again devastated. Later that day, after Jan's father left to take Trixie to the farm, an older neighbor boy saw Jan crying in the front yard of her home. He asked what she was "blubbering about," and Jan told him that Trixie had to go live at a farm. The older boy laughed and explained to Jan, "That's what adults always say when they don't want a dog anymore. Your dog isn't going to a farm; they are going to kill it so they don't have to deal with it anymore." The boy then jumped up and left Jan to process this scenario. All of a sudden, Jan "remembered" all the little comments her Dad had made about the dog over the two months that Jan had the cast: "How can dogs eat this much? I'm going to have to get a second job to feed this mutt"; "How can one animal smell so terrible? Did it eat something dead?" and so on. Instantly, Jan knew the truth. Her father was not taking Trixie to a farm; he was going to kill her, and he lied about it. From that point on, Jan made up her mind that her father could not be trusted. Jan never spoke of the "truth" she had uncovered, but she began to believe that everything she knew about her father had been a lie.

While Jan was recounting this story to me, I noticed that these events were very real for her, and she was responding as if they had just occurred the day before, even though it had been nearly 30 years since this had taken place. She was very angry, hurt, and betrayed. Suddenly, her eyes popped open with conviction, and "Bill is just like my father!" she declared. "I feel the same way about him. He cannot be trusted. I'm sure he is lying to me, just like my dad." From experience, I knew that this memory held an incredible amount of influence over the way Jan was representing Bill. We worked on the memory and eventually made peace with everyone involved. After that initial session, Jan felt much lighter and freer, but I knew we weren't done yet. She was shocked to realize how much that memory (which she claimed she had forgotten about) had been influencing her. She felt much more empowered to reexamine her relationship with Bill and set up her next session.

I didn't hear from Jan between sessions, but the next time we met, I could tell that something was different. Normally, clients are very excited to share all the positive changes they have been experiencing since our last session. Jan looked like she had seen a ghost. I inquired how things had been going since I had seen her last. "Honestly," she began slowly, "I'm not sure what is even real anymore." That was a first for me, and I waited for her to explain. "After our last session, I felt so good. I even felt like I could call my father and forgive him for the incident with Trixie. So I called him. Of course, he was very surprised. We rarely talk, so it was a bit awkward at first. After initial pleasantries, I got to the point. I told him that I had been doing some work from my childhood and that I was finally ready to forgive him for the Trixie incident." Jan paused for a minute, trying to find the words to keep going. "My dad had no idea what I was talking about. At first, I was tempted to react and think that he was lying again. But after the work we did, I knew that I could offer up forgiveness even if he was not sorry or validating my pain. So I continued and explained that I forgave him for taking Trixie away and having her killed. I told him that I had made peace with the situation and that I knew he was doing what he thought was best for me." Jan continued, "My dad seemed completely shocked. Like, genuinely taken aback." "You mean that old dog we borrowed that summer you broke your leg?" Jan's dad asked. "What do you mean *borrowed*?" Jan asked tentatively. Jan's father went on to explain that she had been depressed and despondent after breaking her leg. All she could do was focus on how much fun everyone else was going to have, and her whole summer was ruined. Jan's father was explaining this to an acquaintance in town one day when the old man mentioned that a dog might cheer Jan up. Jan's father had never had a dog and didn't really want the commitment of taking care of an animal. The old man came up with a genius solution. They could borrow his dog. Trixie was a farm dog and didn't get much attention anyway. She would probably enjoy spending the summer being doted on by a little girl. Jan's father thought that might just be a good idea and went to fetch Trixie.

After Trixie's arrival, little Jan was transformed. Instead of feeling terrible about her leg being broken, she now believed that she was the lucky one because none of her friends had a dog. Jan's father said he felt terrible having to give the dog back, but that they were not in a position to keep the dog long term because one of Jan's siblings was allergic. Besides, Trixie belonged to the old man. Jan's father said they had explained that Trixie needed to go back to her real home and that it was a beautiful farm where she could run free and play with the other animals. Jan could hardly believe what she was hearing, because the "other truth" had become so real to her. In fact, she *didn't* fully believe what she was hearing. She asked her father if she could speak to her mother. Jan detailed the story to her mother, and to Jan's surprise, her mother corroborated the events exactly as her father had told her. Jan got off the phone and quickly called her older brother. He, too, recounted the story that her parents had told her, except he added the detail that he hated that summer because they kept that "stupid dog" for almost two months even though he was allergic and miserable. Jan told him the story of the neighborhood boy and what he had told her. "That was probably John Dorty," her brother said. "That kid didn't have a nice bone in him. He loved to bully the younger kids in the neighborhood and was a source of constant drama."

Jan felt like she was in the Twilight Zone. The memory of her father "killing Trixie" was so real to her. She had made up pictures about the way he did it, how Trixie must have felt, and even how her father could do it to *her* if she ever became an inconvenience. "At that point," Jan said, "everything unraveled. I was convinced that Trixie had been part of my life since before I could remember, when in truth, we only had her for about two months!" Jan continued, "I realized that I had hated and feared my father since I was seven years old, based on a lie. I never looked at him the same. I wasted so many years!" Luckily, we were able to work through all the associations and make the necessary changes within Jan's subconscious mind so that she was free to have a loving relationship with her father. Interestingly, her marriage issues resolved. I put together that her marriage issues began when her own daughter had turned seven years old. Unbeknownst to her, Jan began projecting her unresolved anger, fear, and hurt toward her own father onto her child's father, her husband. To keep her safe from further hurt from those she trusted, she developed a belief that "men who say they love you will lie to you and hurt you in the end." Over time, Jan was able to see how that belief had infiltrated many areas of her life and caused her to be controlling, fearful, and suspicious with people she got close to.

I'm happy to report that Jan continues to flourish and now reports closer relationships with all her family members, especially her husband. It was a valuable lesson for her to realize that memory is not always reliable and that many of our current issues are a result of unresolved past hurt.

CHAPTER 10

THE TRAUMA CYCLE

We don't like loose ends. Have you ever had a song stuck in your head? Generally (and annoyingly), it is usually just one refrain from the music, playing over and over again in our head. And very frequently, we don't even like the song! This phenomenon is called an earworm. This odd mental habit demonstrates just how little conscious control we usually have over our thoughts. After all, if we hate it so much, why can't we make it stop?

Researchers have attributed this to the Zeigarnik effect, in which our minds get stuck on incomplete mental processes. Zeigarnik's findings suggest that when we fail to resolve something from our life, it can create underlying cognitive tension. This tension results in greater subconscious effort and rehearsal in order to keep the issue at the forefront of awareness, in an effort to find resolution. Once this feedback loop is satisfactorily resolved, the mind is then able to let go of these efforts.[55]

We all have trauma. That is part of existing in a fallen world. The Bible makes it clear that we will experience troubles in this life.

> *For troubles without number surround me;*
> *my sins have overtaken me, and I cannot see.*
> *They are more than the hairs of my head,*
> *and my heart fails within me.*
>
> **Psalm 40:12**

---

[55] Denmark, FL. *Zeigarnik Effect.* The Corsini Encyclopedia of Psychology. New York: John Wiley & Sons; 2010.

Praise be to the God and Father of our Lord Jesus Christ, the Father of compassion and the God of all comfort, who comforts us in all our troubles.

2 Corinthians 1:3–4

What is traumatic for one person may seem trivial to another. We tend to judge one another's experiences through our own lenses, and trauma cannot be approached in this way. What we do know is that most people have and will experience trauma in their lives. What is also abundantly clear is that, as a society, we have been grossly underequipped in *how to deal with it*. In fact, we have become experts in *not* dealing with trauma. Instead, we "cope." Though I have found this to be true across the board, I find that Christians can be particularly skilled at this. There is much talk about "being forgiven" and "having faith" and things being "in God's hands," but the fruit of those confessions is not matching up. Often, we equate "not feeling it" or "not thinking about it" as dealing with something. If it doesn't bother me, it doesn't exist. The problem is that it doesn't "bother" us because we simply don't acknowledge it (the "it" being our unpleasant feelings, experiences, thoughts, or past). This is the way I handled my past for much of my life. I could easily speak about the abuse, neglect, and trauma. I would routinely say that I was no longer bothered with it. "The past is in the past. You can't change it, so why think about it." This was my mantra for daily living.

Consciously, we can avoid thinking about those negative experiences. But subconsciously, they are alive and well and usually gaining momentum. It's like an earworm, playing and replaying until it finds true resolution or completion. Remember, it's our *subconscious* that dictates our daily thoughts, attitudes, and behaviors. It's automatic, the inevitable *out*put of what we have *in*put over time. But we have settled for simply "not thinking about it" and considering that a victory. Or we just default to Philippians 4:8 and admonish ourselves to simply "think positive." Now, I am *not* saying it's a victory to be in constant thought about the negative experiences of our lives. That is emotional suicide. What I am saying is that we shouldn't settle for just being okay on the outside. Ideally, when we clean up the inside, the outside will reflect that. Consider the words of Jesus in the book of Matthew:

> *Woe to you, teachers of the law and Pharisees, you hypocrites! You clean the outside of the cup and dish, but inside they are full of greed and self-indulgence. Blind Pharisee! First clean the inside of the cup and dish, and then the outside also will be clean.*
>
> **Matthew 23:25–26**

If you have seen the show *Hoarders*, you will understand this concept. People don't start out as hoarders. It's a gradual accumulation. And it always has a deeper motivation than "having more stuff." Often, you don't know someone is a hoarder from the outside of the house. It's only when you open the door that it becomes apparent. But left alone for a period, the hoard cannot be kept in; it starts to "leak out." First, it's the closet, then the house, then the garage, then the yard. People often notice an unpleasant smell coming from the property or see increased pest activity like cockroaches or rats. This is a lot like our minds. We are very concerned with the outside of the house looking good, but often at the interior's expense.

COPING MECHANISMS: KEEPING IN THE HOARD

We are expert avoiders. And one of the key ways that we avoid is with coping mechanisms. In fact, we have turned coping into a *trillion-dollar* business. To *feel* good, we have to *look* good. So the fitness and beauty industries thrive. We are so busy giving our power away to the things, people, and situations that make us feel bad that we employ the same tactic to feel better.

"If I find the right diet, lifestyle, job, mate, body, hobby, etc., I will feel good."
"If I can find a successful career, I will overcome the feelings I had about growing up poor."
"If I have the right body or beauty, I will find the right partner."

"If I can find the right partner, I will overcome the knowledge that nobody ever loved me for me."

We give our power away and feel *bad*, and then we give it away *again* to feel *good*. I think you have probably witnessed that this doesn't work. It's never enough. Why? Because we believe the power to have a good life is outside us.

We are cope-aholics. We don't want to *feel*. We work, play, read, exercise, Facebook, Instagram, have sex, eat, join support groups, watch TV—anything to keep us busy and distracted from the reality that we are not satisfied with our lives. Or we keep the expectations so low that we could never be disappointed because we never really expected much.

Eating is good, vital even. But when we do it to feel better, it's a coping mechanism, acting like there is actually love in that chocolate bar or donut. Working out is great. But what are we running from? Work is necessary and fulfilling at times. But do we use it to escape and stay busy? Are we filling our hours and days with busywork to avoid the quiet that may ensue? What would your mind do? What thoughts might arise? What feelings would creep to the surface? Do you think that it is a coincidence that we have lost the art and heart of the Sabbath—God's perfect plan to give our busy minds a rest? Most of us cannot risk sitting with our self for a few minutes, let alone an entire day.

For some of us, like the hoarders, the "mess" looks too big. That is if you were to really look to see what has become of your inner self. Most hoarders have little pathways throughout their house. Around them, trash and accumulated "stuff" towers over them on each side of the paths. Entire rooms or wings of the house are blocked completely. We look at that and are horrified that people would have built such walls of rubbish around them that they only follow narrow paths to one or two rooms of their house. But how many of us mentally live that same way? We have "packed away" so much rubbish from our lives mentally and emotionally that there are only a few small areas that are safe.

You will recognize these people. They find offense in everything. If you dare tread outside the "safe" zones, it's like their very life is in danger, and they will attack. Don't mention the smell. Or the strange oozing of emotions that don't seem to fit the situation. Their inner world is so precariously constructed that one misstep could bring it all down.

THE SURVIVAL LOOP: HOW TRAUMA KEEPS US STUCK

Dr. Peter Levine, the creator of Somatic Experiencing®, is a leading expert in our body's response to trauma. Observing animals in the wild, Dr. Levine noticed that animals that had experienced a perceived life-threatening trauma would have a strange "whole-body" shaking once they had reached safety.[56] In his video, *Nature's Lessons in Healing Trauma: An Introduction to Somatic Experiencing*, you can see an example with a polar bear.[57] It has been recognized that this whole-body-tremor effect is the physical release and elimination of all the "trauma" experienced from the event. Based on this tremoring, Dr. David Berceli developed a technique called TRE (Tension & Trauma Releasing Exercises).[58]

For instance, let's say a gazelle happens to escape the jaws of a lioness and finds itself in safety. You can witness a process that this animal goes through to release and discharge this experience from its body. The process happens in stages, including moments of literal body shaking. Research has shown that if animals are not able to complete this process, they risk debilitating effects on their health, and even death. They were not actually mortally harmed by the attack itself but from the impact of the trauma on the mind/body. Clearly, trauma has effects and consequences that go beyond just "feeling" scared. A great example of this is in a YouTube video of an impala escaping an attack.[59]

Humans usually do not do this trauma discharge. Not only are we taught to "suck it up" or "be strong," we aren't aware that there is anything we *can* do about it. Severe shaking and coming back *through* the trauma does not seem like

---

[56] Somatic Experiencing Trauma Institute. https://traumahealing.org/

[57] YouTube. *Somatic Experiencing Trauma Institute.* https://www.youtube.com, Oct 15, 2014

[58] Trauma Prevention. *What is TRE?* https://traumaprevention.com

[59] YouTube. *Impala in and slowly out of collapsed immobility.* https://www.youtube.com

a logical or safe option to our thinking brain. As children, we are taught *not* to act out when we feel strong emotions, so that we don't have to feel. But seeing this process play out in the animal kingdom makes it clear that we might be missing something with regard to trauma processing. Matt Schwenteck of TRE says, "only two kinds of mammals have forgotten how to do this life-saving tremoring: zoo animals and humans."[60]

The Bible mentions wailing women in both the Old and New Testaments (2 Samuel 1:24; Ezekiel 32:16–18; Luke 8:52, 23:27–28; Matthew 11:17). In biblical times, mourning was a communal activity. Professional wailing women were invited to funerals and other somber events, to lead the community in a shared expression of grief. The term used for wailing women could also be translated as "wise women" or "skilled women," suggesting that the art of mourning was a skill that had to be learned (Jeremiah 9:17). The role of the wailing women constituted a professional trade that required strict training. Their laments led the community's response in the face of extreme trauma. People would tear their clothes, putting on sackcloth and ashes. These "wise women" led their communities in expressing both sorrow and joy, which fostered solidarity, empathy, and healing.

Many Jews, in biblical times, would mourn their parents' deaths for up to a year! Today, on the other hand, we tend to move on from anything hard, problematic, or traumatic because life carries on. Think about the typical modern mother who goes back to work soon after giving birth. Or those who attend the funeral of a relative or close friend on a Saturday, and head back to work on Monday. Worse still, there are those who are raped and instead of moving through the grief and trauma, they choose to act as if nothing happened. We "get over" these things and "move on," while burying the anguish deep within. But is this really how we were created to deal with trauma, stress, or life?

---

[60] Brous, Kathy. *Healing Tools for Trauma.* https://attachmentdisorderhealing.com

THE SCIENCE OF SURVIVAL

Trauma has an impact on the entire human system. The brain, mind, and body all process trauma with different systems and responses. This cycle is complex and intricate.

In my opinion, Dr. Bessel Van Der Kolk, author of *The Body Keeps Score*, is one of the foremost experts in the field of trauma on the human body. A psychiatry professor at Boston University School of Medicine, he did some of the leading research in PTSD patients. Dr. Van Der Kolk explains that we are preprogrammed with a "brain alarm system" that automatically activates when we perceive or encounter any threat. This engages the oldest part of the brain, the reptilian brain. When the reptilian brain is in control, it partially shuts down the higher brain, our prefrontal cortex or neocortex, our rational or thinking brain. It generally has three primary responses: fight, flight, or freeze.[61]

In response to acute stress, the amygdala becomes activated. The amygdala's job is to determine whether the current event is a threat. It does this in less than a millisecond based on sensory input that we are not even consciously aware of. To help make the decision, it engages the hippocampus, which is where all the "file folders" (memories) are stored. It scans through past experiences to help identify possible threats. If the amygdala decides that a potential threat is present, it engages the body's autonomic nervous system, which creates a sudden release of hormones. The sympathetic nervous system stimulates the adrenal glands, thereby activating the release of catecholamines, which include cortisol, adrenaline, and noradrenaline. These hormones result in various, whole-body responses. Our senses are heightened, our heart beats faster, and we can have moments of increased strength or speed. We are specifically built to go "superhuman" for brief moments of time to help us stay alive. This is an *amazing* system! But we are not meant to remain in that state for any length of time.

Functioning "normally," the most evolved part of our brain, the prefrontal cortex, plays a vital role in this process. While the amygdala is ready to "take action" at the first sign of danger, our frontal lobes can restore peace in our

---

[61] Van der Kolk, B. A. *The body keeps the score: Brain, mind, and body in the healing of trauma.* New York: Viking, 2014.

systems if it deems the threat a "false alarm." For instance, imagine you are in a city park with your children when you suddenly hear tires screeching. Before you are consciously aware of it, you have jumped to your feet and moved toward your child. When you regain awareness (thank you, frontal lobes), you realize that the street is nowhere close to the park and your child is safe. Likely, you settle down quickly and take a few deep breaths, even finding your reaction a bit humorous. With your prefrontal cortex back in control, you have consciously assessed the situation and decided you and your child were not in danger. The amygdala is quieted; it released few or no hormones, making it easier to come back to homeostasis (normal).

Our prefrontal cortex helps us be mindful of our situations, seeing different possible perspectives before reacting or making decisions. It helps us understand that other people's emotions are a state of *their* well-being and have little to do with us personally. It helps us have deep and meaningful relationships with those around us, as we can observe our own thoughts and feelings. This system allows us to patiently apply the brakes in the car when someone pulls out in front of us and assume the other driver simply did not see us.

The problem is, in times of prolonged stress, this "danger detecting" system gets a little more trigger-happy. We all know that practice makes perfect. If the amygdala has been overly engaged, especially as a child, it can become accustomed to "taking control." Research has shown that repeated trauma, or what I call perceived negative experiences (PNEs), can increase the sensitivity of the amygdala. This increases the risk that situations will be interpreted as dangerous. Even small "glitches" in this system can lead to relationship turmoil. You sense that your partner might be angry with you, and from past negative experiences, you quickly engage your "fight-back" response. Unfortunately, the frontal lobes are "offline," which doesn't allow you to think clearly at all. When the thinking/reasoning part of our brain is inhibited, we are left to our primal responses and actions. This is when tempers suddenly flare over the slightest thing, making them unpredictable. Or someone may completely freeze or withdraw when put on the spot. Fear has been practiced so often that it is the go-to response to keep the body safe.

Neuroimaging studies of the brain in people suffering with PTSD show significantly increased activity in the subcortical regions of the brain.[62] The areas that regulate fear, sadness, pain, and anger are more active, and they seem "stuck" in the emotional brain. After a trauma, especially repeated trauma, the nervous system responds differently. This can cause increased hormone production, keeping the body in a constant state of low-level reactivity. Now the body must reroute precious energy and focus in order to suppress the hair-trigger reactions. When this person lashes out in pain, fear, or anger out of context, this can cause further trauma and withdrawal. Because the person is stuck in the emotional brain, they rarely engage the prefrontal region to get a "higher perspective." This becomes a vicious cycle. Now every new experience is tainted by the perpetual state of looking for, and reacting to, trauma. The body is forced to defend itself daily against a threat produced by the mind. The constant vigilance and energy it takes to maintain this cycle can take a hefty emotional and physical toll on the body.

PNEs – PERCEIVED NEGATIVE EXPERIENCES

Remember, trauma is subjective. Even though we all possess the same basic "warning and response" system, how we *in*put an experience within our unique model of the world will significantly impact how the experience is filed. Also, our individual perceptions of trauma are different. A child could be yelled at by a teacher in school, and depending on this child's previous experiences, this could be devastating or largely ignored. Even children who are raised in the same home can have vastly different reactions to the same experiences.

It is my opinion that most of us hold some form of trauma. We all have some experience in our life that continues to haunt us. Granted, someone who felt like they were a bit ignored as a child may not have the same outward effects that a survivor of incest may exhibit, but the hurt is there nonetheless. Our society is good at comparing. And we often gauge our suffering by the suffering of others.

---

62 Centers for Disease Control and Prevention. *The Adverse Childhood Experiences (ACE) Study.* http://cdc.gov. Atlanta, Georgia, December 27, 2015.

"Yeah, my father wasn't around much, but at least he didn't beat me."
"I was bullied terribly in school, but wasn't everyone?"
"My mother was an alcoholic, but not as bad as other people I know."

At first glance, these statements seem like the better of two options. You know the other one, the "Woe is me; I had it worse than anyone" type of person. The trouble is, both these people are hurting. They both have had hurtful, negative experiences, but the latter type tends to get a worse reputation. Of course, we can see why. Most of us are just trying to keep all those negative memories, thoughts, and emotions at bay. We don't need some poor-me individual constantly reminding us of just how fragile our own grip is on "normal."

What if we have another option? What if we each can acknowledge our own hurts and experiences, but rather than broadcasting them day and night, or stuffing them down into the subconscious abyss, or denying them altogether, we could actually deal with them?

It is my belief that nearly all "dis-ease" in the body and mind comes from one thing: perceived negative experiences. Unfortunately, no amount of positive thought, positive affirmations, yoga, drugs, booze, sex, or makeup can cover these up forever. Some of these things will seem to help, even for long stretches of time. But it always shows up somewhere. In the book, *Feelings Buried Alive Never Die*, Karol K. Truman explains that most, if not all, of the problems we face in life are from unresolved feelings.[63] As discussed previously, we know that feelings are just chemical responses to our memories.

As much as we would like to "keep the past in the past," PNEs will keep showing up if they need to be processed and resolved. I will discuss this in more length soon, but for now, the important thing to realize is that if *we* are producing and holding these negative experiences, *we* can also decide and learn to let them go! The power is in our hands.

---

[63] Truman, Karol K. *Feelings Buried Alive Never Die.* Olympus Distribution Corp, August 28, 2014.

TRAUMA CAN BE GENETICALLY PASSED DOWN

One of the most important diagnostic tools is something anyone can create: a family tree. Have you noticed that health problems and negative behavioral outcomes seem to repeat themselves from one generation to another? Sometimes specific health or behavioral issues even skip a generation and keep on trucking. Odd, isn't it? Yet this is a truth that we continue to find in parent-child relationships physically, emotionally, and even spiritually. Countless psychologists have noted that specific characteristics and behaviors such as rage, anger, and molestation tend to roll over to the next generation.[64]

> *Do not bow in worship to them, and do not serve them; for I, the Lord your God, am a jealous God, bringing the consequences of the fathers' iniquity on the children to the third and fourth generations of those who hate me.*
>
> **Exodus 20:5** CSB

> *Do not bow in worship to them, and do not serve them, because I, the Lord your God, am a jealous God, bringing the consequences of the fathers' iniquity on the children to the third and fourth generations of those who hate me.*
>
> **Deuteronomy 5:9** CSB

> *Those of you who are left will waste away in the lands of their enemies because of their sins; also because of their ancestors' sins they will waste away. But if they will confess their sins and the sins of their ancestors…*
>
> **Leviticus 26:39–40**

These scriptures became well known to the Jews, who realized the reason for their captivity in Babylon centuries later. In the books of Ezra and Nehemiah, we

---

[64] Wright, Dr. Henry W. *A More Excellent Way.* Be in Health, Inc. Whitaker House, New Kensington, PA. 2009.

read about the amazing outcome when the people understand how their parents' and grandparents' choices and sin have affected them for generations. What do they do? Sulk and lament about being victims of their ancestors' issues? No! They break the cycle by confessing and repenting and moving forward as victors!

> *Those of Israelite descent had separated themselves from all foreigners. They stood in their places and confessed their sins and the sins of their ancestors.*
>
> **Nehemiah 9:2**

These amazing people took the power back into their hands by changing their minds, taking responsibility, and creating a different outcome.

> *But see, we are slaves today, slaves in the land you gave our ancestors so they could eat its fruit and the other good things it produces. Because of our sins, its abundant harvest goes to the kings you have placed over us. They rule over our bodies and our cattle as they please. We are in great distress. In view of all this, we are making a binding agreement, putting it in writing, and our leaders, our Levites and our priests are affixing their seals to it."*
>
> **Nehemiah 9:36–38**

No blame or shame. No fear or rage. A simple mind change changed everything! Let's take a look at another passage in Ezekiel.

> *For everyone belongs to me, the parent as well as the child—both alike belong to me. The one who sins is the one who will die. "Suppose there is a righteous man who does what is just and right. He does not eat at the mountain shrines or look to the idols of Israel. He does not defile his neighbor's wife or have sexual relations with a woman during her period. He does not oppress*

> *anyone, but returns what he took in pledge for a loan. He does not commit robbery but gives his food to the hungry and provides clothing for the naked. He does not lend to them at interest or take a profit from them. He withholds his hand from doing wrong and judges fairly between two parties. He follows my decrees and faithfully keeps my laws. That man is righteous; he will surely live, declares the Sovereign Lord... "Yet you ask, 'Why does the son not share the guilt of his father?' Since the son has done what is just and right and has been careful to keep all my decrees, he will surely live. The one who sins is the one who will die. The child will not share the guilt of the parent, nor will the parent share the guilt of the child. The righteousness of the righteous will be credited to them, and the wickedness of the wicked will be charged against them... If a righteous person turns from their righteousness and commits sin, they will die for it; because of the sin they have committed they will die. But if a wicked person turns away from the wickedness they have committed and does what is just and right, they will save their life... Rid yourselves of all the offenses you have committed, and get a new heart and a new spirit... For I take no pleasure in the death of anyone, declares the Sovereign Lord. Repent and live!*
>
> **Ezekiel 18:4–9, 19–20, 26–27, 31–32**

So, which passage is true? Are we all going to suffer from our ancestors' trauma, sin, thoughts, and behavior? Or are we going to live free because we repent? The choice is *yours*! The cycle can continue, or it can come to a screeching halt. Remember that it is not the guilt of sin that is passed down, but rather the consequences of sin that become the legacy. But notice that in both scriptures, repentance is the only thing that allows us to be forgiven so we can break the cycle and live anew. Even if we are genetically predisposed to something (through our parents), there is the promise that we *can* change, that we can "repent and live!"

EPIGENETICS

Through the ground-breaking study of epigenetics, we now know that genes can be changed. By our thoughts, no less! Simply put, epigenetics explains how our thought life and environment can cause changes in our DNA. This field of study has also revealed that traumatic events in the lives of parents or grandparents can be handed down genetically. The belief that we can "pass on" traits from one generation to the next is not a recent theory. We all know that eye color, hair color, and biological dispositions can be passed down genetically, but what if other things can be passed on as well? What if *acquired* traits could follow along to the next generation? Fears, hurts, traumas, addictions. In the late 1700s to early 1800s, Jean-Baptiste Lamarck, a French biologist known for his own theories on evolution, proposed that organisms pass down acquired traits to future generations.[65] Science now shows that Lamarck may not have been far off base. Some of the most fascinating research on this matter comes from the study of children of Holocaust survivors. In 2012, the Department of Psychiatry, São Paulo School of Medicine, published a research article entitled "Transgenerational transmission of trauma and resilience: a qualitative study with Brazilian offspring of Holocaust survivors." This study concluded by showing that "traumatic experiences can be transmitted to and developed by the second generation."[66]

The study was built on a similar one published in 1997. "Trauma in children of Holocaust survivors: transgenerational effects," by Sorscher and Cohen, found that "Holocaust trauma has psychological impacts on the children of survivors, such as higher levels of childhood trauma, increased vulnerability to PTSD, and other psychiatric disorders."[67]

---

65 Burkhardt, Richard W. *Jean-Baptiste Lamarck*, Encyclopedia Britannica, 2019.

66 Braga, Mello and Fiks, *Transgenerational transmission of trauma and resilience: a qualitative study with Brazilian offspring of Holocaust survivors.* BMC Psychiatry, 2012.

67 Sorscher N, Cohen LJ. *Trauma in children of Holocaust survivors: transgenerational effects,* Columbia Presbyterian Medical Center, New York, July 1997.

Rachel Yehuda, a psychiatry and neuroscience professor and the Director of the Traumatic Stress Studies Division at the Mount Sinai School of Medicine, is pioneering some of the latest data with Holocaust survivors. Yehuda states, "Holocaust offspring had the same neuroendocrine or hormonal abnormalities that we were viewing in Holocaust survivors and persons with post-traumatic stress disorder."[68] Epigenetics sees that genes can be turned on and off and expressed differently through changes in environment and behavior. Long before I ever considered the mind-body connection, I had my own seemingly epigenetic experience.

In 2001, I worked for an ambulatory equine vet clinic and lived on a ranch in Malibu. Every morning before my shift, I felt so nauseous that I would end up in the clinic restroom throwing up. I had been losing weight and had menstrual bleeding for about nine months straight. For any "normal" person, this may have been cause for alarm, but I was extremely accustomed to random symptoms and frequent ailments by this point in my life. Besides, I didn't have insurance and wasn't making much money. One morning, I was driving with the primary doctor of the clinic for some farm calls. Either someone had mentioned my morning ritual or, as a doctor, he noticed some things were not right with me.

As was part of my illness "program," I was commonly ashamed of ailments. I would mostly suffer in silence, preferring that I be perceived as strong and healthy. But after a little prodding, I came out with my myriad of symptoms, including my bleeding. I had ridden with this doctor many times and knew him to be wise and caring. He immediately suggested that I see a friend of his who was a general practitioner, but he suspected I might have endometriosis. After many tests and two surgeries to deal with the endometriosis, I was still unwell. Though the constant bleeding had stopped, I was still throwing up, and now I was also falling asleep at all times of the day, even while driving.

I had gone to visit my cousin who lived in Redondo Beach at the time, and she was telling me that she had recently been diagnosed with celiac disease. After hearing my symptoms, she said I should be tested for celiac disease because it

[68] Yehuda, Rachel. *How Trauma and Resilience Cross Generations*, On Being, July 30, 2015.

was genetic. I immediately started eating gluten-free and eventually was able to secure an appointment at a clinic. Very quickly after stopping the gluten, I saw an improvement in my symptoms. It just so happened that my morning breakfast for the last year had been a few slices of sourdough bread with butter. When I finally saw the doctor and explained all the symptoms, my improvement after stopping the gluten, and my cousin's diagnosis, he felt pretty sure that celiac disease was also my problem. But he couldn't be sure without an intestinal biopsy.

Again, having no insurance made this impossible, not to mention that I had already begun improving without any invasive procedures. I thought I had found the answer. What a miracle! Just by avoiding gluten, I could live a "normal" life. I was still referred to a gastroenterologist for follow-up. During my appointment with him, I mentioned that I had no intention of doing the biopsy because it would require that I begin eating gluten again. At this time, the gold-standard diagnostic tool was the biopsy (by now, many advancements have been made in this area). Because I was opting out of the biopsy, I was given a comprehensive health history questionnaire instead.

I remember distinctly one of the first questions I was asked: "Did you have any traumatic events happen to you in childhood?" I laughed out loud at this question, thinking, "*Take your pick, doc!*" I briefly explained that, yes, I had quite a few traumatic events in childhood, and he nodded and made notes on his paper. This was the first time I had ever been asked anything about my past by a medical professional, besides a medical history. I was caught a little off guard by this and couldn't help but demand an explanation of this intrusive line of questioning. The doctor explained that celiac disease is genetic and that certain people are genetically predisposed to developing it, but that it doesn't manifest in everyone that carries the genetic disposition. Research had shown that this gene gets "turned on like a switch" at some point in the person's life. They had linked the switch being flipped to traumatic events in people's lives.[69]

At the time, I remember thinking, "*Great! Just another little gift from my crummy past! Thanks, Mom and Dad!*" Some 15 years later, during the infancy of

---

[69] Ratner, Amy. *Eating Gluten One Time Might Be Enough of a Challenge To Diagnose Celiac Disease.* htpps://BeyondCeliac.com, September 27, 2017.

my journey down the "rabbit hole" of the mind-body connection, I would remember this doctor's words. It turned out that avoiding gluten wasn't going to be my "miracle cure," because the gluten wasn't exactly the culprit, even though it was showing up in my genes.

The genetic revolution promised to hold all the answers to health and wellness. Upon discovering the obesity gene, the cancer gene, the diabetes gene, and many other possible disease indicators, the scientific and medical communities thought they had found the holy grail of information. Unfortunately, it only brought more questions. Why did some people carry the gene for breast cancer and *not* manifest breast cancer, while others who didn't carry the gene did develop the disease?

Again, I am taking years of research and science and "dumbing it down" into my personal takeaways. The research on this subject is fascinating and scientifically dense. It is also still quite controversial. But when I first learned about epigenetics, my own diagnosis with celiac disease came into focus. If traumatic events can "turn on" or influence the disposition of our genes, could they also not be "turned off"? That is my theory and the belief that I operate from. Just as we can remodel a house to suit our preferences and needs, we can also remodel our genes!

Several years back, we bought a house in Maui. Though we have had many fixer-upper homes in the past, we purchased this one believing that it only needed minor updates. We were wrong. As we began removing the old Formica countertops to replace them with granite, we quickly realized that everything was not as it seemed. We lifted the old countertops, only to watch the cabinets below practically disintegrate before our eyes. Years of water and pest damage had left them riddled with rot. Oh, how I wish that were all! We ended up gutting the entire house down to the studs. This was not in the plan. Many hours and dollars later, we had rebuilt everything to our personal taste and quality. It was very comforting knowing what was behind each wall because we were the ones who put it there. We were building on someone else's foundation. Some things were good. The actual framework and foundation were solid. But the electrical work was in shambles and not up to code, requiring a complete overhaul. I thought a lot about our pasts and our minds during the long hours of remodeling and about how similar our lives are to the remodeling of a house. We could have simply left it. We could have patched up the ever-increasing "flaws" that would inevitably pop up. So often, we live our lives like this. "Cracks" show up in our health, and rather than remodel, we patch. We medicate, operate, and succumb to limitations.

Thankfully, it doesn't have to be that way! We can change our thoughts and remodel our memories. Yes, *we can change anything—even our genes!* How? By changing our thoughts and reshaping our memories.

CHAPTER 11

SANCTIFICATION THROUGH SICKNESS AND SUFFERING

We are about to enter enemy territory. A person who has a deep relationship with their sickness, their hurt, their pain, or their suffering will usually defend it to the degree they would their own child. I have wrestled with this chapter in my heart, but I ultimately feel that I would be doing you a great disservice by ignoring this topic. I warn you now that this chapter will challenge you. It flies in the face of some of our most deeply ingrained societal beliefs and asks us to dig deeper into the truth of the Scriptures. I would humbly ask you to approach the following material with an open heart and mind. Just consider, for a moment, that what I am saying contains truth. In the end, you are welcome to return to what you know if the information is too uncomfortable. Not everyone is ready, and that is okay. Some seeds take longer than others to bear fruit.

Let me ask you a question, and I want you to take a moment to really think about it: does God still heal today? Take a moment to observe your answer. Does your answer sound something similar to "Yes, I believe that God heals today, *but* only if it's his will." We will address numerous "*buts*" in the following pages. First, let us get a baseline understanding of what we see in the Bible concerning sickness, illness, and mental maladies. To do this, we must acknowledge how beliefs form and know that we approach the Bible in the same way we approach any other learning: seeing is believing.

DOES GOD STILL HEAL?

To answer this question honestly, you will undoubtedly need to take into account your own experiences. Have you ever prayed for someone to be healed, and it didn't happen? Did God say no? If that person wasn't healed, how do you reconcile that? It's too big a question to leave unanswered. I have heard countless theological discussions on this topic, trying to deal with the fear and the doubt that a sick or suffering Christian leaves in the hearts of their fellow brothers and sisters. This problem is too huge to be left unquestioned.

It is my opinion that no other topic has been more biblically maligned than the topic of sickness and suffering among believers. The reason? We are indoctrinated culturally, societally, and emotionally about this subject. We see too many inconsistencies in our own churches, families, and lives. What if we have let our own fear, doubt, and sentimentality about this topic blind us to the truth? Please take a moment to, again, consider this familiar passage:

> *Do not conform to the pattern of this world, but be transformed by the renewing of your mind. Then you will be able to test and approve what God's will is—his good, pleasing and perfect will.*
>
> **Romans 12:2**

In order to "not conform," we must address what the modernly held views on the subject are. Most of us in the modern, Western world are not comfortable with miracles. Still today, as in the first-century culture of the New Testament, many non-Western cultures are open to the possibility of miraculous healing. Though many of us in the Western Christian world would *say* that we believe God capable of miraculous healing, we are far more secular in our expectations of it. We would be naïve at best if we neglected to acknowledge that the majority of us come from a secular worldview. Remember our previous discussion about our personal models of the world. We cannot choose the worldview we are born into, in the same way that we cannot choose our parents who contributed to our DNA. But when we confess our allegiance to God and commit our lives to following Jesus, we must consistently question our worldview to see where it does not align with the Bible. Ken Blue, author of *Authority to Heal,* addresses this challenge beautifully:

> *This is why the secular world view is not so much a weed which chokes out good seed, but rather the polluted ground in which the seed is planted. Our view of reality is not skewed by one*

> *particular erroneous thought but by a whole system of thought. Gaining some perspective on the modern world view is the first step towards being able to resist it.*

Later in the same chapter, Blue elaborates on his position that our worldview renders God as a nonessential in our healing.

> *We Western Christians may be theist in our heads, but we tend to act like secularists in our daily activities. The real authority in our world view today and the touchstone of truth for our society is science. Science is our savior, provider and fixer.*[70]

It is impossible to view the message of Jesus without addressing healing. His ministry was a ministry of healing and restoration. Jesus was a healer. He didn't come to lay down a new set of theological regulations to be followed and used as a banner of protection. He came to salvage, save, heal, and restore the relationship between God and his lost children. For Jesus, teaching was not an intellectual endeavor, but a way to open hearts to becoming whole again. Think about the mission and purpose of Jesus in his own words, "*For the Son of Man came to seek and to save the lost*" (Luke 19:10).

The Greek word for "save" here is *sōzō*. This word, *sōzō*, is translated into several different phrases in the Bible: save, make whole, heal, be whole (refer back to Chapter 7 on wholeness and healing for an in-depth look).[71]

Humans are physical, social, intellectual, emotional, and spiritual beings. If we experience a disruption in any one of these five dimensions, there is a loss of the *wholeness* we were created to have. As we observe in the Gospels, Jesus rarely healed for the sake of healing alone. The physical healings he administered revealed the redemptive power of God. Today, many Christians look at the healing ministry of Jesus from a purely physiological perspective. When they

---

[70] Blue, K. "The Secular World View." *Authority to Heal.* Madison, WI: InterVarsity Press. 1987.

[71] Strong's Greek Lexicon. https://www.blueletterbible.org/

experience physical illness or disease, they hope that God will intervene and provide physical healing. If healing does not occur, people become disheartened and often lose faith. We must figure out how to reconcile a loving God who wants "*to prosper…and not to harm*" his children with his apparent decision to let us suffer. Perhaps the issue that needed healing was not physical in nature to begin with. Maybe the healing ministry of Jesus was more centered around the greater concept of salvation. Jesus' mission is to see God's children restored to wholeness in mind, body, and spirit.

> *May God himself, the God of peace, sanctify you through and through. May your whole spirit, soul and body be kept blameless at the coming of our Lord Jesus Christ.*
>
> **1 Thessalonians 5:23**

The Bible is replete with scriptures connecting a separation from God with physical illness, as well as our deliverance from sin with the healing of our bodies.

> *Praise the Lord, my soul,*
> *and forget not all his benefits—*
> *who forgives all your sins*
> *and heals all your diseases.*
>
> **Psalm 103:2–3**

> *Beloved, I pray that you may prosper in all things and be in health, just as your soul prospers.*
>
> **3 John 1:2 NKJV**

> *A heart at peace gives life to the body,*
> *but envy rots the bones.*
>
> **Proverbs 14:30**

In the overall theological perspective, we see a basic connection between the entrance of sin into the world through Adam and Eve and the introduction of death, pain, and disease. In the first three chapters of Genesis, we find that death and physical afflictions are established as consequences of sin. Because of sin, pain/death/illness became a normal part of the human experience. However, it is abundantly clear that this was not God's original design. The Good News, through Jesus Christ, was that humanity could be restored back to wholeness with God. Salvation and healing were synonymous to Jesus. We find that whenever Christ offered to heal a physical ailment, he also illustrated our ability to be free from the consequences of sin. In this, Jesus is able to provide humanity with a visible example of the freedom we are offered in body, mind, and spirit. Observe the distinction when addressing the ministry of John the Baptist versus Jesus' own ministry focus:

> *Jesus replied, "Go back and report to John what you hear and see: The blind receive sight, the lame walk, those who have leprosy are cleansed, the deaf hear, the dead are raised, and the good news is proclaimed to the poor. Blessed is anyone who does not stumble on account of me."*
>
> **Matthew 11:4–6**

John the Baptist was preaching a message of repentance by behavior modification: "Change your life by changing your actions so as to avoid the wrath to come." Jesus revealed the difference between the "good-works gospel" taught by the Jews and the "complete change of mind," or "new birth" gospel—which is required for restoration to wholeness and holiness. When John heard that Jesus' followers were experiencing true healing of body and spirit, he knew that this Jesus was the Christ. This should still be a defining factor in who we are following today.

SALVATION = HEALING

To properly view the connection between physical and spiritual healing, we must consider some of the original language of those terms. The following excerpts are taken from StudyLight.org, a Hebrew language studies site.

> ישע *yâsha'* is the Hebrew verb *to save*, occurring some 205 times, from which we get the name Jesus (ישוע Yeshu'a) and the word *hosanna*. *Yeshû'âh* is the noun, *salvation* derived from it. But neither of these words has the sense of being whisked away to heaven. Rather, they are salvation in the here and now words. *Yâsha'* can also mean *to deliver*, or *liberate* from evil, setting free into a spacious rather than a constricted place. It is commonly translated by such terms as *safety, welfare, prosperity, health* and *victory*. Salvation is thus realistic and holistic, not only spiritual; it includes God's practical intervention in healing, deliverance, and provision.
>
> The verb is first used in Exodus 2:17 of Moses in Egypt helping/ saving the daughters of the priest of Midian who were bullied away by shepherds. The salvation he offered was practical. The very next use in the Bible and the first used of God is the Lord's salvation of the Israelites through the Red Sea, allowing Israel to pass through to the other side unharmed (Exodus 14:30). The majority of *salvation* verses in the [Old Testament] were to do with physical deliverance from enemies.
>
> The Greek words *sôzô* and *sôter*, to *save*, and *salvation*, [in the New Testament] have a similar breadth of meaning as *yâsha'*. They can be translated by *deliver, protect, heal, save, preserve, do well* and *be whole*. *Sôzô* is used of healing in Matthew 9:21–22, of deliverance and wholeness in Luke 8:35–36, of resurrection in Luke 8:49–55 and of care and provision in 2 Timothy 4:18. Thus, salvation in both testaments is not only of

> the soul, but of the whole person, life and liberty. Indeed, soul is a Hebrew euphemism for the whole person anyway.[72]

Understanding the Old Testament and New Testament biblical definitions of salvation on a broader scale, as presented here, can help us understand even further the mind-body-spirit connection. Yes—God wants to save our souls and redeem us on a spiritual level. But he also integrates the spiritual, physical, mental, and emotional sides of us, revealing that they all work together. God wants us to be saved, safe, delivered, prosperous, protected, healed, healthy, victorious, and whole.

It is very common for Christians today to consider sin as a legal transgression or "crime" rather than a sickness. "Sin as crime" versus "sin as sickness" has been a theological debate for thousands of years. The historical and theological research on these matters is plentiful, dense, and fascinating. I have come to the conclusion that it can be both. Regardless, whether sin is manifesting as crime or sickness, the consequences are usually not pleasant. If we view sin as deviation, as discussed in the previous chapters, both "sin as crime" and "sin as sickness" call out for reconciliation and a return to holiness. Let me provide you with an example.

We are all familiar with the fact that HIV can be passed through delivery from the mother to the baby. If we take into account that the mother contracted HIV through having unprotected sex with an infected partner, we might easily see the parallel of her sickness being caused by sin. But what if the infected partner was her husband, and she was unaware of his condition, which was due to infidelity. Sin is still the problem. And though it was not *her* sin that resulted in contracting the virus, the virus is still a deviation from health. Should she, therefore, not treat the virus because it was not her sin that caused it? Of course not! The problem so often revolves around the concept of guilt and blame. What happens when that sexual encounter that left the mother infected also ends up with a pregnancy? Now the baby is likely infected. Is that an absolute? Not

72 Went, K. *Hebrew Thoughts: Language Studies*. https://www.studylight.org/

always. Babies can be born virus-free from an infected mother. If the baby *is* infected, do we blame the child? No, but this sickness is still a result of sin. Do you see the connections? Should we fail to treat the child because they were not directly involved with the infection? By no means! The goal of medicine and the goal of Christianity is to restore wholeness to the mind, body, and spirit. Knowing that the child contracted the disease by behavior that was a deviation from God's loving design for us can help the child in the long run. Why? So they can *blame* their father and hold him responsible for the malady? No. I would argue that having that kind of reaction would only hinder the body's ability to heal. Instead, knowing that a deviation was responsible for the disease allows the child to have the power to make different choices about their own sexual decisions.

If you narrow your view of sickness to "environmental forces outside our control," you miss the obvious connection that Jesus makes between healing and forgiveness of sins. Likewise, to view sickness only as punishment for some heavenly infraction, you perpetuate the idea that every person struggling with a physical ailment is *at fault* for the illness.

In the Gospel of John, Jesus encounters a blame-based mindset from his followers: "*As he went along, he saw a man blind from birth. His disciples asked him, 'Rabbi, who sinned, this man or his parents, that he was born blind?'*" (John 9:1–2). It's easy for us to look for something or someone to blame for an ailment or hardship of some kind. But Jesus helps us understand that blame and shame are never the answers. We live in a magnificent world occupied by the ever-present problem of sin. Therefore, we will find deviations (spiritually and physically) as long as we live.

Jesus responds to this victim mindset by sharing how God always works to bring opportunities for healing. "*'Neither this man nor his parents sinned,' said Jesus, 'but this happened so that the works of God might be displayed in him'*" (John 9:3). Placing fault is never Jesus' intention. Instead, healing that points people back to God is always Jesus' heart.

SICKNESS = COMMUNICATION

Through my own experiences and study, I have come to understand that sickness/illness/pain is communication. God designed our bodies to be messengers of the mind. If I fall off my horse and break my leg, my body will produce pain in alignment with the circumstance. Why? Because my leg needs attention. There is a deviation in the design of my leg. It won't function to the best of its ability with a fracture in the bone. If I do not listen to the signals my mind is giving me through my body, then I risk causing even further harm or damage to my body. I am not the first to make this connection. It was the foundational belief of the early fathers of medicine.

> *This is the reason why the cure of so many diseases is unknown to the physicians of Hellas; they are ignorant of the whole. For this is the great error of our day in the treatment of the human body, that the physicians separate the mind from the body.*[73]
>
> — Socrates

Hippocrates, a Greek physician who lived from about 460 BCE to 375 BCE, is widely known as the "father of medicine." Many medical school graduates today still recite the Hippocratic Oath. This famous quote is attributed to this man: "*It is more important to know what sort of person has a disease than to know what sort of disease a person has*."[74]

WHAT ABOUT PHARMACEUTICAL DRUGS?

We all are very aware that the world is on drugs. Seriously. According to the Mayo Clinic study of prescription medication in 2013, nearly 70 percent of the US population is on at least one prescription drug. More than 50 percent of the population takes two medications, and 20 percent of patients are on five or more

---

[73] Jowett, Benjamin. *The Dialogues of Plato: Charmides*. Third Edition, Five Volumes. London: Oxford: Overs Press, 1892.

[74] Schubert, Charlotte; Scholl, Reinhold. *The Hippocratic Oath: How many covenants, how many oaths?* http://www.Science.gov. 2005.

prescription medications. The Medical Research Center says the top prescribed drugs are antibiotics, antidepressants, and painkilling opioids. Does the Bible have anything to say about the use of drugs? James Sanders of Greencastle, Indiana, wrote an article for *Truth Magazine* years back, a portion of which I'd like to share with you, regarding a Greek word in the Bible that many broadly misunderstand: *pharmakeia*.

> *Since the beginning of time, nearly every culture has identified our mental, spiritual, and emotional well-being as a direct link to our physical well-being. The Bible is full of references showing the connection between mind and body. Proverbs 17:22 says, "A cheerful heart is good medicine, but a crushed spirit dries up the bones." We, as a society, are deeply entrenched in the way we do "health care." The pharmaceutical companies are quite happy with the direction we have been going. It lines their pockets but keeps people sicker than ever. Paul, in his epistle to the Galatians enumerated a concise list of the works of the flesh. Contained in that list is the Greek word, pharmakeia. The King James scholar translated pharmakeia as "witchcraft" but a more probable rendering is that of "sorcery" and is so given by the American Standard Version. Sorcery is far closer to the meaning of the term. Pharmakeia (sorcery) is a form of the Greek root from which we get our English words pharmacy, pharmacist, and pharmaceutical. Pharmakeia (sorcery) fundamentally has to do with drugs or medicine. In the New Testament, pharmakeia carried with it the idea of sorcery, occultism, and black magic. It is in this sense that Paul used the term in Galatians 5:20. When Paul spoke of pharmakeia he certainly did not have in mind witches on broomsticks, black cats, and silly superstitions. The Apostle was speaking of sorcery—the evil abuse of drugs.*

Pharmakeia primarily signified the use of medicine, drugs, spells; then, poisoning; then sorcery.[75]

We all know that drugs have an effect on our bodies. We also know of the healing remedies God has placed on this earth for us to find and discover. Research has also shown that we can produce chemicals in our body that most drugs are trying to synthesize and produce for us. Rather than make a political or even definitive, biblical, black-and-white statement here, I want to focus on this situation's positive reality: our health is in our hands.

Though you may not have heard anything about the degree to which our emotional and thought life affects our physical health, that doesn't mean that the information hasn't been there. For centuries, even back to the time of Hippocrates, people were aware of this connection. In the Bible, Proverbs 23:7 is often quoted as saying, "*As a man thinks, so he shall be*."

Louise Hay published her first book, *Heal Your Body*, in 1976. She was instrumental in illustrating the mind-body connection and connecting various limiting beliefs to specific ailments or diseases in the body. She wasn't the first to do so but is arguably the best known. Inna Segal, the author of *The Secret Language of Your Body*, is another individual who linked specific illnesses to life events or negative feelings/emotions. These authors were instrumental in my own journey to wellness. Being someone who wasn't particularly skilled at "feeling my feelings," their texts became a reference system for what was going on with me emotionally.

For instance, I had long suffered from pain in my lower back. Though I had seen countless doctors, tried various forms of treatments from steroid injections/ painkillers/muscle relaxers to yoga and Pilates, nothing seemed to work. I was told genetics were at play as well as lifestyle. Being a horse trainer in my earlier years and suffering numerous falls definitely provided an easy explanation of why my back always seemed to hurt. Interestingly, it didn't always hurt the same way. Sometimes I could barely feel it, and at other times I was lying on a hospital

---

[75] Sanders, James. *Pharmakeia: The Abuse of Drugs.* Truth Magazine. http://truthmagazine.com/ December 10, 1970

gurney writhing in pain despite every available painkiller. If it was something purely physical, why did the symptoms change so drastically?

It wasn't until I began addressing my past physical abuse that I saw the first real relief in the pain. Louise Hay, in *You Can Heal Your Life*, says that back pain is about support. Specifically, lower back pain can indicate "fear of money and lack of financial support."[76] That definitely could fit, but when I referenced Inna Segal's book *The Secret Language of Your Body*, she had this to say about the pain: "Feeling unsupported and alone. Not knowing who or where to ask for help. Feeling that the world is an unsafe place to live in. Trying to protect yourself from pain and hurt."[77] That definitely resonated with me! Her book even broke it down further into the different vertebrae. I knew that I had been diagnosed with herniations in the L4 and L5 regions, so I looked those up. In the L5 description, it said, "Holding on to feelings of betrayal, abandonment, and isolation. Difficulty trusting people and following through with plans. Frequent self-sabotage, anger, and anxiety. A tendency to see yourself as a victim." *Bingo*!

These insights allowed me to further understand the problem areas in my life. I was quickly transported back to the first time I felt or believed these things and found myself back in my childhood. I thought that my back was the problem. I had MRIs and scans to show the "damage," but I just wanted to feel better. My spine surgeon (who had previously operated on my neck and fused two of my vertebrae…another story!) said something to me during the discussions of yet another surgery on my spine. When discussing my herniations, I asked why it hurt so much. He said that they didn't know and that much of what happens with the spine is still a mystery. He went on to tell me that he had scanned thousands of spines over the years. He had seen people with much worse herniations than mine who felt no pain whatsoever and some with even smaller ones who were in constant, unbearable pain.

This very well respected and educated surgeon told me that they had no idea what the connection is, but that they often do surgery just hoping to alleviate

---

[76] Hay, Louise. *You can heal your body.* Hay House, Inc. 1984.

[77] Segal, Inna. *Secret Messages of the Body.* Blue Angel Gallery. 2007.

some pain, and that the outcomes are unreliable at best. This information caused me to pause and think. What if the pain had little or nothing to do with what the scans showed, but something else altogether? It wasn't until I found myself down the rabbit hole of my own mind-body healing journey that his words came back to me. What if the pain had a message for me?

Though Inna Segal and Louise Hay were pivotal in my journey of communicating with my body, I eventually moved to even more in-depth resources. I was shocked to find many resources that go into incredible detail about the "emotional drivers" behind dis-ease and illness. Over the years, these have become invaluable tools as I continue to explore the body messages to myself and my clients.

I have come to see illness, disease, syndromes, and ailments as communication. I no longer think, "*What did I eat?*" "*What might I have?*" "*Maybe I should go see a doctor.*" My first reaction is to find out what my mind is trying to communicate to me through my body. I am particularly skilled in having my body deliver messages to me. I believe this is something I developed over time because I was not well versed in feeling emotions. I beat myself up over this for many years as an adult. I had interacted with enough people at this point to realize that I wasn't a very "emotional" person. It seemed that I had two main emotions—"mad" or "fine." That was about it. I didn't get "hurt," I got mad. From someone who was formerly diagnosed with bipolar disorder, this might seem like a good, happy medium! But it didn't serve me well, especially because I had children.

Although I had multiple physical issues before, the conception and birth of my children were a huge catalyst in the downfall of my health. I know now that the emotional components to that were my stressed relationship with my own mother and my fears of being a parent. All I knew about parenting was my view of my own parents, and the way I felt growing up. I didn't think that I possessed any skills to do it differently, and this wreaked havoc on my body. My body was screaming out to deal with these things, but I continued to worsen over time because I didn't know how to listen.

Before embarking on the mind-body journey about my inability to feel, I spoke to a friend who also happened to be a therapist. He was aware of my tumultuous upbringing and reframed it for me in a beautiful way: "Thank God you *didn't* feel much as a kid. What a gift! Can you imagine what your life would have been like if you had *felt* every bad thing that had happened to you and you were aware of it? Your mind was protecting you. What a wonderful skill it provided you with. The problem is, though it kept you alive and sane as a child, it no longer serves you as an adult."

Yes! That was it. At that moment, rather than beat myself up for "not feeling," I loved myself for taking such good care of ME. Luckily, this was right before I began finding the answers to how to change those programs and beliefs, even if they once kept me safe.

Someone might say, "Okay, I could see how some autoimmune syndrome might be associated with feelings, but what about a broken arm? Huh? That surely can't be emotional. Am I supposed to just *feel* the bone back together?" Do you get the feeling I have been asked this before?

Here is what I have to say about that. First of all, I have fallen off horses more times than I can count. And though I have broken many bones, I don't always break something when I fall. Is it just the way I fall? Maybe. But there is also an insight into what seems like random events.

Which arm did I break? The right? The left? Questions such as these hold possible clues to a message from the mind. *Is it possible that I have been feeling something that I haven't been dealing with? Am I having to reevaluate my usual way of doing things because my way is no longer effective?*

Knowing this will not un-break an arm. But it can aid in the healing. It can also fortify areas of your life or belief systems that might be weak so that your arms are strengthened.

At the same time, working on the emotional drivers can heal issues you did not even recognize were there before. I remember working with a young woman, just 23 years old. She came to me because she had a lot of physical ailments that she wanted to heal but also felt that she wasn't really thriving in her Christian faith. She never really felt "good enough" and also believed that she couldn't measure up in the eyes of God. As we dove into her life and her past, there were many relational and ancestral issues to unravel. In our work together, something surfaced that she had previously not been aware of: she was afraid to live as a woman in what she felt was a patriarchal society. It didn't feel safe. This fear was the root of her job issues, boss issues, relationships with men, and view of God. It also was an emotional foundation for one of her main physical issues: she had only menstruated two or three times in her entire life. Of course, this problem would have a direct impact on her ability to have children in the future.

One of the first things we addressed was the unhealthy relationship she had with her father. Over time, she cleared her fears, shame, and guilt that she had been carrying since childhood. She was able to forgive her father, which opened her heart to God in a way she had previously been unable to achieve. Through the sessions, she felt free and ready to be the amazing woman she already was. Lo and behold, at our next session, she proudly and comfortably let me know that she got her period (and she has been regular ever since). Even more amazing was how fulfilled she felt in her walk with God. "I thought that this kind of intimacy with God was something only *other* people could have. Not me. Now I see it was there for me the whole time. And I'm finally ready to receive it!" When we feel safe, the body will come back into alignment. I want to share another case study that will hopefully help illustrate this further.

A CASE STUDY

Addie was referred to me by another client who had resolved her chronic illness. As I looked over Addie's listed illnesses and disorders, I could see that she was headed down the same path that many people have been on, collecting disease after disease, syndrome after syndrome. When I next glanced at Addie's paperwork, I was a little surprised to see so few traumas listed. When I first met with Addie, she was just on the heels of her latest diagnosis, fibromyalgia. She had already been diagnosed with depression, a thyroid condition, migraines, and CFS (chronic fatigue syndrome). I am quite familiar with this sequence of autoimmune disorders and knew that a Lyme disease diagnosis was probably not too far off. But for now, Addie was sufficiently worried about the proclamation of an "incurable" and oft untreatable diagnosis of fibromyalgia.

As I asked Addie about her childhood, she seemed a bit perplexed as to why it mattered. From her perspective, she had a "normal" childhood and didn't seem to remember any traumas. From my experience, CFS is often a result of a deep subconscious need to be "on guard." This results in the body being in a constant state of fight or flight, as if there is always a possible danger lurking. This causes the adrenals to work overtime and many of the body's resources to be used up by its hypervigilance to survive. Though this can be a natural result of a traumatic event, it can also be a young child's best adaptation in a tumultuous home environment. As I explored Addie's childhood experiences more, it became clear that she grew up in a very controlling and critical family. Her father had been an elder in their local congregation. Though highly respected and much loved within his church community, he was very harsh and critical of his children and his wife. Addie remembered feeling that she needed to be obedient and respectful at all times, especially in front of people at church. In addition, she was taught never to question someone in authority.

Addie's mother was a quiet woman who lived to please her husband. Addie felt that her mother loved her and the other children, but she also felt that her mother was reluctant to show too much affection because Addie's father disapproved of "coddling" the children. Addie remembered having happy and loving times with her mother during the daytime, but as the afternoon approached, the level of anxiety would rise as they all awaited her father's arrival from work. Addie remembered how tense everyone would get, knowing that Dad would be home soon. Everyone needed to be on their best behavior and not make anything unpleasant for him once he got home. If any of the children whined, cried, or complained, Addie's father would shake his head disapprovingly and withhold any love, attention, or eye contact with the children or his wife. He would also berate Addie's mother for not being able to handle the "one job" she had: raising the children. Addie said she felt as though she could never measure up to her father's standards, no matter how much she tried. She also began resenting her mother's "weakness" and vowed that she would never follow in her footsteps by letting a man dominate her.

Addie left the house as soon as she was able. While in college, she reveled in her newfound freedom. She soon became involved romantically with a boy on campus who was well respected within the university for his athletic abilities. At first, Addie was swept away by his confidence and take-charge attitude. Eventually, his confidence gave way to domineering and controlling behavior. Addie once again felt trapped by a man whom she could never make happy, no matter how hard she tried. After breaking up with this young man, Addie began dating someone who was "nothing like her father." Jeff was quiet, dutiful, and seemed very interested in supporting Addie in her own dreams and endeavors. Addie quickly found herself in the driver's seat of this relationship and quite enjoyed the change of scenery. Jeff and Addie married as soon as they finished college. Jeff continued to support Addie and encouraged her to follow her dreams of opening a bakery.

The first few years were fun, exciting, and a *lot* of hard work. Addie threw herself into the business, working long days with little or no time off. Eventually, she became pregnant. The thought of having a baby both excited and terrified her. The bakery was so busy, and Addie was not very good with boundaries. Employees would often call in sick or take advantage of her willingness to cover shifts and take the bulk of the workload. After the birth of their daughter, Jeff and Addie decided it would be best for Jeff to stay home with the baby while Addie continued to work at the bakery. It all seemed like a great plan. Soon, Addie began to resent Jeff for all the time he was able to spend with the baby. Why did she have to work so hard and provide financially while Jeff got to stay home all day with their little one? Not long after, Addie began to feel unwell. At first, it was just the common cold every month or so. But with each cold, she never felt like she quite recovered fully. Also, she began to feel like she wasn't getting good sleep each night. After a year, it had gotten so bad, she decided to see her doctor. The doctor eventually landed on a diagnosis of adrenal fatigue and a sluggish thyroid. Addie took some dietary steps to resolve the adrenal fatigue and also began taking thyroid medication. Within a few months, she was feeling worse than ever. She had begun to miss more and more work but also felt less and less able to care for her baby. After many more doctor visits, she was given another diagnosis: CFS.

Jeff had no ability nor any desire to try to work at the bakery. He had also made no effort to pursue any further education or training while he had assumed the role of a stay-at-home parent. He began feeling that Addie was "exaggerating" her symptoms so that she could have an excuse to stay home. By the time Addie came to see me, she had all but lost the bakery, was mostly homebound, and was barely on speaking terms with her husband. She had just been told by yet another doctor that they couldn't find anything "concrete" but had been given the newest diagnosis to add to her growing list of conditions: fibromyalgia.

In our work together, we quickly identified a strongly reinforced belief that she was not worthy of love. Any and all affection, nurturing, or approval she had felt had come as a result of her working hard to perform. She felt that too many people relied on her and that she was responsible for keeping everyone "happy and healthy." She felt that she had failed the most important people in her life. When I asked her who was responsible for Addie, who was looking out for her needs and happiness, she broke down in tears. I helped Addie see that through the coping skills she received from her own parents, she was still stuck in the cycle of "not good enough" and trying to earn her love/acceptance/nurturing through her actions. Though she had physically left her parents' house, she was still staying in alignment with their model of the world.

As we dove deeper in, Addie realized that her father had been doing the best he could with the limited skills he had been given. His own father had been killed in the war when he was very young, and his mother remarried a harsh man who had no real love for this "other man's child." As he grew into an adult, he had no skills in how to love and connect with his children. Respect and authority were all he knew of parenting. Addie also recognized that, in trying to get away from her father's oppressive reign over the family, she became just like him in her own marriage. Finding a husband who resembled the character of her mother allowed Addie to have the control she so desperately wanted as a child. As with many women, the birth of her first child sparked a landslide of unresolved emotional trauma that was calling out to be healed. As someone who had made up her mind that she would never "be weak," she stopped listening to her own body when it demanded some attention. Eventually, her body screamed louder and louder (through dis-ease) until it finally got her notice.

Addie was afraid that she wouldn't know who she was or what her place in the world would be without feeling the need to work for love and approval. Eventually, we were able to change her mind, bringing her back into congruency with who she really was, and was created to be. We gave her the knowledge and proof that she *was* lovable and worthy of love, just for being who she was intrinsically. As she began to love and nurture herself in a more abundant way, she was finally free to love others without condition. This allowed her to set healthy boundaries for herself and for others. Today, Addie no longer needs to do CFS, fibromyalgia, thyroid disorders, or anything else physically to get the attention and care she so deeply deserves. She is able to give and receive love in abundance. Jeff has also learned to love himself in a deeper way and has begun to explore his own passions. Addie is more connected to her husband and her daughter than she ever thought possible. Now that she listens to her body, it no longer needs to speak the language of dis-ease. Addie is free.

CHAPTER 12

WILL THIS WORK FOR ME?

A woman was there who had been subject to bleeding for twelve years. She had suffered a great deal under the care of many doctors and had spent all she had, yet instead of getting better she grew worse. When she heard about Jesus, she came up behind him in the crowd and touched his cloak, because she thought, "If I just touch his clothes, I will be healed." Immediately her bleeding stopped and she felt in her body that she was freed from her suffering... He said to her, "Daughter, your faith has healed you. Go in peace and be freed from your suffering."

Mark 5:25–29, 34

"But if you can do anything, take pity on us and help us."
"'If you can'?" said Jesus. "Everything is possible for one who believes."

Immediately the boy's father exclaimed, "I do believe; help me overcome my unbelief!"

Mark 9:22–24

I am often asked what kind of people the Metanoia Method works for, and I usually say that it works for people who have problems. When they ask what kind of problems, I typically respond with, "Any problem you can think of." I sometimes add that it helps if they have a brain, since that is what we will be working with! But most of the people I work with have a very good reason for asking. They have "tried everything" and are still just as bad, if not worse. Why?

It's not because they don't want healing. It's not because they haven't tried enough, or prayed enough, or that they don't deserve it. It's not because they aren't good enough, smart enough, or strong enough. People question whether this will work because they *know how* to put all their hope, money, and energy into something and have it fail. They weren't consciously trying to fail. In fact, according to the subconscious mind, they succeeded—they succeeded in keeping things just the way they are because it's often not perceived to be safe enough to change.

SECONDARY GAINS

As I mentioned before, if we are doing something, we likely have a very good reason for it. Otherwise, we wouldn't be doing it. A problem isn't a failure; it's a success. You aren't failing at being healthy, you are successful at being sick! If you stopped being successful, you would fail to be sick. Clear as mud?

Here's the deal: we need to start seeing our lives as a success: I am successful at not losing weight. I am successful at producing this cancer. I am successful at sabotaging good opportunities in my life. The reason we need to see it this way is, if we can be successful at some things, it presupposes that we can be successful at other things. A problem is just an undesired success. So we can choose to be successful at something else! Remember, God made us powerful creators, in his image.

Often, we see something as a problem but neglect to acknowledge the benefits we get from it. When we benefit from something that on the surface looks negative, we call this secondary gains.

"*If I'm overweight, someone will finally love me for who I am and not what I look like.*"
"*If I self-sabotage good job opportunities, I won't ever have to face the pressure that comes with maintaining success.*"
"*If I am sick, I won't be expected to do all those things that drain me emotionally.*"

And so on. It may not be easy to identify the secondary gains in our lives. Our subconscious mind keeps these safely guarded. We are often reluctant to give up certain undesirable outcomes if there are "good things" that come from it, especially if the subconscious mind has used this to keep us safe at some point in our life.

The statistics and research linking obesity with prior sexual abuse are plentiful. Weight gain is often a metaphoric "barrier" of protection, almost like emotional padding. It's also a deterrent from unwanted sexual attention. Note that these are conclusions made by the subconscious mind, since we are not often consciously aware of these connections. A friend of mine who has been using the Metanoia Method for many years was talking about her experience with secondary gains as a Christian. She has this wisdom to share:

> *Another reason I have seen Christians protect their secondary gains is because we are so steeped in judgment of self. If we acknowledge that we are doing it to ourselves, the blame and shame are too overwhelming. We believe this is right, that we are supposed to be highly critical of ourselves (in the name of discipling) even though Romans 8 says there is no condemnation for those in Christ.*

This was a vastly enlightening revelation in her own walk with God, and something that many of us can relate to.

QUESTIONS AND EXCUSES

We wanted to address some of the common questions, objections, and resistance that are common among Christians regarding this work. Most of the following questions stem from subconscious programs (patterns of thinking to keep the person "safe" on a fundamental level). Sometimes, the first several sessions I have with a client are spent dealing specifically with these objections or fears. Here are some examples:

"I've tried everything. Nothing works for me."

This program comes from a file folder that has many "proofs" or "references" that it is a fact. This is often an indicator that there may be secondary gains from the problem. We typically need to address the "what if's" behind the person getting better. A common fear associated with this is, "Who will I be if I don't have this problem?" To deal with this, we often need to go back and find out why it's so important to them that it *doesn't* work. People are often flustered by this, being completely ignorant of the "good" that the subconscious mind is trying to protect.

"I have prayed/fasted/asked God to take this away, yet I still have it. Does that mean that God is just saying no? Shouldn't I just accept this?"

This was me (Heather). I had prayed, fasted, asked others to pray, been anointed with oil, and had the church elders pray over me, yet I was still sick. And now I'm well! We know from Scripture that God wants *all* people to be saved, and from my experience, his heart also yearns for *all* people to be healed —but we have to be willing.

"So, are you saying you need something more than the Bible to heal?"

No. Instead, we are revealing that everything in the Bible is there to help us learn *how* to heal from the inside out. This book could have been 10 times as long, quoting and analyzing every scripture on healing, repentance, and the mind-body connection. But we hope that, by now, you have been supplied with enough material to show you just how amazing God created us to be. And we encourage you to keep learning more!

"How is this different from New Age thinking about healing?"

We have found that all cultures across the world have various forms of thinking when it comes to healing. People are searching for something to heal the pain, the scars, and the problems they encounter. Many modalities will claim a "new" find as the course to all healing. So how is the Metanoia Method different? We give God all the credit. God offers us "*everything we need for life and godliness*" (2 Peter 1:3). Be willing to discover this amazing world and our amazing brains that he created. "*I pray that the eyes of your heart may be enlightened in order that you may know the hope to which he has called you*" (Ephesians 1:18).

"Aren't you kind of taking God out of this?"

Absolutely not. "*For it is God who works in you to will and to act in order to fulfill his good purpose... so that you may become blameless and pure, 'children of God without fault in a warped and crooked generation.' Then you will shine among them like stars in the sky as you hold firmly to the word of life*" (Philippians 2:13–16). We firmly believe that "*with man this is impossible, but not with God; all things are possible with God*" (Mark 10:27). Only because of how God created us can any of this be possible. We absolutely keep God at the center of our healing.

"But where does the Holy Spirit come into play?"

One of the greatest gifts God has given to those who turn to him is the indwelling of the Holy Spirit. I believe the counsel and help that is provided by the Holy Spirit is a marvelous mystery and an integral part of what allows us to change. I think the Holy Spirit is instrumental in helping us reveal the places inside us that need healing. Ultimately, this book is not about how the Holy Spirit works. It is about God enabling us to inherently transform—mind, body, soul.

"This sounds to me like another version of the 'health and wealth gospel.' What's the difference?"

To answer this question, let's first look a little more closely at the "health and wealth gospel" and define what it is. Also known as the prosperity gospel or the Word of Faith movement, this belief system is an offshoot of the Protestant church and more recently affiliated with the Pentecostal and charismatic movements. This theology is mostly centered around material wealth and physical healing. It depends on a very contractual relationship with God and the Bible. Poverty or illness are viewed as curses that result from a lack of faith. An overarching message in this "gospel" is that the more you give financially, the more God will give you in return.

This movement is the basis for what became televangelism. Proponents of this belief maintain that if they contribute financially and "confess positively," they will be granted dominion over their souls and material objects around them. Therefore, they can claim whatever they desire of God, simply by speaking it, and God must grant that request.[78] Prominent leaders in this movement assert that possession of wealth, significant income, and lack of illness is proof of heavenly favor.

Health and wealth theology has gained increasing popularity among poor Americans seeking advancement in their health and social status. This kind of teaching also has a psychological component that is particularly attractive to individuals who seek connection and belonging. Members feel like they are part of a "gift-exchange" system. They give to God, and then he gives to them. Prosperity is proof of connection with God.[79]

I hope that it is clear that the Metanoia Method does not align with this theology. Although we *do* believe that God wants his people to live abundantly (John 10:10), we *do not* believe that material wealth or physical health is proof of God's favor. Similarly, we do not believe that poverty or illness equates to distance or dissatisfaction from God. It is our belief, based on Scripture, that God loves his creation abundantly and purposes us and equips us for every good work (2 Timothy 3:17). We believe that God works for the good of those who love him (Romans 8:28). We also believe that all people will experience hardship of some form or fashion. We are, after all, in a world inhabited by sin. The degree to which hardship occurs is no reflection of God's favor or lack thereof. We do not believe that financial wealth is either good or bad, and we don't believe that God cares very much about that either way. We *do* believe that sickness, illness in the body, relationship issues, mental health concerns, and many other problems have more to do with what is happening inside us rather than outside us; this belief is supported biblically and scientifically. We believe we are God's handiwork and

---

78 Coleman, Simon. *The Globalisation of Charismatic Christianity: Spreading the Gospel of Prosperity.* Cambridge University Press, 2010.

79 Robbins, Joel. *Studying Global Pentecostalism: Theories and Methods.* Michael Bergunder, André Droogers, and Cornelis van der Laan, University of California Press, 2010.

were created to do good works (Ephesians 2:10), but we also believe that God grants us free will and gives us the right to reject his involvement.

Overall, it is our opinion that the health and wealth gospel is no gospel at all. We believe that Jesus is our Redeemer, the way, the truth, and the life—not a means by which to gain material wealth and power. As for the abundance we frequently speak of throughout these pages, we will leave you with one of our guiding passages in 2 Corinthians 9:8: "*And God is able to bless you abundantly, so that in all things at all times, having all that you need, you will abound in every good work.*"

"Yes, but my disease/illness/diagnosis is REAL. I have proof!"

Again, I will say, *yes*, your issue is real—to you. I know that you feel it or can see it. You likely have some sort of diagnostic proof to back up your reality. This was the case for me. I had a medical file the size of three stacked encyclopedias. I had blood tests, MRIs, X-rays, and other tests that "proved" my many conditions. In the past, I looked at that stack of information, and it confirmed what I had always felt: "There is something wrong with me." That all changed when I found out about the power of the mind. After that, I looked at that same stack and was *amazed!* I was SO powerful that I had brilliantly created each one of these conditions and diseases. I was *amazing!* There wasn't anything *wrong* with me. I had just spent my time and energy creating things that no longer served me. With that knowledge, I began to deconstruct all that I had built while also building the future that I wanted.

"Okay, but my disease/illness/ailment is genetic!"

Please refer to the section in Chapter 10 on "Epigenetics."

"I don't want to dig up the past. Shouldn't I just think positive thoughts?"

People who believe this are under the impression that "the past is in the past." Unfortunately, that is not true. Our present and our future are built with the building blocks of our past. I am all for positive thinking. I just spent the last few pages and many other chapters saying that our thoughts can create our realities.

But positive thinking, though a clearly preferable coping mechanism, is still *usually* a coping mechanism. "Yeah, a lot of really horrible things happened to me as a child, but I'm just going to think positive."

When you do that, what happens in your mind is this: The conscious mind becomes aware of negative feelings, sensations, and pictures—then it decides that this is uncomfortable and logically thinks that there is really no good reason to focus on these "bad" feelings. So you try to think of something different, something positive. But remember, it's the subconscious mind that ultimately dictates the outcome of our thinking. The subconscious mind has a very good reason to hold onto the things that happened as a child, especially if they were hard or painful. And it has built an entire belief system around those childhood memories. If those experiences were painful, the subconscious mind flagged them and has been seeking out similar circumstances, to keep you safe and stay within that belief system.

A negative core belief is often stored as an irrevocable truth. For instance, let's say you were raised in a home where it seemed like any "negative" emotion was unacceptable. If you cried, complained, got angry, or talked back, you were made to feel "bad" or sinful. On the other hand, when you seemed compliant or virtuous in any way, you were held up as a model child. A core belief that could be developed from this experience is that you are only "good" when you feel good. If you feel bad, you *are* bad. You would eventually learn that any negative feelings, thoughts, and emotions meant that you weren't good enough. You could grow up not trusting your emotions, and in turn, yourself. You could grow up to believe that vulnerability or any discomfort was weak, sinful, or an inconvenience to those around you. As a result, you would believe that the only way to be "acceptable" to others is to be perfect and/or quiet. Of course, it is completely unrealistic to feel good all the time. So when this individual feels bad or reaches out for help in any way, they may feel so uncomfortable and so rejected already that they end up sabotaging the bid for attention. This only deepens the belief and continues the cycle.

Another common example would be accepting feedback. If you grew up feeling like your worth was based on whether you had the approval of those around you, it is likely you will continually seek outside validation. Being able to ask for and accept feedback in a healthy way is vital to our growth and connection with others. But for someone whose worth is wrapped up in these interactions, getting feedback can seem like a life-threatening venture. If the feedback is "good," you feel validated and worthy as a human. If the feedback is "bad," it is a direct reflection on you as a person. You will process "work that could use improvement in a certain area," as *I myself need improvement and I, myself, am being rejected*. This individual will not be able to hear anything but what they ultimately believe about themselves. You cannot positive-think your way around these belief systems; they need to be fundamentally changed. You can continue to bury trauma behind lots of positive thinking, but the subconscious beliefs and past experiences will always win the war. As I mentioned before, it *will* "leak out" eventually.

Positive thinking is like putting on a fresh coat of paint. If you paint over a solidly built wall, it looks beautiful and can really enhance the room. If you paint over a wall with cracks or leaks behind it, the paint will soon begin to show the water stains, the mold, the cracks, and the rot. You will have to put on more and more paint. For some people, that is preferable. And that is okay. They have very good reasons for not opening those walls. It can be scary, and it can be a lot of work. Some people don't feel equipped for remodeling. My goal is to give hope to these people, along with the "do-it-yourselfers." The methods I will share with you in Part 2 are simple. You go as fast and as far as you want to. This is *your* remodeling project. Positive thinking plays a huge role in the process, but only after the foundations have been examined and, if necessary, rebuilt.

"I'm too sick/tired/busy/stressed to do this work."

I would say that you are too sick/tired/busy/stressed *not* to do this work. This can be done from your home, from your bed, on the way to work, or anywhere you choose. You may need some initial assistance to recognize your power to change, but it's possible! For *anyone*.

"I don't feel comfortable sharing all the horrible things that were done to me/ that I have done."

That's okay. I have helped hundreds of people heal and change their minds without ever knowing what we were working on. This is because the change is within *your* mind. Often, I can help my clients change something they do not want to discuss without them ever mentioning the content at all. Why? Because your brain already knows the specifics. Part of the reason I love what I do is that I *don't* have to know all the "grimy details." I commonly work with people who say to me, "This is something I've never even wanted to admit to *myself*, let alone others."

Listen, I am not a magician. Neither am I a wonderfully intuitive healer. I don't shift energy, balance chakras, or have any special "miraculous healing gift from God." Many people have ascribed those descriptions to me and the work I do, but I see it a little more simply. I *facilitate*. I help others help themselves. I work with the brain and the mind, and the body follows.

It would be a much more lucrative business model if I could convince you that you *need me* to make your life better. But it's not the truth. Granted, we all need some help at times, and often we need someone to support us as we transition from the victim model into the victor model. But ultimately, the power is in *your* hands: the power to get well *and* the power to stay exactly where you are.

Why do I say this now? Because no matter what has happened to you, you are not stuck. The work I do is not magic. It's simple and easy to understand once you "get it." I don't need to know the details because you already do. Please don't ever believe you are "too far gone," "too broken," or "too indoctrinated." If you have a brain (which I'm going to assume that you do if you are reading this), you can change. Even if you believe that you are past the point of no return, you can change that too, because these methods *work* with beliefs!

"My childhood was pretty good. I don't really think I have any traumas. How can this help me?"

I am thrilled that you had a good childhood. I have heard this many times, yet the person is in my office. Why? In some ways, it doesn't matter. We all deserve to have the life of our dreams. Are you living it? Great! Drop this book and go enjoy it! Give it to someone who isn't living their *best* life. These methods can help sick people get well. Diseased people become healthy. Overweight people find the body they can love and accept. It can heal relationships, even with people who have long passed on. It can reverse addictions and mend broken hearts. It can help people become more successful in business, sports, and hobbies.

If you had a great childhood, you are already on your way to having the life you want. But if you need more tools in your toolbelt or find that pesky little "programs" keep popping up in your life, this can work for you. That being said, I have worked with many clients who claimed to have had a happy childhood, only to find out it was a lovely little coping mechanism to keep them safe from seeing what really went on in their lives. Again, it's a more socially acceptable and preferable coping skill than many others: rather than drugs, alcohol, or pornography, this person uses the "I had a great childhood, so I have no excuse for feeling the way I do" skill. But if this isn't "true" in any part of their internal resources, it will find a way to leak out eventually. These are the individuals who "have everything," yet keep up the relentless pursuit for more. This could include the high-powered executive who never "found the time" to get married or have a relationship of any worth. Or perhaps it's the mental-health guru who now develops a debilitating disease. Even still, this could be the healthy, fit marathon runner who drops dead of a heart attack at age 45.

It doesn't have to be a traumatic childhood. It can be war, heartbreak, the loss of a loved one, a natural disaster. It can be religious trauma, a car accident, or betrayal by a close friend.

I'd like to share the story of a client to illustrate this point. Amanda was referred to me because she was a 40-year-old woman with four kids, and she didn't drive. It had caused great strain on her marriage, especially as her children reached school age and the driving demands became increasingly difficult for her husband to manage alone. In the initial consultation, I thought that Amanda had never learned to drive and had no desire to learn. She was terrified at the very idea. She had even begun to fear the mere idea of riding in a car and would sit nearly paralyzed with fear as her husband drove, screaming with every bump and turn.

When Amanda arrived for the session, dropped off by her husband, I was met by a small, timid woman. She carefully averted her gaze and was clearly nervous about our time together. As always, I took an inventory of past experiences and found that Amanda had a happy and loving childhood. Other than the occasional sibling squabble, she could only remember positive experiences growing up. When I further investigated her driving experiences, I found that she had learned to drive and obtained her license at 16. When she was 17, she was driving and had hit a patch of wet road, and the car spun out of control. Nobody was hurt, but it frightened her tremendously. This was not enough to cause the full-blown phobia I was witnessing before me, so I probed deeper. Amanda grew visibly more anxious and practically shrunk into her seat as she began recalling the next memory. At 18, she was a passenger in a car with her brother. As they drove through town, a bicyclist suddenly appeared on Amanda's side of the car. Her brother did not see the cyclist in time and hit the man.

With great detail, Amanda recalled feeling the tires run over the man and his bike. It was clear to me that she was reliving the incident. I stopped her, knowing that we had already found the source of her phobia. Going into further details was not necessary at that time. Amanda was representing this trauma visually in her mind. She had very clear pictures, and as is common with rehearsed traumatic events, she also had clear sounds and feelings associated with this event.

I had a colleague working with me during this session, and we quickly addressed the trauma Amanda was experiencing. After a relatively short time, she began to relax, and soon we could enable her to view the story and event without being in the situation. We worked on every aspect of the accident, the pictures, the sounds, and the feelings. Soon, she was able to retell the story in a different way, seeing things the way she would have liked to have seen them and making peace with her brother, the man, and herself.

Knowing that a well-rehearsed traumatic memory can be stored physically within the body, I knew we needed to clear that as well. So I signaled to my colleague that I was about to tip Amanda's chair a little as she was in the "trance" of her story, to simulate hitting a bump in the road. We had cleared enough of the trauma at this point that I felt sure that she would be able to handle this without regressing to the original state. This was important to do because, without addressing this, she could easily transport back into a part of the event with even the smallest bump in the road. Our goal is always to be as thorough as possible with these memories, not leaving any "negative information" within the files.

As Amanda began walking us through the new memory, I took hold of her chair and gave it a quick jostle. Amanda immediately screamed and grabbed the arms of the chair for dear life. Expecting this reaction, we immediately addressed the physical memory and calmed down her system, retraining her mind and body with a new reaction. I kept tipping the chair, jostling it harder and harder each time. Within minutes, Amanda was squealing with joy as she naturally linked this movement to the excitement of riding a roller-coaster rather than to running over a man.

Within two hours, Amanda was transformed. Toward the end of the session, she began sitting up in her chair, rather than the reclusive slouching position she had held in the beginning. She also removed her low ponytail, and her hair flowed naturally to her shoulders. Suddenly, this soft-spoken and shy woman blossomed into a chatty and vibrant individual. We moved the session outside into one of the vehicles. First, we had her sit in the passenger side without the car being started. We ensured that no negative associations arose, but instead, feelings of excitement and power. When we were sure that she was successful, we moved her into the driver's seat, again without the car being started. We had her go through the motions of starting the car, buckling her belt, and pretending to drive around the neighborhood. At one point, she had her arm out the window, imagining the breeze blowing through her hair as she drove down the freeway. She was laughing and enjoying herself. We asked her if she was ready to drive, and she enthusiastically agreed. Of course, without a license, we didn't feel that it would be an actual option.

About this time, her husband arrived to pick Amanda up from the session. He was in complete shock at what he was seeing! We decided to test out her new neuropathways even further. We enlisted her husband to help. I quietly pulled him to the side and asked him to drive us around the neighborhood, but with a few minor adjustments. I asked him to brake suddenly at times and swerve dramatically once in a while. Amanda jumped into the passenger side, and my colleague and I got into the back, letting her know we would be there to help her through any residual anxiety.

Upon the first sudden slam on the breaks, Amanda instinctively braced herself and reached for the safety bar while letting out a little yelp. We quickly worked with her through this and moved along. Within minutes, Amanda was easily navigating the quick stops and the sudden swerves with laughter, even letting out a boisterous "WHEEE!" at one particular swerve, immediately connecting to the rollercoaster feeling.

After our adventurous ride, we planned for Amanda to enroll in a driving course and work toward getting her license. Her husband was speechless and could barely believe what he was seeing. We gave Amanda some "homework," which was just exercises in strengthening her fledgling neuropathways and replaying the new memory. I followed up with Amanda later, and she happily reported that she was enrolled in a driving course and would likely be getting her license soon.

Amanda didn't have a traumatic childhood, but she did have a traumatic event. Though she knew that particular experience was not one that she liked to think about, she had no idea how much power it had over her. See, every time she was faced with the idea of driving or riding in a car, she likely played that memory in her subconscious mind. She had to have a very good reason for not driving, and her mind offered up a landslide of pictures/emotions/feelings to support that choice. Now, though she knows that event happened in the past, she no longer has the pictures/feelings/sensations/sounds/smells to support it. She has something different there instead. Now she automatically produces a different response to the idea of driving.

"I don't really want to change my memories. They make me who I am. Who will I be without my memories?" / "Won't I be lying to myself if I change a memory?"

First of all, it's important to remember that memory isn't "real" anyway. It has been irrevocably changed by your own perceptions, filters, and experiences. This method does not "take away" memories, nor does it make fairytales up in your mind. Through this method, we help you clear negative associations so that you can see distinctly what you need to keep and what you can release. Remember, what you hold within is what you give to others. So then, the question is, do you like what is currently being produced in your life? If so, great! If not, then it makes sense to go back and let go of what doesn't serve you, and give yourself something better. Don't you deserve that? It's *your* mind; you get to choose what you keep and what you let go of. One of our associate practitioners, Cara Ugolini, likes to put it this way:

> *What if you were able to see everything in your life and past, even the negative experiences, through a lens of love? If you could see it all the way God sees it, through the eyes of love, peace, forgiveness, compassion? That is really what we are after: changing memories much like changing perception to reflect the truth of God's love.*

"I don't have the money to spend on getting sessions or getting trained on how to do these techniques."

It is important to realize that a "lack" in finances is almost always a program related to money. The way we feel about money and the relationship we have with finances are closely related to the way we feel about ourselves. It's very similar to our relationship with food. I had the same thought when it came to this information. I had been on disability for years. My husband and I had spent about

$100,000 out of pocket on my health challenges over the years. We were not in a financial place to spend any more money.

But I was scheduled to have yet another spinal surgery, and I was going for IV infusions every other day. I was on close to 180 meds, supplements, and tinctures *every day* until my liver and kidneys gave out. It was costing me an astronomical amount of money to stay sick. Even with excellent insurance, I couldn't afford to continue supporting myself in the illness.

My question would be, *can you afford not to get help*? I had to face this exact same dilemma. I can now safely say that I would have paid triple the amount of money I had to, to learn this material. More, in fact. This information is priceless. I totally understand that financial duress is a very real thing. Anyone can learn and use these tools. My goal with this book is to make this knowledge and these tools accessible for everyone. Again, some problems are more complex and may need an expert to get the ball rolling. But these tools were never meant to line a practitioner's pocket. My goal is ALWAYS to equip my clients with the ability to do this work themselves.

"I've tried therapy/EFT/hypnosis/EMDR/etc., and it didn't work for me. How is this any different?"

Obviously, without knowing you personally, I cannot speak to your experiences. What I can say is that I get many clients who come from other modalities; even practitioners of these systems often come to me for help. Is it that these modalities are ineffective? I would say no. Most of the information contained in this book comes from the application and research associated with these techniques. I have found extremely valuable tools from each one of these methods.

What I believe makes the Metanoia Method even quicker and more effective is that I have endeavored to find out *why* the things that *do* work, work. Each of these systems (and more) have made incredible contributions in the field of health and wellness. So, like many before me, I have cherry-picked the best of each system and put them together so that mind, body, science, and faith all converge to give you the best possible tools for changing your life.

On a side note, it's important to remember that some people have spent 20, 30, or 40 years or more developing the coping skills that they are now using. These things rarely fall apart overnight (although they can). But think about it: let's say it's taken you 20 years to build a phobia or a disease or an addiction. That means it has been practiced, unconsciously, daily for 20 years. You are an expert at it. But now you are ready for something different. We are now on the journey to *disassemble* the very coping mechanism that has "kept you safe" all these years. This is no small feat! But it is more than doable.

If you can address the root cause, the secondary gains associated, *and* have a properly constructed *alternative* outcome, it is rare to have the Metanoia Method *not* work. Also, please go back to the first question in this section. It's possible that you may be running the "nothing works for me" program. If that is the case, that belief would need to be dealt with first. Otherwise, you will keep producing the result that things "don't work." We are incredibly powerful creators!

Also, don't forget the Reticular Activating System discussed in Chapter 8. When you ask the question, "What if this *doesn't* work for me?" your mind *will* answer that question. You will fantasize about all the adverse outcomes, and you will further reinforce all the "danger" associated with trying to change. Even if you take the leap and try, the RAS will begin looking for what you are focused on: all the ways this is *not* working. The RAS is like a bloodhound! It *always* finds what it's looking for. Does this sound familiar? Have you tried to change before and found this to be the case?

Luckily, the Metanoia Method deals with beliefs. Therefore we can ask better questions for your mind to answer. What if this *does* work? If the mind finds any "good" reasons that it wouldn't be safe for it to work, we can deal with that as well! Really, it's a win-win situation. The only people with whom I have experienced that these techniques did not work are those who found *more benefit in staying where they were rather than changing*. The problem is, they were not consciously aware of that "benefit." The investment they have in their particular "problem" is too great at this point. Please hear me say this: there is *no* judgment on these people. For those who *are* ready, the tools are there.

"If all this information is true, why haven't I heard about it before?"

Again, I'm going to have to reference the RAS. After reading this book, or even while reading it, you will begin to notice how many people are talking about it. You'll overhear conversations, see interviews, listen to a podcast. Believe me. You will start to hear more about it as you begin to listen.

That being said, human beings are in a constant state of evolution. New developments in science and technology are happening daily. We understand much more about the brain than we did 20 years ago. We typically wait for science and PhDs to study, research, experiment, and then break it down so the general public can digest it. Innovation and information happen almost *too* fast these days. It's challenging to keep up! Our entire social structure is set up in such a way that we wait for "authorities" to tell us what to do, what to eat, and what to believe. Then when they figure out what they have been saying is wrong, they just tell us that "research *now shows*" something else, and we blindly follow.

Just look at smoking and the tobacco industry. Or the food pyramid. What we were originally told is far different from the current recommendations. Obviously, it wouldn't be news to you to say that the almighty dollar plays a massive role in what the public hears. I have no intention to get all "conspiracy theory" with what I'm about to say, so don't read too much into it. But the things that I am saying and the tools that I have to offer are not going to *ever* be very popular. Why? For the most part, nobody can monetize it. My sole intention is to give the power back to *you*. If the power to be happy, successful, and well is in *your* hands, there is no single person or entity that can "corner the market" on that.

If no drug, therapist, facility, food group, or supplement holds the power to your wellness, then nobody makes a fortune off you getting better. If there is no money, there is no research. If there is no research, there is no "proof" that these methods work. This means it's likely that you will not be hearing about this from the "medical world" anytime soon. So the burden of response lies solely where it needs to be: in your lap. Those willing to accept that their personal healing really is *personal* are already one step ahead of the game. Those who are still giving their power away to some "higher authority" will continue to wait for the right pill, diet, surgery, or guru.

In our modern-day society, faith is also not a popular commodity. We are a generation of "seeing is believing." Yet "*Jesus said, 'So, you believe because you've seen with your own eyes. Even better blessings are in store for those who believe without seeing*'" (John 20:29 MSG). I encourage you to take that step on the water and to take a leap of faith. The truth is out there, ripe for the taking.

The previous questions are just a few of the many "concerns" that I have encountered. Obviously, I cannot address all of them here. But for a moment, I would ask you to suspend any further judgment until you have fully processed all the information held in these pages. The changing of one's mind is no small feat. Be patient with yourself. It is time to transition from the "why" to the "how." In Part 2, I will discuss *how* to take back the power God has placed inside each of us and how to change your mind.

Part 2

The Metanoia Method

Part 2 Overview

The Metanoia Method

You have let go of the commands of God and are holding on to human traditions.

Mark 7:8

You're not stuck. You're just committed to certain patterns of behavior because they helped you in the past. Now those behaviors have become more harmful than helpful. The reason why you can't move forward is because you keep applying an old formula to a new level in your life. Change the formula to get a different result.

— Emily Maroutian

I'm beginning to suspect that the second half of life is about learning to let go of everything I feverishly collected over the first half that wasn't loving or human.

– Michael Xavier

WHAT IS THE METANOIA METHOD?

Are you ready to let go of what you thought you knew and grab hold of our God-given ability to transform from the inside out? If you are anything like me, you are ready for the practicals. You've been gearing up to get at the issues and "get 'em gone." You may even have skipped ahead to this part of the book to see if the how-to's of this method are appealing to you or if they are "something you have already tried." Again, I get it! If that is you, I will appeal to you to please go back and read all of Part 1 before moving on. Though comprehending the *how* and *why* of what we do is rarely powerful enough to change it, I have found that it significantly helps set the mind up for change.

Part 2 Overview

I have broken Part 2 into easy-to-understand, actionable practicals. I would suggest reading through everything first, at least once, before applying them. Again, I believe in the power of seeing the "macro" version of the entire process before diving in.

Love is one of the most prominent overarching themes to self-work. "*Love covers over a multitude of sins*" (1 Peter 4:8). Love yourself enough to take the time and energy to invest in this process *and* be loving to yourself in the process.

Remember, the things you want to change result from subconsciously "practicing" them for years, sometimes decades or even several lifetimes! Considering everything we mentioned about epigenetics, some of our destructive (subconscious) thought patterns may have been passed down over centuries. Having a "mind change" about your problem, life, or disease takes considerably less time to transform than it did to build it. But we still ask that you give yourself the time and space to do so. Let's address *the* most common question I get with the work I do:

"*How long will it take for me to change my problem?*"

Because your "problem" is unique to you and your programming, I can't answer that with any definitive time frame. Two people can come to see me with nearly identical issues, and the time it takes for resolution of the problem will differ significantly because no two "problems" are built the same. What I can say is that, in my experience, these methods provide the fastest route to change I have ever encountered. Problems *can* change within one session. I see that happen all the time. It was my personal experience. Within one session, my life was forever altered. People from all over the world who have heard my story always ask me the same question, "How were you able to heal so quickly? What did you do?" I always say that it came down to one clear understanding: *I was doing it to me*. And rather than getting defensive (like I usually would have) and trying to defend how "real" my issues were and all the medical "proof" I had that I was dying, I made a life-changing decision to *change my mind*. Blaming it on other people or things wasn't working for me. I had beat that horse to the ground. So what if it *was* me? For the first time, maybe in my life, I felt empowered. If I was doing it, I could stop it. So I believed. I changed my mind completely, and it gave me the power. I now realized that I had the power to create the life of my dreams instead of countless rare diseases. I had the power to finally *deal* with my past and stop running from it.

> *And what more shall I say? I do not have time to tell about Gideon, Barak, Samson and Jephthah, about David and Samuel and the prophets, who through faith conquered kingdoms, administered justice, and gained what was promised; who shut the mouths of lions, quenched the fury of the flames, and escaped the edge of the sword; whose weakness was turned to strength.*
>
> **Hebrews 11:32–34**

> *Therefore, since we are surrounded by such a great cloud of witnesses, let us throw off everything that hinders and the sin that so easily entangles. And let us run with perseverance the race marked out for us, fixing our eyes on Jesus, the pioneer and perfecter of faith.*
>
> **Hebrews 12:1–2**

> *You can change anything you want to change, and you can do it very fast. That's another satanic sucker-punch—that it takes years and years and eons of eternity to repent. It takes exactly as long to repent as it takes you to say, "I'll change"—and mean it... You may well spend (indeed you had better spend) the rest of your life proving your repentance by its permanence. But change, growth, renewal, and repentance can come for you instantaneously.*[80]
>
> – Robert Reynolds

---

[80] Reynolds, Robert. *Unstuck: How the Savior Frees Us from Our Favorite Sins.* Deseret Book, 2015

Part 2 Overview

Utilizing the Metanoia Method can create change instantaneously, yet lasts a lifetime! In the following chapters, we will lay out a step-by-step plan to help you change your mind. The following terms will be helpful for you to understand:

- **Metanoia Manifesto:** This will help you identify exactly what you would like to see in your future so that you can know where you are going.
- **Metanoia GPS:** These will be your "directions" and tools to get where you are going. We will teach you how to utilize your **G**ratitude, **P**ositive Affirmations, and **S**miles (happy memories) to begin creating your dreams.
- **PaNE CuRe List:** This powerful tool will help you identify the past negative experiences, limiting beliefs, and programs that are keeping you stuck in some of your unpleasant patterns.
- **Pattern Interrupts:** Learning this tool and the power behind it is a key piece to overcoming the things holding you back.
- **The Process:** Utilizing all of the above tools, we break down the Metanoia Method into a simple-to-use program to help you take the power back in your own life!

This work is not for the timid. It is for the brave. Those who are ready to take on everything they *think* they know and turn it upside down will tap into a power they only dreamed possible. The most challenging and best knowledge we must face is that we have a choice.

I love the *Matrix* movies. If you haven't seen them, please put down this book and go and watch the first one. They were profoundly ahead of their time and remain underrated. The Metanoia Method is like the matrix. You won't be able to "unknow" this information or this power. You can continue to run from it, but it will be like the little unscratchable itch in your brain. *What if?* What if *you* have the power? I leave you with these little nuggets from *The Matrix*. See you on the other side!

"This is your last chance. After this, there is no turning back. You take the blue pill—the story ends, you wake up in your bed and believe whatever you want to believe. You take the red pill—you stay in Wonderland, and I show you how deep the rabbit hole goes... "You have to let it all go... Fear, doubt, disbelief... "I'm trying to free your mind, Neo. But I can only show you the door. You're the one that has to walk through it."[81]

— Morpheus, *The Matrix*

[81] Wachowski, L., and Wachowski, L. *The Matrix.* Warner Bros. Copy, 1999.

CHAPTER 13

THE PERFECTLY WORKING YOU

The body is the servant of the mind. It obeys the operations of the mind, whether they be deliberately chosen or automatically expressed.

– James Allen

Repentance must dig the foundations, but holiness shall erect the structure, and bring forth the top-stone. Repentance is the clearing away of the rubbish of the past temple of sin; holiness builds the new temple which the Lord our God shall inherit. Repentance and desires after holiness never can be separated.

– Charles H. Spurgeon

But unless you repent, you too will perish.

– Jesus

The first thing I would like to remind you of is this: there is likely nothing *wrong* with you. No, I'm not saying that your problem is "only in your head." I believe and know from experience that the body can produce very "real" symptoms, diseases, feelings, and emotions in accordance with what is going on with us. You may have stage 4 cancer, or lupus, or an MS diagnosis, and have turned to the information in this book as a last-ditch effort. I am here to say that I know the fear, pain, and uncertainty that accompanies physical dis-ease. But that doesn't necessarily mean something is *malfunctioning* within you. On the contrary, you are likely working perfectly according to the way we function as humans. If you persist with the belief that "something is wrong with me," then your body (which is the obedient slave to the mind) *will* eventually produce something that will prove you right; it may have already taken that route.

We often cite the story of Job as one of undeserved suffering. It seems that, by no fault of his own, Job is subjected to attacks from Satan. We want desperately to relate to this story, in that we often feel that we are being unfairly persecuted or punished, and that it is by some cosmic dealings apart from our own will. But a little verse early in the Book of Job gives us some possible insight. This insight is not w*hy,* but *how* Job suffers in the ways he does: "*Truly the thing that I fear comes upon me, and what I dread befalls me*" (Job 3:25).

It seems it's possible that the way in which Satan decided to attack Job was a personalized fulfillment of Job's own fears and worries. Does this mean that Job is *to blame* for his affliction? Not at all. But it does give us a possible perspective of the story of Job within the framework of a fundamental spiritual truth: we have the power to create our own life experiences according to the choices we make.

Jesus was very clear in all he taught, especially when it came to total transformation: "*According to your faith, your trust and confidence in my power and my ability to heal, it will be done to you*" (Matthew 9:29 AMP). If we do not deal with the programming (from our past influences and experiences) that we have, those protective mechanisms will make our choices for us. Then, we will inevitably look for (and subconsciously worry about) the things we *don't* want to have happen to us. We will focus on the things that scare or endanger us. Thus, we are subconsciously expressing a *faith* in a potentially negative outcome, which then controls our thoughts, feelings, and behavior. And life follows suit. But what would happen if, instead, our faith, trust, and confidence were in Jesus, the ultimate healer and the One who empowers? What would the outcome be then?

Hopefully (if you have read Part 1), you now know that what we contain in our subconscious "filing system" supports and feeds our automatic mode of operation. So if you are producing illness, depression, anxiety, or dis-ease, you have a very good reason for doing it. Understanding this is a crucial *first step* in changing your mind.

Remember I mentioned before that we remodeled the house I am living in now. There are a couple of things that are little "quirks" in my home. For instance, though we had a lot of electrical rewiring done (the original wiring was a complete mess), there were a few things we left alone. One of those things is the light switch for the dining room. This light is wired into two different panels, but with only one master switch. This means it can be shut off and turned on from two panels in two different locations, but if the master-switch side is flipped in a particular direction, the other switch does absolutely nothing! So I often spend a few minutes trying to figure out which switch is flipped which way so that I can get the silly light to turn on. So here is the question: is my light switch "broken"? No, it's not. It's performing precisely the way it was wired to. Unfortunately, it wasn't wired for optimal performance. But it is *not* broken. If this bothered me enough, I would simply rewire it to produce the desired outcome. Frankly, I have far more important concerns in my life!

I also have a faucet on my bathroom sink that we replaced. When we installed it, we accidentally put the hot water knob on the cold-water line. Again, *not* broken; simply installed incorrectly. Are you with me? Many of us have original hardware that just needs some remodeling. It isn't working optimally. That's okay. We just need to rewire. Sometimes it's not even that significant. We simply want to upgrade! Guess what? Go for it! It's *your* mind and *your* body. Make it as great as you choose.

Even though the Metanoia Method is based on years of personal experience and research (scientific and biblical), it's a simple tool. Taking power back over the way your body and emotions respond is relatively easy. Overcoming the fears, doubts, and victim conditioning is not. No matter your background, health limitations, diagnosis, or situation, you can learn to think differently. "*Therefore, if anyone is in Christ, the new creation has come: The old has gone, the new is here!*" (2 Corinthians 5:17).

Stop believing the lie that you are "broken" and start believing the truth: you "*have been remarkably and wonderfully made*" (Psalm 139:14 HCSB). Might you need some rewiring? Probably. Welcome to the club. I want you to take some time and answer the following questions:

1. What have I learned so far that will empower me to change my mind?
2. How has my mind changed already?
3. What tools have I gained from this book and from my life that will make me successful in changing my mind?
4. How do I know that I am ready to use the Metanoia Method to take my power back and live my best life?

I'm trusting that you took the time to complete that exercise. How was it? Whether you are aware of it or not, these answers provide the building blocks that are already at work in your subconscious mind that will facilitate the change. I want you to become aware of some of the patterns and beliefs that emerge as you go through this process.

A POWERFUL EQUATION FOR METANOIA MOMENTS

I would like to give you a simple equation that, if understood and applied, holds the power of changing nearly anything. Ready?

RUMINATION + DECLARATION = CREATION

RUMINATION

Let's break this down a little. *Merriam-Webster Dictionary* defines rumination as:

1. A deep or considered thought about something
2. The action or process of thinking deeply about something

"Ruminate" is derived from a 16th-century word describing how cows chew their cud. "Cud" is a bolus, or lump, of regurgitated food that is brought up and chewed again and again until it is digestible. Rumination is one of the hallmarks of the mind. It is simply our thoughts that occur over and over again. We "regurgitate" past experiences and then subconsciously go over them, again and again, to try to make sense of them. These thoughts are sometimes in our conscious awareness but are often subconscious. Regardless, they are the building blocks for our belief systems. Also known as the "little voice inside my head," the "broken record," or the "phrase/picture/sound that keeps popping into my head," these are examples of ruminating. Often, we think these thoughts so regularly that they seem naturally "hardwired" into our thinking. Ruminations are not *good* or *bad*. They are just thoughts. If we judge our thoughts, we are simply thinking more thoughts about our thoughts. Let me illustrate.

You are rushing out the door in the morning and realize you cannot find your keys. As you frantically search, thoughts fill your mind:

"*I can't believe I did this again! I'm such an idiot.*"
"*Great! Now I'm going to be even later and probably get fired.*"
"*This kind of thing always happens to me.*"

The list goes on. But if you were to take a time-out and reflect on these thoughts, you probably would agree that they are not the most productive if you are trying to find your keys, feel good, and get going. You may even go as far as beating yourself up over these thoughts. Now deeper-layered thoughts flood your mind:

"*I'm such a bully to myself.*"
"*I know better than to let negative thinking get in my way. What an idiot I am.*"
"*I will never be able to stop being so hard on myself.*"
"*I'm supposed to have the Holy Spirit, so what is wrong with me?*"
"*I'm just being faithless.*"
"*Am I even a Christian?*"

Those are just thoughts *about* your thoughts. Generally, not helpful. What if, on the other hand, you were to take a time-out and listen. Rather than judge the thoughts, take a moment to hear what they are saying. Notice them. They are there for a reason. They are your creation from past experiences: your beliefs. It's very helpful to know what we ruminate about. This is invaluable feedback! Becoming aware of our ruminations can enable us to make better choices. We are the gatekeepers of our minds. We only have to let in what we want. Consider a gardening analogy and think of it this way: *My mind is my garden. It's wonderful that weeds pop up and show themselves. Why? Because then I can pull them out! Luckily, the weeds aren't happening underground where I can't see them. Otherwise, I may not know they are there. If something is in my garden that either I didn't plant, or I no longer want to grow there, it makes no sense for me to judge it. I can just as easily pull it out with a happy and grateful mood, knowing that my garden will be better for it.*

The most significant area of sin in our lives is not overt and obvious from the outside—instead, it is the sin (*kakos*/evil) within our thought life. As Jesus said in Mark 7:21, "*It is from within, out of a person's heart, that evil thoughts come.*" Our ruminations control our thought life. But what if our ruminations, those tracks that play continuously in our minds, were full of gratitude and joy and encouragement from God's heart?

> *Blessed, happy, and prosperous is the man who walks and lives not in the counsel of the ungodly... But his delight and desire are in the law of the Lord, and on his precepts and teachings, he habitually meditates, ponders, and studies by day and by night.*
>
> **Psalm 1:1–2** AMPC

When we begin to clean up the painful resources within our mind, we can make room to ruminate (meditate) about the word of God.

Ruminations are like seeds in our garden. With food and water, some will grow up to be nourishing, beautiful plants. Others will grow up to reveal the weeds that they are. Once we are aware of which kind of plant they are, we can keep them or pluck them out! Ruminations are powerful and can ultimately dictate many of our feelings and behaviors, but combined with the next step, they are even more powerful.

DECLARATION

To declare is to formally and confidently announce something. Usually, this is a verbal act, though it can also be a nonverbal declaration. A large smile can be a declaration of happiness or humor. A raised fist can be a declaration that says, "You better run, or I'll clobber you!" Declarations are usually a result of our ruminations, but now we are formally announcing them. Plucked from our minds, we now speak them into existence, giving them a voice and allowing them to be heard. "*For out of the overflow of the heart, the mouth speaks*" (Luke 6:45). The word for speak is λαλέω (*laleó*), meaning "to use words in order to declare one's mind and disclose one's thoughts." And then we have the word for heart, καρδία (*kardia*), which we noted back at the beginning of the book as "the heart, mind, character, inner self, will, intention, center."[82] As Jesus tells us, we will declare whatever we continue to ruminate on.

Think back to "what is real." If we can touch it, taste it, hear it, or see it, it is "real." By speaking this thought into existence *outside* your body, you are now giving it life and an opportunity to become "real." Are you beginning to see just how powerful you are? Your mouth spoke it, but your ears heard it. The body will now respond by creating a feeling to deal with what it just heard. None of us like to be liars, even if you are someone who commonly uses it as a coping skill. If we say it, it must be true, at least to some part of us. When you speak the words, "I am an idiot!" or "Nobody loves me," or "Life is so unfair. This always happens to me," you are moving to the next step of creating its truth.

> *Death and life are in the power of the tongue,*
> *and those who love it will eat its fruit.*
>
> **Proverbs 18:21**

> *For by your words you will be justified, and by your words you will be condemned.*
>
> **Matthew 12:37**

---

[82] Thayer's Greek Lexicon. http://www.BibleHub.com, Electronic Database, 2020

Anxiety in the heart of man causes depression,
but a good word makes it glad.

Proverbs 12:25 NKJV

Do not call to mind the former things,
Or ponder things of the past.
Behold, I will do something new.
Now it will spring forth;
Will you not be aware of it?
I will even make a roadway in the wilderness,
Rivers in the desert.

Isaiah 43:18–19

What goes into someone's mouth does not defile them, but what comes out of their mouth, that is what defiles them.

Matthew 15:11

This is where we step into a place of believing the reality of God's truth for our lives, despite what the facts might be saying. When we "declare" something, we are activating various powerful systems within our mind and body. The system that regulates hormones needs to produce "feeling" in alignment with what is being declared. The RAS is brought online to look for other "proof" that this is true. The subconscious filing system is now searching through all its data to figure out where this should be filed; it looks for similar occurrences, which only reinforces the negative cycle.

CREATION

If we are ruminating on things that do not serve us, then declaring them, we are creating. We may feel "set in our ways," but we are constantly creating. We are often busy creating more of what we already have, simply practicing old beliefs/patterns/feelings. In essence, what we are creating is the illusion of being "stuck." But we *are* creating, nonetheless.

God is our ultimate Creator. We are created in his image and have the immense responsibility (and gift) of free will. This ultimately means that we are the master designers of our own life. As Christians, our goal is to realign our purpose and unique contributions with the purposes of our Creator. Don't misunderstand me here. I am not saying that we are more powerful than God or that we are somehow responsible for our own creation—far from it. Rather, I intend to illustrate how God, in his wisdom and love, has given us the ability to choose the filters we use to view (or distort) our realities.

Though God has given us the freedom to choose, we often outsource this important job to others around us. Some people will take issue with this sentiment, wrongly believing that I am saying that we are somehow equal to God or even more powerful than God in our ability to create. On the contrary, I believe that it is our own misunderstanding of the mind and its effect on the gift of free will. Although we may recoil at the idea that we are somehow powerful enough to create our own unique way of looking at and processing the world, in truth, we give this power away freely every day. But not to God, as we would like to imagine! We are far more likely to let "the world," or at least our personal experience with it, shape our beliefs and create our reality. We let *them* dictate our worth and value ("them" being anyone that we give power of influence to in our lives—parents, teachers, politicians, doctors, pastors, etc.). We collect other people's hurts, pains, and experiences and make them our own. Or we choose to hold on to our own hurts and pains and allow them to define us.

Consider the story of a friend of mine who was diagnosed with kidney stones. She had passed a few with relatively little discomfort and was advised that the rest should pass similarly. Returning to work the next day, she told many of her coworkers about the diagnosis. Instantly, she was inundated with horror stories of other people's experiences with kidney stones. "It's worse than giving birth!" one coworker related. "I peed blood for days and felt like I was going to die!" another said dramatically. Yet another coworker shared the story of her brother, who began having complications with kidney stones and ended up having a seizure!

That whole day, my friend ruminated on these things. Her coworkers repeatedly checked on her, asking her how she was feeling. Each time, she realized and expressed that she was feeling worse. By the time she was ready to end her workday, she was feeling lousy. She called her husband to say, "I think I'm having complications. I'm feeling a lot of strange symptoms." Not surprisingly, she ended up in the emergency room that night in a great deal of pain. The next day, she followed up with her regular doctor, who seemed surprised at her turn for the worse, since X-rays had revealed that the rest of the stones had resolved and had probably passed the day before. How did she do this? Simple: RUMINATION + DECLARATION = CREATION.

But guess what? The opposite is true as well! What do you think would happen if you ruminated on how *good* you feel? How much you have to be grateful for and all the ways that this is true? If you woke up in the morning knowing it was going to be a good day and declaring it to be so, could you also *create* that good day? I used this process in my healing journey. After realizing that I had the power to create health in my body and mind (just as I had created dis-ease), I began to ruminate on healthy thoughts and feelings (God-thoughts). "*How am I going to move my body today?*" "*What am I going to feed this body that is healthy?*" "*How is my relationship with my family going to be enhanced today?*" "*What kinds of things do I want to do with my healthy body?*" "*What kinds of interactions do I want to have with my friends and coworkers?*" I also declared my healing. Many people were aware of how much my (Heather's) health had deteriorated and would frequently check up on me or would inquire about my well-being when we saw each other. "I'm healed!" I would exclaim brightly. "I'm just waiting for my body to catch up!" "Of course I *can* do _____!" "I love to walk/run/work out. It makes me feel so good." And rather quickly, this became natural and normal. Within four months of being practically bedridden and near death, I was in the gym, leg-pressing almost 450 pounds.

This same principle applies not just to health, but to other facets of life as well, even in marriage relationships. Declaring (aloud or in our heads) about the state of affairs in a relationship will create the trajectory of that relationship. I (Kent) used to ruminate on all the ways that my wife was upset with me or some way that I had probably let her down—again! I would ruminate and then declare things such as "You're just mad at me" or "You just don't trust me." And it came to be. Changing your mind from these possible negative outcomes to "What if we had the closest and most passionate marriage ever?" can create a very different neuropathway, which will create a new track to run on.

This method goes beyond positive thinking. It involves being very intentional but also very observational. If we can understand that most situations we find ourselves in are *our own creation*, then we conversely understand that we have the power to create something different.

> *Truly I tell you, if anyone says to this mountain, 'Go, throw yourself into the sea,' and does not doubt in their heart but believes that what they say will happen, it will be done for them.*
>
> **Mark 11:23**

> *You will also decree a thing, and it will be established for you.*
>
> **Job 22:28 NASB** (1995)

> *Whoever keeps his mouth and his tongue [from negativity]*
> *keeps himself out of trouble.*
>
> **Proverbs 21:23 ESV**

> *Finally, brothers and sisters, whatever is true, whatever is noble, whatever is right, whatever is pure, whatever is lovely, whatever is admirable—if anything is excellent or praiseworthy—think about such things. Whatever you have learned or received or heard from me, or seen in me—put it into practice. And the God of peace will be with you.*
>
> **Philippians 4:8–9**

Even when speaking about the very fabric of our salvation and justification, we see the principle of the R + D = C equation being employed: "*If you declare with your mouth, 'Jesus is Lord,' and believe in your heart that God raised him from the dead, you will be saved*" (Romans 10:9). You see, the first step to changing your mind is to understand that you are working perfectly in accordance with the equation:

RUMINATION + DECLARATION = CREATION

If we know that we can create our environment by observing and changing our ruminations and declarations, why don't we? Often, we don't know how. And if we do, we have strong and powerful "objections" to our desired outcomes. This is where the next step comes in.

CHAPTER 14

METANOIA MANIFESTO

If you don't know where you are going, you'll end up someplace else.

– Yogi Berra

Our goals can only be reached through a vehicle of a plan, in which we must fervently believe, and upon which we must vigorously act. There is no other route to success.

– Pablo Picasso

To share out your soul freely, that is what metanoia (a change of mind, or repentance) really refers to: A mental product of love. A change of mind, or love for the undemonstrable. And you throw off every conceptual cloak of self-defense, you give up the fleshly resistance of your ego. Repentance has nothing to do with self-regarding sorrow for legal transgressions. It is an ecstatic erotic self-emptying. A change of mind about the mode of thinking and being.

– Christos Yannaras

Arguably, the most crucial step of the Metanoia Method is changing your mind! For many people, it is difficult to see beyond what is directly in front of them. Many people *want* a better life. They want a healthy body, a happy marriage, a good job, financial security. They "hope" and "wish." But I've learned that it can be difficult for people to see this play out in their future.

In the Bible, the prophet Habakkuk was complaining to God. It seems that Habakkuk is distraught with the perceived condition of the world at the time and whether God is even listening or sympathetic to their cause. Habakkuk has a problem. He cannot see a way out of the current situation. He is focused on violence, wrongdoing, strife, and conflict. Haven't we all been there? We wonder where God is in our distress. We have a hard time envisioning something different from what we see all around us. We believe we have gathered a large amount of "proof" that things are getting *worse* rather than better. God has an answer for Habakkuk, and it has to do with a vision. He has a plan, but he needs Habakkuk and the people to grab hold of it. Without the vision and the plan, the people won't be able to see all the ways God *is* working for their favor. In chapter 2, God answers Habakkuk with his plan:

> *Write down the revelation*
> *and make it plain on tablets*
> *so that a herald may run with it.*
> *For the revelation awaits an appointed time;*
> *it speaks of the end*
> *and will not prove false.*
> *Though it linger, wait for it;*
> *it will certainly come*
> *and will not delay.*
>
> **Habakkuk 2:2–3**

Habakkuk needed to see God's vision. He needed to stop focusing on the narrow perspective of what *was* and start seeing through the lens of what *could be*. This is one of the greatest gifts that God gives us: the ability to tap into his vision and see through the lens of his power and purpose.

WANTING WHAT YOU DON'T WANT

One of the questions I usually ask any client before we begin working to change their mind is this: "*What do you want?*" It sounds like a relatively easy question, right? Let me explain what I am talking about with an example conversation. Let's say that Mike comes to see me. Mike's marriage is tanking.

His wife has spoken of divorce. His kids avoid him as much as possible. And he just can't seem to get promoted at work no matter how hard he tries.

MIKE: I am just so stuck. I can barely get a word in edgewise with my kids. No matter how much I try to build them up or ask them questions, they seem to have an attitude with me. Everything I say or do also seems to trigger my wife. She doesn't want to spend time with me because, inevitably, I will do something hurtful. She doesn't want to engage sexually because she doesn't find me attractive anymore, even though I'm in better shape than ever! And my boss definitely doesn't like me. I have more seniority and talent than any other guy in the office, but I never get the promotions. I'm even working overtime every week! I don't think I will ever get a better-paying position, which leaves my wife unhappy with me, saying that I'm not stepping out on faith. And how am I supposed to support my kids going to college soon if I can't even afford to take my family on that vacation I keep promising? Even my friendships are deteriorating. I'm getting invited way less to outings and activities that I used to do all the time. And now I'm feeling more and more run-down, tired, and unmotivated. In fact, everything just seems to get worse every day!

ME: So, Mike, what do you want?

MIKE: I don't want to feel lonely anymore! I don't want every word I say to my wife to be taken as something offensive, like nothing I do is good enough. I don't want to be such a turn-off to the woman I married! I don't want to watch my children grow up around me but not be able to really be with them. I don't want to wake up, go to work, and do the same mundane thing every day without any progress. I don't want to keep losing my friends and feeling unwanted. I don't want to get worse every day, feeling more and more run down. I don't want to live like this!

ME: So, Mike, I hear what you *don't* want. What *do* you want?

MIKE: (looking slightly confused) I told you. I don't want to be stuck where I am in my relationship with my wife and kids and boss and friends anymore. I don't want to be robbed of my wife and my children. I don't want to be overlooked, unwanted, and underappreciated. I don't want to miss out on my life!

ME: Mike, that is what you *don't* want. The things you *already have*. What do you want different? What *do* you want?
MIKE: Okay, well, I guess I want to be free and happy and connected. I don't want to feel this way anymore. I want my old life back. I want things to go back to the way they were before I had all these problems. I don't want to be stuck in the life I am in!

Mike is not alone. I can't begin to explain how common this interaction is. Do you see the problem? Mike is very well versed in what he *doesn't want*. He could fill pages of what he no longer wants to do, feel, or experience. But when given a chance to see outside those things, he quickly circles back to what he knows. Why is that? Jesus asks this question of the blind man in Luke 18 and Mark 10. He asks it again of the paralytic in John 5. Why ask a question with an obvious answer? Maybe the answer isn't as obvious as we think. As humans, we can become quite comfortable with what we know, even if it's extremely "uncomfortable." Many times, we cannot *see* a way out of where we are. We just know we want out. For many people, the fear of the unknown can be even more "real" than the possibility of freedom.

Simply put, we can't go where we don't know. If I told you about the Land of Flisse and somehow convinced you that you needed to go there, how would you go about getting started? Even if you *really, really* want to get there, you can't without a starting place. First of all, what the heck is the Land of Flisse? Well, I just made it up. But it illustrates the point. Many people who are in the depths of their problem will face the same issue as you would with the Land of Flisse. It seems like a fairytale. They are so unfamiliar with it that they cannot begin to conceive what the first step would even be. It's easy to judge this idea or the people. "Come on, how hard is it to envision feeling happy? Weren't you connected at one time? It's not like that is a made-up place!" True. But for some people, their reality has been this other place for so long that it truly seems impossible to see outside it. But seeing outside it is, ultimately, the first step to getting out of it.

THE POWER OF VISUALIZATION

The Bible is full of scriptures relating to how we see things and what kind of mindset we have. Here are a few translations of Proverbs 29:18.

Where there is no vision, the people decay. (GNV)

Where there is no vision, the people perish. (KJV)

If people can't see what God is doing, they stumble all over themselves; But when they attend to what he reveals, they are most blessed. (MSG)

The power of visualization is far from a New Age, "woo-woo" concept. As far back as 450 BCE, Thucydides, an early Greek philosopher, said these words: "*The bravest are surely those who have the clearest vision of what is before them, glory and danger alike, and yet notwithstanding, go out to meet it.*" Our minds' power to create our future has been tapped for centuries, and we see it illustrated, time and time again, throughout the Bible. The power to visualize is a God-given gift to do good in the world. But like many gifts that God intended for good, we misuse it. Think of the amount of power, energy, and visualization it takes to imagine every possible bad scenario when we are preparing for something important. For example, our children aren't home by curfew. Within minutes, we have likely envisioned them kidnapped, in an accident, lying in a hospital bed, or dead on the side of the road. And it isn't just pictures we are creating. We can actually *feel* the entire range of emotions that stem from these imagined happenings. Why are we so comfortable with these kinds of visualizations, yet question that God would want us to visualize *good* things for our lives? Think about this in relation to the bleeding woman in Matthew 9. Obviously, she had done some intentional and productive visualization to imagine that she could get close enough to Jesus to be healed. Her mission was so clearly mapped out that she knew that the same results could be accomplished by merely touching the garment of Jesus. Wow! That is some powerful visualization. The result? Not only was she healed, but Jesus lifted her up as an example of faith among her peers, clearly stating that it was *her* faith that resulted in the healing. Faith in what? Faith in what she had hoped for and envisioned but had not yet personally experienced. If we follow God's word and see his ultimate vision, imagine his desired outcome for our situations, and visualize the fulfillment of his abundant love in our lives, then we can rest assured that we are on the right path. I also love the example of God himself, who "*calls things that are not as though they are*" all the time. By giving people new names before they become worthy of them, God practices that same power even while allowing people to retain their freedom to choose (free will).

Denis Waitley, PhD, a psychologist, decided to use the power of visualization in the 1980s and 1990s Olympics programs. After the great success of this exercise, Waitley stated:

> *When you visualize, then you materialize. We took Olympic athletes, and then hooked them up to sophisticated biofeedback equipment, and had them run their event only in their mind. Incredibly, the same muscles fired in the same sequence when they were running the race in their minds as when they were running on the track. How could this be? Because the mind cannot distinguish whether you're really doing it, or whether it's just a practice. I believe if you've been there in the mind, you'll go there in the body too.*[83]

Let's look at a few well-known examples of people who harnessed the power of visualization:

• Air Force Colonel George Hall: A Vietnam POW, Hall was held in a North Vietnamese prison camp for seven years, suffering unthinkable conditions. To pass the time, Hall would play a full game of golf in his mind, going through

---

[83] Albright, Judith. *Envisioning Success: The Power Of Visualization*. Regenerate, April 30, 2014.

each motion meticulously: arriving at the green, selecting his club, and making each shot. After being released from the POW camp, he entered the Greater New Orleans Open and shot a 76. This was *one week* after his release!

• Vera Fryling, MD: Fryling was a teenager when she was hiding in Berlin during the Holocaust. Being a Jew, Fryling was staying undercover just to stay alive. While hiding, Fryling passed the time by imagining that she was a doctor. She dreamed of becoming a psychiatrist in a free land, practicing the images and feelings over and over again. Not surprisingly, Fryling ended up escaping the Nazis and went on to become a member of the faculty at the San Francisco School of Medicine.

• Nikola Tesla: Said to be the inventor of the modern world, Tesla was a prolific creator. It is said that before he ever sketched a single idea, he would first spend months to years visualizing it. Tesla would change the construction of, make improvements to, and even operate the device mentally. He could accurately give the measurements of all parts to workers, simply from the mental construction. When completed, all the pieces fit, just as if they had been drawn to specification. Tesla would even test his innovations in his mind, feeling that this practice was equally as valuable as actual testing. Tesla claimed that the inventions he conceived in this way always worked.

• Jim Carrey: As early as Carrey could remember, he wanted to be an actor. In the early 1990s, Carrey was still an unknown actor and struggling to get by. One day, Carrey decided to write a check to himself for $10 million. He wrote the date as 1994, and at the bottom of the check, he wrote, "for acting services rendered." He reportedly carried it in his wallet for daily inspiration. Carrey was later cast for one of the leads in *Dumb and Dumbe*r. He found out that he would make a salary of $10 million for that movie. It was shot in 1994.

The stories go on and on. Professional athletes, famous sports teams, singers, and people who are given fatal diagnoses have had incredible results, all using the power of visualization to achieve their goals. But everyone knows someone this *didn't* work for. Maybe even you. Many just chalk it up to luck or privilege.

But what if we all possess this ability but have yet to harness it? Let's look at some of the key pieces of using this power to create our best life.

IT'S SO HARD TO PERCEIVE THE GOOD

The good man from his inner good treasure flings forth good things, and the evil man out of his inner evil storehouse flings forth evil things.

Matthew 12:35 AMPC

The Lord saw how great the wickedness of the human race had become on the earth, and that every inclination of the thoughts of the human heart was only evil all the time.

Genesis 6:5

Professor Roy Baumeister, a social psychologist at Florida State University, states the following in his published article regarding negative thinking:

The greater power of bad events over good ones is found in everyday events, major life events (e.g., trauma), close relationship outcomes, social network patterns, interpersonal interactions, and learning processes. Bad emotions, bad parents, and bad feedback have more impact than good ones, and bad information is processed more thoroughly than good. The self is more motivated to avoid bad self-definitions than to pursue good ones. Bad impressions and bad stereotypes are quicker to form and more resistant to disconfirmation than good ones.[84]

Remember when we discussed how memories are formed? You may recall that more of our senses are engaged when a "bad" memory is being processed.

---

[84] Baumeister, Bratslavsky, Finkenauer, Vohs. *Bad is stronger than good.* Review of General Psychology, 2001.

Because of our primal inclination toward safety, anything that is perceived as a threat engages our sensory inputs more acutely. Also, the quality of our current life is almost solely dictated by the way we perceive the events that shaped us. Therefore, if we view our past in a negative light, it stands to reason that we are fine-tuned to see the negative in every situation. That takes us squarely back to our victim model of thinking, discussed in Part 1.

But just as you learned to perceive the negative by practicing it, you can also learn to perceive the positive. Whichever you do more will ultimately be the winning perception. You may have heard the tale of the Two Wolves:

> *An old Cherokee is teaching his grandson about life. "A fight is going on inside me," the old man said to the boy. "It is a terrible fight, and it is between two wolves. One is evil—he is anger, envy, sorrow, regret, greed, arrogance, self-pity, guilt, resentment, inferiority, lies, false pride, superiority, and ego." He continued, "The other is good—he is joy, peace, love, hope, serenity, humility, kindness, benevolence, empathy, generosity, truth, compassion, and faith. The same fight is going on inside you—and inside every other person, too."*
> *The grandson thought about it for a minute and then asked his grandfather, "Which wolf will win?"*
> *The old Cherokee simply replied, "The one you feed the most."*

This beloved fable illustrates our choice in a winning perception. We must choose what we think, what we focus on, and what we create. Visualization is a powerful tool.

HOW TO VISUALIZE YOUR FUTURE

Are you resistant to this practice? The fact is that you already do it, probably every day. Are you sick? Every night, you likely go to bed, wondering how you will feel the next morning. You visualize the worst-case scenario. "Will I feel worse? Will a new symptom appear?" You begin to create visual pictures or feelings in your body to represent your tomorrow. You are creating! Good job. But do you like the outcome? No? Change it!

I have worked with countless insomniacs. The biggest problem with insomniacs is the *fear* of not sleeping. Nearly every day, they think about that night. "Will I sleep?" How long will it last tonight?" I've even known people who come up with a list of things to do that night—while they are *not sleeping!* Talk about planning. Everything becomes a "trigger" to *not* sleep. Even the bedroom becomes an uncomfortable place because of the worrisome, sleepless thoughts it evokes. They have a detailed plan on how *not* to sleep that night. And the body follows!

The single most common defense I hear for this type of planning is, "But I don't want to be disappointed when _____ doesn't happen!" Do you see it? Even the defense is in alignment with what you expect to happen. People feel the need to "be prepared" for the worst. Unfortunately, this usually ends up creating the very thing they say they don't want. Where is faith in this equation?

Now, hear me say this. For many people, just the act of visualization is enough to create an alternate outcome. For others, they have very good reasons for holding onto all the Perceived Negative Experiences that are supporting their problem. For those people, like me, the visualization is just *part* of the process. But its importance must not be minimized. So, how do you begin this process? Let's venture on.

CREATING YOUR METANOIA MANIFESTO

We recommend finding a journal or notebook to dedicate to this practice. Ideally, even the sight of it will evoke a good feeling. I want you to think of this document as if it holds magical powers. What you write can come true. Don't hold back. Make it the BEST! This is the place to plan out exactly what you want for the future. This is way more than a "goals list." This is a story. It needs details, images, sounds, feelings, and character development. It's also, always, a work in progress. It can be refined, fine-tuned, upgraded. It must only possess words of hope and positivity. It can have pictures, poems, quotes, cards—

anything you want that makes you feel good. It can even have glitter if that's your thing.

A small caution about your wording: our words have immense power. Remember our creation equation?

RUMINATION + DECLARATION = CREATION

This is your declaration. Words such as "don't want," "can't have," or any other words that make you *feel* bad are not allowed. NLP, as we've spoken about before, is the study of the way language patterns can be used to program our brains to achieve certain outcomes. Neuro refers to the brain, linguistic refers to the study of words or language, and programming refers to the ability of our mind to be programmed into creating the results and behaviors we desire. The study of NLP has been a huge benefit to me in helping to change my thinking by being aware of what I am saying.

It is widely believed in the personal growth and development industry that the subconscious mind cannot "hear" negatives, meaning that if you were to say, "I don't want to be fat," the mind only hears the "fat," not the "don't." What we say and how we say it impacts what our mind "pulls up" from our resources. The mind responds to whatever is being focused on as it looks for feelings or proof to support that belief. The mind then builds with the resources it is given. The reason "I don't want to be fat" translates into "I'm fat" is because the mind understands all the feelings of being fat. Your mind will find all the people in your life who are or were fat, or all the negative feelings people have toward the word. It has tapped into all the resources that make this true for you. If you changed that statement to, "I want to be fit and healthy," your brain now has to find any resources it holds to build a skill to be "fit and healthy."

People who continue to say, "I'm broke," miraculously always seem to *be* broke. My (Heather's) maiden name is Bolton. My father has a saying, "Well, that's just life on Bolton Boulevard!" This always came after a hardship, usually financial in nature. Though I didn't realize it growing up, this mantra provided support for my belief that getting ahead in life came easy for the rich but hard for the "poor." "Bolton Boulevard" signified the ancestral idea that I was stuck on this street! This was all a subconscious message that I didn't realize until later in life.

As a young kid, in my (Kent's) quest to be like Jesus, I tried to keep humble. Unfortunately, humility, to me, meant to be "less than" and think of myself as "lowly." I thought that it was sinful to talk about how wonderful and talented and amazing I am as God's creation. I needed to stay "humble," and in so doing, I lived many years of my life in an insecure mentality full of negative self-talk like *"I'll never be good enough."* Yet I thought I was being like Jesus! Only when I finally listened to God's unfiltered voice and let go of my deviated self-declarations was I able to live free, full, and fantastically in a manner worthy of the calling I have received.

For your manifesto, make sure that your wording is positive and affirms what you want more of. Remember the admonition from Philippians 4:8: *"Finally, brothers and sisters, whatever is true, whatever is noble, whatever is right, whatever is pure, whatever is lovely, whatever is admirable—if anything is excellent or praiseworthy—think about such things."* This is not the time to restrain yourself. Your future is only limited to what you can imagine. Go big! I *will* ask you to restrain your "but I don't want to be let down" program and your "I'm just trying to be realistic" program and your "I just want to be humble" program and *dream big!* If those thoughts pop up, don't ignore or judge them. Instead, you can jot them down on a separate piece of paper. We will put them on another list described in a further chapter. This notebook is only for what you *do* want.

For some, this step will come easily. You have no problem writing your litany of wants, dreams, and desires. For others, this could prove a little more challenging. If you find yourself in the latter category, don't despair. It only means that you are out of practice with using your imagination for the good. That doesn't mean you don't use your imagination. You have probably just gotten used to imagining all the *bad* things that could happen. Or all the ways it *won't* work out. Remember, the bad and the good are both your imagination. You might as well start practicing imagining the good! It will take practice, but it is more than worth it.

A (VERY IMPORTANT) SIDE NOTE: CHRISTIAN CULTURE

I have had the privilege of interacting with (far too many to count) different churches and church leaders in my lifetime, ranging from coast to coast, country to country, and continent to continent. As we all know, each culture or society has a particular way of thinking that is developed over time. I love many of the church cultures I have been a part of. The big-city churches have the audio/visual effects enhanced to the max for the benefit of people being fully engaged in church services. South African churches that I've been a part of dance in the middle of the aisles during the worship songs. Here on Maui, a good portion of our services are held on the beach, where we preach, sing, and fellowship in our bathing suits! Some churches have regimented schedules, while others fellowship more organically. There is no "one right way" to gather and worship and grow spiritually. But I *do* believe there are destructive ways of trying to create a Christlike culture.

Sadly, I have encountered far too many of these unfortunate mentalities in the church. One of the most destructive cultures I have witnessed is the way fellow Christians "help" one another. Hear me out: I believe everyone is doing the best they can with what they have been given and how they have learned and been trained. But something insidious has seeped into many churches. I have seen it play out in three categories: *false humility*, *self-deprecation*, and *dis-encouragement*.

False humility is when someone de-emphasizes their merits or discredits themselves when credit is due. Remember to "*give to everyone what you owe them... if respect, then respect; if honor, then honor*" (Romans 13:7). Jesus reminds us of the second greatest command, to "*love your neighbor as yourself*" (Matthew 19:19). How are we supposed to love, respect, and honor others if we do not have that respect and honor for ourselves? I have witnessed people trying to become more like Jesus by *not* seeing the amazing aspects of who they are. And just *who* do you think made you so amazing? Honor God by honoring the incredibleness that is you! When someone says, "Your sermon really inspired me," it's okay to respond with gratitude and excitement about how God uses you. "*In the same way, let your light shine before others, that they may see your good deeds and glorify your Father in heaven*" (Matthew 5:16). God is throwing a party for you just because you are his child: "*I tell you, there is rejoicing in the presence of the angels of God over one sinner who repents*" (Luke 15:10). So you, too, rejoice and celebrate you! You are God's!

Self-deprecation is a variation of false humility, but this time, instead of avoiding being celebrated, you dump on yourself (metaphorically). Comments sound something like "You know I'm just a sinner" or "It's a good thing I have Jesus, because I am a wretch and worthless without him" or even "That's my character, but thanks be to God for his grace." *Yes*, all these statements could technically be true in themselves. But they do not come from a humble place of desiring to give God the glory. Instead, these come from a place of insecurity, thinking, "*I will never be enough.*" But the Bible clearly states that "*his divine power has given us everything we need for a godly life through our knowledge of him who called us by his own glory and goodness*" (2 Peter 1:3). Jesus says, "*Very truly I tell you, whoever believes in me will do the works I have been doing, and they will do even greater things than these*" (John 14:12). Jesus himself told us that we, mere humans, would do even greater things than he did! How awesome we must be in God's eyes! Can you imagine Paul or Peter or John saying anything like, "God is so great, but I am just a sinner. I know my life is a mess, but I'm just grateful that I have God in my life." Peter "*fell at Jesus' knees and said, 'Go away from me, Lord; I am a sinful man!'*" when he first encountered Jesus (Luke 5:8), but Jesus did not want this kind of fear or self-deprecation. Instead, he responded by saying to Simon, "*Don't be afraid; from now on you will fish for people*" (Luke 5:10). Jesus saw Simon Peter through God's perspective.

So does God want us to claim his greatness, but see ourselves in some tainted, broken manner? No way! Remember from Chapter 8 that Paul did not boast because he was weak. Go back and read that part of the book. Peter became a rock for the church. John was a son of thunder. Yes, these guys each had their much-needed growth opportunities, but they were each on fire for God, fully confident in whatever they did because they decided to see themselves through God's eyes as incredible creations. You can too!

Dis-encouragement is the final facet of this destructive culture. I am not talking about discouragement, although that would also be something to avoid. First, let's understand what it means to *encourage*. To encourage literally means to put courage into or to instill confidence by giving support. Encouragement has to do with stimulating someone's state of mind toward continuing in their path. Notice this has nothing to do with the person *giving* the encouragement, but everything to do with the courageous and confident outcome *received*. Therefore, *dis*-encouragement is to strip away or extinguish the courage that is already held within another person. It is to passively, discretely, and manipulatively lower someone's heightened spirit and confidence. To dis-encourage is to take away the hope someone has, so as to deter them from their current path. This can be intentional or completely unintentional, all the while instilling doubt or fear of possible consequences. Do you see this in your church? Let me answer that by asking some questions:

What kinds of sermons are being preached regularly? Is your gospel the *good* news? How is the cross of Jesus being reflected? Is there any shame or guilt involved, or are there any "shoulds"? Is your "good standing" as a disciple based on sinning less? Are your conversations flooded with what you need to be doing better? Does anything ever allude to "God may be disappointed" in you? Are our small groups' topics mostly about the sin that needs to be dealt with? Are church meetings mostly to address the problems with people? Are people drawn to the unconditional, nonjudgmental love that they see in Jesus? Is there a "system" that needs to be followed or else you're out? What about your one-on-one conversations? How much is about the tragedies or hardships of life? When someone needs help spiritually, how are they viewed or spoken about? If you are a mentor or leader or facilitator or somehow helping someone in your fellowship, what kind of advice or help are you giving them? Do you fan their flame, or do you keep them manageable, "safe," and with their flame low? Are you focused more on what is done wrong that needs to change or what we can do moving forward from here on out?

I believe in the call for repentance; I believe that faith requires action. And I believe that we need to be in each other's lives to call one another higher. But we need to remember two things:

1) Jesus tells us to love as he loved us, and that by our love for one another, the world will know that we are his disciples (John 13:34–35).
2) People typically seek God because they want to be loved, accepted, and connected.

Let's make certain that we never put out the Spirit's fire. "*Never dampen the fire of the Spirit, and never despise what is spoken in the name of the Lord. By all means, use your judgment, and* ***hold on to whatever is really good***" (1 Thessalonians 5:19 PHILLIPS, emphasis added). When you are with others, "*Let your conversation be always full of grace, seasoned with salt*" (Colossians 4:6). Let's "*encourage one another daily,*" and in so doing, build up the kingdom of God (Hebrews 3:13).

What if your entire fellowship rid themselves of false humility, self-deprecation, and dis-encouragement? What if people honored and declared the amazingness of who God created them to be? What if each of the members declared only what is noble and true and excellent, speaking about their victories in the Lord and how they continue to overcome? What if each member's passion and purpose were to infuse one another with confidence to keep moving forward in their growth? What if fellowship meant finding out what the other person is doing well and fanning into flame their confidence to take it to the next level because you both know they already have what it takes? Imagine if we were a part of a fellowship who loved one another so much that all interactions (encouragement or growth opportunities) culminated in spurring one another on to love and good deeds. What if every day were a new opportunity to harmonize with the others and with the earth that God created for us? What if you helped people feel accepted as Christ accepts you? What if you made people feel loved the way Christ loves you? And what if you held space for people who are not quite where they need or want to be, giving them every opportunity to make the choices to grow and change?

An atmosphere of authenticity, vision, and courage would surely ensue. This is precisely why God created the church: to gather people, transform lives, and expand love. That's the kind of church Jesus lived for, died for, and resurrected for—a church in which we can thrive.

TIPS FOR SUCCEEDING

Let's get back to how to write your Metanoia Manifesto. Use language that indicates you *already have it*. For instance, rather than writing: "I want to be fit and healthy," you would write, "I am fit and healthy. And with this fit and healthy body, I exercise three to five times a week and enjoy it immensely." Instead of writing, "I want to be like Jesus and change my impatience and lack of faith," you would write, "I am like Jesus, continually growing and overcoming. Patience is a strength, and every challenge that comes my way reveals my solid faith more as I charge forward in faithfulness every day." Write this beginning part *as if* you already possess the desired thing. Remember Jesus' direction that "*whatever you ask for in prayer, believe that you have received it, and it will be yours*" (Mark 11:24).

Here is an excerpt of my (Heather's) personal Metanoia Manifesto from 2015. It was in my five-year-plan section. (Interesting side note: *every single one* of these things has now manifested for me in one form or another!)

> *I am fit and healthy, working out in the gym and lifting weights. My body is strong and can easily communicate emotions. I am self-employed and self-supporting, doing what I love and helping people all over the world. I am a speaker, an author, and an authority on mind-body wellness. I love myself in a deeper way than ever before, and I give myself the time I need. I have a healthy relationship with food and easily and effortlessly maintain a healthy weight. I love my body more and more. I look*

> *and feel younger because I take care of myself accordingly. I live on a tropical island. There is plenty of sunshine, and I enjoy the outdoors regularly. My children enjoy the beach, and we are able to surf, hike, and relax in the sun. I keep a healthy work/family balance. I am surrounded by friends and people who call me higher. Opportunities are abundant. As I learn and grow, I am free to help others do the same. This comes naturally and easily. Money flows to me, and my needs are met. Kent* (my husband) *and I can dream even bigger and can be partners in every adventure. My children are confident and feel loved. They are healthy and feel free to be themselves.*

Again, this is just a sample of my personal manifesto. In 2015, I planned where I was going. At the time, I was living in South Africa and had no idea how I would ever end up on a tropical island. It seemed farfetched and "wishful thinking." It was! But the more I concentrated on clarifying *where* I was going, the paths to that place began to reveal themselves. As I declared and wrote those things, I felt like I *didn't* and *couldn't* have them. But I knew that I had to make a pathway out, if even just in my mind. The Metanoia Manifesto is your pathway out! It's the first step in knowing where you are going and how you will feel once you get there.

Here are some good questions to get you thinking about what you will write:

- **Who would I want to be if I were the *best* me?** Step out of yourself and see yourself as you'd *like* to be. See yourself the way God sees you (if this isn't pleasant, you know you have some work to do around what God says about you versus what YOU say about you). This can include character traits, feelings, attributes. If you were the best person you knew, what would you be like?

- **What would I do if I succeeded in every venture?** Dare to imagine yourself as a success in everything you do. Often, the main thing holding us back from becoming what we want is the *fear of failing*. It paralyzes us to the point that we don't even try. Try envisioning yourself as a perpetual success. How would this change your dreams?

• **How do I choose to serve others and provide value to every relationship?** Giving to others and feeling valued go hand in hand. You may give and give, but you will only end up depleted if you don't feel valued. Create situations that will be a win-win for both parties.

• **What skills do I already possess that get me closer to attaining my goals and objectives?** It's a good idea and practice to reflect on your life with the intent of finding tools and skills that you have already attained, and then recognize how you can use those to get even more.

• **What relationships do I have that support and value my vision?** Think about people who "have your back." Even if they are no longer living, see yourself through their eyes. Notice how they already believe in you and can help you go even further.

• **If I woke up every morning feeling the best I ever have, what would that feel like?** Be specific on the visual and the feeling of this scenario. What would you do if you woke up every day like this? How would your life change?

• **If I had a magic wand and could have anything and everything I desired, what would I have?** Don't limit yourself to tangible ways of achieving things. We often unknowingly limit ourselves because our reality is so restricted. Allow yourself the freedom to "magically" get things. That way, you can see an unrestricted version of what you want.

• **What is great about my life now, and what would I want to make it even better?** The power of gratitude cannot be overestimated. This practice alone will make huge strides in feeling better about your life. Taking your gratitude and using it to make more gratitude is an essential "life hack"!

• **If I had a great and loving childhood, in which everyone was doing the best they could, what would it have felt like?** This question holds the key to healing many hurts and pains. Even if you believe you had a horrific childhood, give yourself a moment to see it differently. If your parents really were doing the best job they could (and they likely were, even if it was awful), find some of the wonderful treasures that you may have overlooked in the past. Write a story as if you had the childhood that you wished you had. Rather than getting bogged down with what *should have been*, take a moment to be specific about what you would have wanted. Remember, write as if you *already* have it.

These are just some of the wonderful questions that will help you build a powerful Metanoia Manifesto. Read it frequently, take planned time to envision it, feel it, touch it, taste it. Become so familiar with this plan and destination that you could recite it by memory. When you do this, you will soon begin to notice how many things are already true and how many others are becoming true.

If you find resistance, that is okay. It can even be good. Resistance is an indicator of investment. It's good to see what beliefs you are really invested in. Just jot it down and turn back to your Metanoia Manifesto. That resistance will get the attention it needs. This is an organic document, meaning it will grow and be modified. It's meant to be changeable. As you attract more and more of the things on your list, you will be able to adjust and even dream bigger. This manifesto will also become a weighty testament to the power of your mind and the One who created it. In the near future, you will look back and realize how many of your "dreams" have become reality, and your gratitude will overflow. This allows for even more greatness and growth! It's a wild and wonderful ride!

CHAPTER 15

METANOIA GPS & SAFE HAVEN

I am not one to journal. Not that I haven't made countless attempts. If you look on my shelf, I have a handful of prayer journals that have five to 10 days of consistently written prayers, then a gap of two to six months (sometimes years). The next entry recaps the gap, and I continue my prayers. But consistency in a journal of any sort is just not my thing. However, it is imperative to have a place where we can store and remember our joyous times. We are reminded throughout the Bible to meditate on the Lord's precepts and to fill our minds with thankfulness. Many of the feasts and festivals that God commanded in the Old Testament were scheduled opportunities to remember the good things. Once you start your Metanoia Manifesto, it will become clearer *where* you are going. Now you need to recognize the tools you have to get there. This is where the Metanoia GPS comes into play. A GPS gives us all the tools to arrive at our desired destination. What will be included in your GPS? The "**G**" stands for *Gratitude*, the "**P**" stands for *Positive Affirmations*, and the "**S**" stands for *Smiles*. I will explain a little more about this later in the chapter. A lot of people carry around a "record of wrongs" in their hearts: a detailed list of how they've been hurt, and who did it. But we encourage people to have a record of "rights": an intentional list of things that are good in your life and people who have contributed to the good. That is what your GPS is! This will be highly beneficial to your Metanoia Method practice.

Remember, everything is a skill. Even happiness! If our life has been in a particularly rough place for any extended period, it's clear that we have been "practicing" a lot less joy than we need to. Practice makes perfect.

One way to practice our happiness, gratitude, and joy is to record them. It's the mindset behind photo albums, Facebook feeds, and Instagram accounts—a way to record all the wonderful things that happen to us. We look back on our memories and see the smiling faces, and we can hardly help but smile now. Yes, sometimes it makes us nostalgic, which we often mistake for sadness. But in reality, we are often just looking back and wishing we had been more present, aware, and grateful *then*. Keeping track of these times and reminding ourselves of all the fantastic "happiness skills" we possess is an incredible tool.

It may be of no surprise to you to note that gratitude and the "record-keeping" of blessings have been studied and researched for many years. In one recent study, researchers recruited 300 college students who were seeking mental health counseling at a university. The participants were studied just before they began their first session of counseling. The majority reported clinically low levels of mental health at the time. At the conclusion of the study, researchers found that the participants who engaged in gratitude activities reported significantly better mental health immediately following the study. But remarkably, they also reported benefits up to 12 weeks *after* the exercise ended.[85]

Another gratitude study, using adults with congenital and neuromuscular disorders (NMD), showed similar findings. Compared to the control group, the participants who recorded their blessings every night reported more hours of sleep each night and feeling more refreshed upon awakening. They also reported more satisfaction with their lives as a whole. Members of the gratitude group also felt more optimistic about each upcoming week and reported feeling more connected with others than did participants in the control group. Incredibly, the positive changes in the gratitude group were markedly noticeable to others. According to the researchers, "Spouses of the participants in the gratitude (group) reported that the participants appeared to have higher subjective well-being than did the spouses of the participants in the control (group)."[86]

Gratitude builds on itself. Researchers note that daily practice is superior to weekly practice. The brain changes with experience, so the more often gratitude

---

[85] Wong, Owen, Gabana, Brown, McInnis, Toth and Gilman. *Does gratitude writing improve the mental health of psychotherapy clients?* Psychotherapy Research, 2018.

[86] Robbins, Ocean. *The Neuroscience of Why Gratitude Makes Us Healthier.* Life, November 4, 2011.

is focused on, the more the brain learns to tune in to the world's positive things.[87] Though it may take a little extra effort, the payoff should not be downplayed. However you do decide to do this, please don't skip this step. Even if you've "tried it before," I implore you to try it again. In conjunction with the other tools you will receive in this book, you will have a powerful recipe for health and happiness. God created us to utilize gratitude as a powerful tool for happiness and health. We *need* gratitude in our lives to thrive. In all that we are writing about, we are simply tapping into the ways that God designed us.

MAKE A METANOIA GPS

This is fairly self-explanatory. Find a journal or notebook in which you can record the things that make you feel happy, grateful, blessed, hopeful, euphoric, and inspired. In our modern world, this can be done in various ways:

- **Written Journal:** A book or binder of blank pages that you use to write things down with a pen, markers, crayons, or other tools.
- **Electronic Journal:** This can be any word-processing document system that you can write into: Google docs, notepad, Microsoft Word, Pages, etc. This is also the easiest to combine with pictures or music.
- **Scrapbook/Photo Journal:** Track your joyous events through pictures, stamps, or drawings. You can add a few captions here and there, inspirational quotes, cards, letters, drawings, or anything that makes you feel good. You can also add song lyrics, poems, or printed pictures.
- **Combo Journal:** Use any combination of the above ideas to create your own masterpiece.

Remember, the basic components are:

G: Gratitude – This can be a daily list of things that you are grateful for. Even entering five items every day can be a powerful tool toward getting more of

[87] Hey Sigmund. Young, Karen. *The Science of Gratitude How it Changes People.* https://www.heysigmund.com

what you want in life. I do this in the evening, before bed. I think through my day and take time to record some things I am grateful for. Even on the worst days, I can find things to be thankful for. Some days, it simply says "coffee." Other days, I make a long list of things. Some things are repeated, day after day. It's all okay. Just log your gratitude, daily if possible. If you miss a day, be grateful the *next* day that you were able to journal that day.

P: Positive Affirmations – Did you know that anything you affirm will become truer to you? We *negatively* affirm all the time. "I'm such a dummy," "I can't do anything right," "I hate my job," "I'm so tired," and so on. All of those are affirmations. In your GPS, we want only *positive* affirmations. These can be little quotes, sayings, or purposeful affirmations used to build you up. Louise Hay, an author and expert in the mind-body field whom we mentioned before, has amazing affirmations in many of her books that counteract certain physical symptoms. Also, you can find numerous affirmations online. Find these and rehearse them. Write them daily and read them aloud if possible. You don't have to believe that these are "true" now, but things you *want* to be true in the future, like, "I am completely and unconditionally loved, just as I am." In a very short time, you will look back at your earlier positive affirmations and realize that some of the things you wrote are absolutely true now! Another powerful practice is to write down scriptures that encourage you, along with statements about who God is and the way he feels about you.

S: Smiles – This is *anything* that makes you smile! This can be photos, song lyrics, funny little stories, or observations. Ideally, this will include happy memories from your past as well as things you have loved or been inspired by in the past (or present), and will also serve as something you can add to daily. Noticing the blessings surrounding even minor topics can help you reinforce gratitude in your life. Even something as simple as gratitude for the sun streaming through the window can be a powerful practice. I saw two lizards having an epic battle for a female lizard's attention. It was beautiful, and I made sure to write it down as soon as I was able. Even now, as I write this, I have a huge smile on my face as I remember that incredible scene. You can also glue in cards, notes, letters, or other little mementos that bring a smile to your face. This will also be a vital section and a crucial part of your Metanoia Method practice because it will be the place where you record your *changed* memories (more on how to change memories in the next chapter).

CREATING A MENTAL SAFE HAVEN

Another powerful practice that I have employed is intentionally creating a "safe haven" in my mind. Anyone who has experienced trauma of any kind can likely explain the importance of "feeling safe" in any given situation. For people who have spent any extended period in a "flight/fight/freeze" response, finding a calm, safe environment can be a key to healing. For this exercise, we capitalize on the knowledge that our mind doesn't know the difference between "happening now" and "already happened" if we are deeply rehearsing the memory. Having a safe haven that we can visit anytime and anywhere is a valuable tool.

Inside my mind, I have created my "happy place." For me, this is an outdoor setting. I can visually represent things powerfully in my mind. For those who are not highly visual, this can be equally powerful using feelings, smells, sounds, and other details. This place is *very* real to me. I have visited it enough in my mind that I know every detail. I know what it looks like, feels like, smells like, and sounds like. I have even added some details that I can taste. This is my happy place. I love going there! I visit it often. I cannot feel bad there. Bad feelings are not allowed. It's a very similar idea to the place that Cosette, the little girl in *Les Miserables*, explains in her song "Castle on a Cloud."

> *There is a castle on a cloud;*
> *I like to go there in my sleep.*
> *Aren't any floors for me to sweep,*
> *Not in my castle on a cloud.*
>
> *There is a room that's full of toys;*
> *There are a hundred boys and girls.*
> *Nobody shouts or talks too loud,*
> *Not in my castle on a cloud.*

There is a lady all in white,
Holds me and sings a lullaby.
She's nice to see and she's soft to touch;
She says, "Cosette, I love you very much."

I know a place where no one's lost;
I know a place where no one cries.
Crying at all is not allowed,
Not in my castle on a cloud.[88]

Like Cosette, we all need a place we can go to that is exactly the way it should be. And with the amazingly creative and imaginative powers of our mind, we can have that place! Let's also consider another example of someone practicing a safe haven. Listen to David as he brings us along in his detailed descriptions of a place that sounds utterly peaceful!

Lord, our Lord,
how majestic is your name in all the earth!
You have set your glory
in the heavens.
Through the praise of children and infants
you have established a stronghold against your enemies,
to silence the foe and the avenger.
When I consider your heavens,
the work of your fingers,
the moon and the stars,
which you have set in place,
what is mankind that you are mindful of them,
human beings that you care for them?
You have made them a little lower than the angels

---

88 Hugo, Victor. *Les Miserables.* "Castle on a Cloud." Copy Translation: Charles E. Wilbour. New York: Random House Modern Library, 1992.

and crowned them with glory and honor.
You made them rulers over the works of your hands;
you put everything under their feet:
all flocks and herds,
and the animals of the wild,
the birds in the sky,
and the fish in the sea,
all that swim the paths of the seas.
Lord, our Lord,
how majestic is your name in all the earth!

Psalm 8

This exercise will be easier for some than others, but I encourage you to keep working on it. For your benefit, I will share a description of my safe haven with you. Remember, this is highly personalized for *me*. It may include details that you do not enjoy. That's okay! This is my place, not yours. That's the point. It's supposed to be *your* safe haven. Make it as good as you want it. But feel free to borrow from mine if you like.

There is a large, crystal-clear lake surrounded by mountains on all sides. The mountains are covered in all sorts of trees. Evergreens, aspens, willows. Out on the lake is a long wooden walkway that leads to a covered dock. At the end of this dock, I sit in a large, reclined chair. It is a large wooden Adirondack chair with a high back. As I sit, I have a warm, soft blanket draped over my legs. It is often morning, and the air still has a slight chill that lingers before burning off into a warm summer day. I hold a hot cup of coffee (or sometimes hot cocoa) in my hands. I can feel the warmth of the mug. I take a sip and savor the deep flavor. The lake is completely calm and flat. Every once in a while, an unseen insect touches the top of the lake and causes a gentle ripple on the surface. The water is clear, and I can see to the bottom of the lake. The color of the water is turquoise blue, turning a deeper blue where the lake deepens. I can hear the birds in the forest, and the leaves rustle when the slight breeze picks up. I just sit, taking it all in. I take deep breaths of the crisp mountain air. The air is sweet, and I can feel it fill up my lungs and cleanse my body. I am completely at peace. I am alone and perfectly at ease. I have nothing to do, nowhere to be. I can stay as long as I choose. I can smell the pine and the earthy scent of the mossy woods. I can also smell the freshness of the water. I can smell the faint aroma of a wood-burning stove in the distance. Here, I am safe. Here, I am whole.

I have never physically been to my safe haven, but it feels as real as any other place I have been to. I'm not sure why I chose the particular details I did. In some ways, they chose me. But I treasure this place. I visit often and have added numerous details over the years. Sometimes, I jump in the cold water and swim with manatees. Other times, I lie in the sun on the dock and take the occasional dive into the crystal waters. A dolphin showed up once! Yes, I know. There are no dolphins in lakes. But one showed up nonetheless! I often see butterflies or beautifully colored blue jays or cardinals. Sometimes I'm wearing a bathing suit and sometimes a sweater. Those little details are flexible and change without my understanding. But some things remain constant.

The more you invest in this place, and this practice, the more powerful it will become for you. Creating a place of safety and comfort is a priceless investment. I understand that some people have not had the luxury of safety in their lives. But this is something that *anyone* can create. Give this to yourself. It's worth it. It will also come in handy later when you begin working through your PaNE CuRe list (more about this in Chapter 16).

Interestingly, a few years ago, I found myself in a very familiar place while visiting somewhere I had never been. Because this work is so effective with addiction, I had the opportunity to go over to the island of Oahu and volunteer my services at Habilitat. Habilitat is a drug and alcohol treatment center that deals with some of the toughest addiction cases in the USA. It is a mandatory 24-month program, and I am honored to have worked with them. My first time at the facility, I was taken out to the "dock." As I stood at the end, I couldn't help but feel like I had been there before. I felt an instant connection and was immediately peaceful. After a few minutes, I was shocked to realize how much it resembled "my dock" in my mind! I have no doubt that I will someday stand at the end of "my dock," somewhere in this world, and I will be flooded with all the wonderful feelings that I practice regularly.

CHAPTER 16

CURING PAIN WITH A PANE CURE LIST

It is for freedom that Christ has set us free. Stand firm, then, and do not let yourselves be burdened again by a yoke of slavery.

Galatians 5:1

Of all acts of man repentance is the most divine. The greatest of all faults is to be conscious of none.

— Thomas Carlyle

I do not understand what I do. For what I want to do I do not do, but what I hate I do. And if I do what I do not want to do, I agree that the law is good. As it is, it is no longer I myself who do it, but it is sin living in me. For I know that good itself does not dwell in me, that is, in my sinful nature. For I have the desire to do what is good, but I cannot carry it out. For I do not do the good I want to do, but the evil I do not want to do—this I keep on doing. Now if I do what I do not want to do, it is no longer I who do it, but it is sin living in me that does it. So I find this law at work: Although I want to do good, evil is right there with me. For in my inner being I delight in God's law; but I see another law at work in me, waging war against the law of my mind and making me a prisoner of the law of sin at work within me.

Romans 7:15–23

Now that you have completed your Metanoia Manifesto, it's time to address any resistance that may have shown up. In addition, it's time to go back and take inventory of the beliefs, memories, and experiences that helped you become who you are right now. Remember, our current life circumstances, beliefs, and operations come from our internal programming. If you have tried many different modalities or theologies on how to "deal with" your past, you may have made the incorrect assumption that it is unchangeable. The adage, "The past is the past; you cannot change it" comes from an inaccurate view of "the past." If the past truly were "the past," we would not be currently dealing with it. But our current reality (and often our future reality) is dictated by what we already know. As much as we would like the past to stay put, where it belongs, we just don't work like that as humans. If you can conjure up something negative (in your mind) from your past right now, then your brain will produce similar or the same neurotoxins from the original event. Therefore, your mind makes that past memory present and real as if it were happening right now. Our subconscious does not understand time or reality as our conscious mind does. Our memory is a crucial and mysterious part of our make-up.

With the Metanoia Method, we don't run from the past. We don't talk about it until you are (along with everyone else) tired of hearing about it. We don't ignore it and we certainly don't judge it. We *change* it! Well, technically *you* change it—we just facilitate the process. Memory is a function of the mind. How you hold memories is unique to your perception. Memories are the building materials you use to construct your current and future realities. Ever wonder why you keep getting the same thing in your life over and over? You are building with the same building blocks! You may decide you are unhappy with your current environment, so you uproot and start over. Still, if you bring the same materials with you to build your new life, you will have basically the same foundational problems. To change the building materials, we must first assess what they are.

We do this by listing our **Pa**st **N**egative **E**xperiences and **Cu**rrent **Re**alities. Take the first letter(s) of those and we get the acronym PaNE CuRe. I wasn't trying to be cute, but it turns out that the "cure for pain" starts with our PaNE CuRe.

MAKING YOUR PaNE CuRe LIST

In a moment, I will give you detailed instructions for making your list. I would highly suggest finishing this book *before* making your list. I will be asking you to do some things that will make a lot more sense once you have finished reading the book. You may experience a range of emotions when considering this task. Some people are very excited, knowing that identifying the "building blocks" of our experiences, beliefs, and realities is the first step in changing them. Others may feel like this task is daunting. First off, give yourself ample time to finish the list. You do not have to do it all in one sitting. Give yourself a specific time frame each day that you will work on it. You may find that you desire to continue after the allotted time. That's fine—keep going until you are finished or feel ready to stop for the day. Otherwise, just work on it for 10, 20, 30, or 60 minutes, and then stop. Pick it back up the next day.

There will be a temptation to get very emotionally involved in this list. As you are writing, it is essential to remind yourself that *this is not actually happening now*. You are safe. Take this opportunity to learn to be an observer. Yes, these things happened, and you have many thoughts, feelings, and sensations surrounding them. We will deal with all of that. But for now, simply record them for future use.

Also, this would be an excellent time to have your Metanoia GPS handy. If, at any point, you feel that you are becoming too emotionally charged by making the list, take a break and look at your GPS. Alternatively, have some funny YouTube videos handy. Whatever makes you uncontrollably happy!

HACK YOUR HAPPY

> *We demolish arguments and every pretension that sets itself up against the knowledge of God, and we take captive every thought to make it obedient to Christ.*
>
> **2 Corinthians 10:5**

> *Repentance is not about earning grace but entering it; not about quenching his wrath but quieting the accusations of our hearts; not about unlocking his mercy but releasing our sin-sick sorrow to the Savior, who already rejoices to receive it.*
>
> – Bryan Chapell

The brain chemicals dopamine, serotonin, oxytocin, and endorphins are the foursome partially responsible for feelings of happiness. Neurotransmitters such as cortisol, glutamate, and norepinephrine are attributed to anxiety, sadness, and depression. Your thoughts produce hormones and chemicals in your body, which leads to emotions and behaviors. For instance, if you choose to focus on something that brings you joy, you actually produce more of the "happy" hormones. We can actually "hack" our happiness!

Think about something "bad" and then shift to thinking of something "good." If the good feelings are powerful enough, they can deconstruct the bad feeling (negative neuropathway). This is merely hacking our biochemistry! We innately know this as humans. How many of you fell down and skinned your knee as a child? A natural response of an adult is to offer a "boo-boo kiss" or a lollipop. Or they try to make the child laugh. We know somehow that distracting from the pain will lessen it. Oh, how right we are! But it goes far deeper than that. I will go into this in detail in the next chapter. But for now, I want you to focus on the power of this "happiness hack."

Dopamine is a naturally occurring neurotransmitter created to give you a surge of reinforcing pleasure when you feel proud of yourself or have achieved a goal. Look back at old photos of your proudest moments. Reread touching cards or letters. Take a peek at your vision board.

Serotonin flows when you feel significant, valued, or grateful. Take a few moments to write down five things you are thankful for. Mentally or verbally affirm yourself in a positive way. You can also go for a walk or have a meal outside. Expose yourself to the sun for 15 to 20 minutes, which enhances serotonin production.

Oxytocin, referred to as the "cuddle hormone," creates intimacy, enhances trust, and strengthens relationships. It's released during orgasm, and by mothers during childbirth and breastfeeding. Give a hug to someone! Also, be sure to hug yourself regularly!

Endorphins help to alleviate anxiety. Exercise often results in a surge of endorphins. Laughter is one of the best ways to induce endorphin release. Even the anticipation and expectation of laughter increases levels of endorphins. Finding several things to laugh at during the day is a great way to keep your endorphins flowing. Also, don't forget to smile. When we smile, specific muscles contract and fire a signal back to the brain, stimulating our reward system, resulting in a boost of endorphins. Even the act of holding a pencil in your teeth for a while can generate "feel good" chemicals.

Can we just stop for a moment and thank God for his forethought and attention to detail? God created our brains and bodies to work in perfect harmony. These powerful neurotransmitters are naturally produced by our bodies when we feel safe, happy, and content. God has given us incredible tools to help us live our best lives. The more you free your mind from the past, the more you create space for all the "happy chemicals" to flood your mind and body.

MAKING THE LIST

Now that you can "hack your happy" at any point, you are ready to make your list. Keeping the above information in mind, prepare yourself to do this by first sitting down and taking 10 deep breaths. Breathing in through your nose and out through your mouth, try to match your inhale to a three-count beat (breathing in for three counts) and exhaling to a four-count beat. When you have completed your breathing, take a moment to invite your subconscious mind to bring forth the information that is needed. You can do this by verbally or mentally acknowledging that you are providing a safe and loving space for this process. When you are ready, you may record this information on paper or on your computer.

It is my suggestion that you use a notebook or journal that is specifically designated for this process. This, like the Manifesto, is an organic document, meaning it will continue to change over time. It is a valuable resource, becoming a record of all the beliefs that you once had. I cannot stress this point enough. As a self-professed non-journaler, I initially experienced resistance to this exercise. But after working with hundreds of clients, I can say that the people who *did* make this list along with a detailed Metanoia Manifesto experienced significantly more changes in the long run. This is, in essence, the "before picture" when you start a workout program. Inevitably, you will need this to form an accurate view of how far you have come.

There can be no judgment here. If you begin to have feelings of shame, blame, or grief, you need to go and "hack your happy." Come back and start again when you are ready. You can create this list in various formats, but we suggest starting from the beginning of your life. Starting from birth (or even stories you've heard predating your birth, if applicable) list every PNE (perceived/past negative experience) in your life. Give the memory a short title and then list two or three emotions, feelings, or sensations generated by this memory. Also rate this memory's emotional intensity next to the title using a scale of 0–10, with zero being you feel nothing and 10 being the worst feeling, as if it's happening right now (examples below). Here are detailed instructions on getting started:

1. List any prebirth or ancestral trauma. These will be stories you were told, or family identities. Include stories about parents or grandparents, aunts or uncles, anything you remember that was an unpleasant trait or story from your ancestry. You may have developed pictures in your mind or have audio recordings of the stories you were told. Examples of events in your mind: "*My grandfather was a Holocaust survivor… My mom almost drowned as a kid… My dad did not want to have any children…*" I would then title this memory, give it a rating (0–10) and list any feelings, emotions, or physical sensations associated with it.

- Holocaust stories: (8) fear, anger, rejection
- Mom's drowning: (6) fear, uncertainty, abandonment
- Dad didn't want me: (9) aloneness, feeling not good enough, bitterness

2. List any birth stories. These will be stories around your birth or conception: an arduous labor, hardships, the difficulty of Mom getting pregnant. Were you unwanted or a "mistake"? Adopted? Were you the "miracle child" they always wanted? A child of rape or abuse?

- Mother nearly died in labor: (6) shame, blame, fear
- Long and terrible labor: (4) hard, stuck, painful

3. Chronologically list all other PNEs. It may be helpful to divide your life into time periods (0–5 years old, 5–10 years old, etc.). Consider each period and try to list 10 or more events. If you remember a specific event but do not have an emotional intensity with it, list it anyway. Title the memory, give it a rating and list any related feelings, emotions, or physical sensations.

Events to include and consider:

- How siblings and family members felt about you, how they treated you
- School experiences: bullying, shaming, embarrassments
- Any sexual abuse or molestation
- First sexual experience: pornography, experimenting
- Emotional or physical abuse
- Religious traumas
- Major moves, changing schools
- Deaths of pets, pet injuries, losses
- Any romantic relationships, especially first boyfriend/girlfriend
- Pivotal points in life with parents, siblings, bosses, coworkers, etc.
- Divorce, relationship breakups, broken friendships
- Deaths, grief and loss, loss of a job, loss of health
- All hurts, anything you felt bad about when it happened
- All major medical illnesses, chronic illnesses, other medical problems

- Accidents and injuries
- Fears/phobias – list each experience that supports the fear
- Recurring beliefs or mantras: "I'm not good enough," "I'll never amount to anything," "I am so stupid!" etc.

4. List all current realities and core beliefs. This will be all the negative or unproductive things you believe about your life now. Examples: "I will never be well," "I don't have enough money," "I'm not good enough," "I have to earn love," "Life is hard," "My marriage is a disaster," "I'm depressed," "I am bad," "Something is wrong with me."

5. List any "unmentionables." These will be things that you feel are too difficult to deal with, something you have never told anyone, family secrets, or things that you aren't sure really happened. For these, you do not need to add any content, and the titles can be unrelated. For example, someone who remembers an incest incident but has never talked about it could list that event here with the title of "Lemonade." Lemonade may have something or nothing to do with the actual event but serves as a title for this particular memory. If you suspect something happened or that you did something, but have no memory of it, you can make up a short version of what might have happened and then title it. You don't have to have a conscious construct of a memory to change it. Your subconscious mind already knows.

Be careful not to indulge in the stories. Stories are merely practice. The more we tell it, the better we get at remembering it and making it true. Remember:

RUMINATION + DECLARATION = CREATION

Once you have completed your list, you now have a starting place for the Metanoia Method. You can begin working your way through this list using the rest of the practicals in this book. Remember, this document can be altered and added to as time goes along. But specify short, intentional times to come back and work on this list. Do not be in continual thought about all the PNEs of your life. Trust that if something else needs to be on the list, your subconscious mind will give it to you at the right time (more details and instructions on what to do with your PaNE CuRe continues in Chapter 17).

Caution: I do not advise trying to deal with highly traumatic events on your own if the emotional charge is too high. You may need the help of a skilled practitioner to facilitate your work on these items. Always ensure that you are in a safe, supportive environment when addressing past traumas. Do not use these methods as a replacement for skilled medical advice.

Chapter 17

Changing Your Mind: Rewiring Your Neuropathways

Neurons that fire together, wire together.

— Donald Hebb, neuropsychologist

Progress is impossible without change, and those who cannot change their minds cannot change anything.

— George Bernard Shaw

Those who live according to the flesh have their minds set on what the flesh desires; but those who live in accordance with the Spirit have their minds set on what the Spirit desires. The mind governed by the flesh is death, but the mind governed by the Spirit is life and peace.

Romans 8:5–6

We are now entering the "nuts and bolts" of the Metanoia Method process. Before telling you how to do it, I'm going to explain to you why it works. For this part, I will ask that you remember much of what we learned in Part 1. Remember Chapter 11, where we learned that "pain is communication." I mentioned that pain, among other things, is a feedback loop. If you hit your thumb with a hammer, you cannot feel pain unless the brain decides that "pain" is the appropriate response. These messages are carried along by synaptic impulses. This process creates a circular loop of communication.

What do you think would happen if we were to derail this feedback loop? If we were to intercept the messages and recode them, do you think the outcome would be different? I'm here to tell you it is! To illustrate this, let me introduce a concept that is crucial to the Metanoia Method. It is the "magic" that God empowers within our beautiful brains.

THE PATTERN INTERRUPT

"Pattern interrupt" is a term that comes from hypnosis and is also used in NLP. It means to change a person's state, pattern, or trance by interruption. Any unexpected event, like a sudden movement or response, can interrupt a pattern. You may have seen this in performance hypnosis through the "handshake induction," where the hypnotist puts someone into a hypnotic state simply by shaking their hand. Introducing an unexpected or uncomfortable moment into a familiar situation causes the brain to reevaluate the response. You probably witness this in action on a daily basis. Have you ever derailed someone's story simply by asking a question? When they try to go back, they have a difficult time regaining their place.

I have had this happen to me many times. For instance, I am retelling a story that is so funny I can barely contain my laughter, and as I get going someone interrupts me to clarify a detail. After I answer, I try to regain my place in the story, and I realize that the situation suddenly doesn't feel as funny as I had previously thought. If I get interrupted again, it's even more difficult for me to find the same amount of humor. After two or three interruptions, I usually give up, saying, "Never mind. It was much funnier when it happened. I guess you had to be there." It may seem like I am annoyed at the interruptions, but often, I simply cannot regain the same momentum I began with and even sometimes forget the story!

We see this with children all the time. I remember a time when my oldest daughter, Cadence, was little, and she fell hard and scraped her knee at the playground. It ripped her pants, and she was bleeding. She let out a blood-curdling cry, and I knew this wasn't going to be an easy consolation. But just as I reached her, a butterfly lit right on her nose! She crossed her eyes to get a better look and was instantly unaware of her hurt knee. The butterfly remained on her nose as she slowly rose to her feet. She was ecstatic! She walked around slowly, careful not to disturb her new friend. Soon after, it took flight, and we discussed it in amazement. Only afterward, I asked her how her knee was. She seemed confused and then remembered the scrape. She examined it, somewhat absently, and determined that it was fine, saying it only hurt a little. She ran off to find more butterflies!

So is this just distraction? Not really. It's deeper than that. Most of the time, we are operating in a "trance." Not the "cluck like a chicken" kind of thing that you see in performance hypnosis. Very simply put, a trance is when we are on a sort of half-conscious autopilot. We do this *most* of the time. We have trances for everything. It's our conditioned response to known stimuli. You are walking down the street, and someone smiles at you, and without thinking, you smile back. Unless you actively engage your conscious awareness, you will have an almost automatic response to most situations. Our experiences program these responses. When you interrupt someone's pattern, they experience momentary confusion, and in some circumstances, momentary amnesia.

I know I'm not alone in the next scenario. Have you ever started to do something and, after being interrupted, can't remember what it was you were doing in the first place? This can cause a "state of confusion" and make you open to suggestion. We can actually *program in* another state of mind within these moments. Not only that, but with enough "interruption," we can completely scramble a well-known program, pathway, or trance. Let me use another example.

Most of you reading this are probably able to recall early CDs. CDs are circular disks that have information encoded into them. If you had a Rolling Stones CD, their songs were "engraved" into (almost undetectable) grooves of data. So when you stick it in your car stereo to play it, the stereo reads those codes and spits out music. So what happens if one of those grooves gets a scratch in it? It skips, right? The severity of the skip depends on the size of the scratch. What happens if you scratch that song enough? It won't play at all.

The information feedback loop between our brain and our body works very similarly. If we understand the cyclical nature of that feedback, we can use it to our advantage. If we are stuck in an undesirable loop, we can interrupt it. Do it enough times, and it won't play any longer! Want to experience this? Let's do a quick exercise to demonstrate.

Think of something that bothered you today or this week. For now, choose something that was mildly bothersome. Got it? Write it down on some paper in front of you. Ask yourself one question: *how do I know this bothered me*? Notice that we are not asking "why." We don't want the story. We want the "how you know." It may be a feeling or a picture, or maybe you can hear the phrase or sounds. Just notice how you know. Jot down a few ways that you know below this event (only one or two words). It can be feelings, details, or things you hear. See below for an example.

Event: Someone cut me off in traffic.
How do I know: I can still see the picture of it. It made me angry, and I honked loudly.

Now rate the level of bother that you feel. Allow yourself to be back in that situation in your mind. Close your eyes if it helps. Notice how you know it bothers you. On a scale of 0–10, give it a rating for how much it bothers you, with 0 being you feel/see/hear nothing negative at all and 10 being as bad as if it were happening right now. If you happen to get a 0 rating, pick another event.

So now you will have the event, how you know it bothered you, and a rating to gauge that bother.

Now close your eyes, and *be there*. For a moment, allow yourself to *be bothered*. If you see a picture, see it clearly and notice how it makes you feel. If it's a feeling, make it stronger. If it's a sound, make it louder. This may even increase the rating a bit. That's okay. When you feel like you have "engaged the bother" and activated the trance, I want you to stop.

Now open your eyes and stand up. Put your right finger on the tip of your nose and recite the alphabet. When you complete it, take your left finger and replace the right finger, allowing your right hand to drop. Recite the alphabet again aloud, this time skipping every other letter. Good job!

Now sit back down and review your event. Ask yourself how bothered you are now. Almost always, you will not be as bothered as you were before. If something bothersome remains, repeat the alphabet tricks until it's at a 0.

Amazing, right? You are not done yet! Now think of the opposite of what bothered you. In my example, someone cut me off in traffic. The opposite of that might be that someone let me go first, or the person waited for me to go by and then gave me a friendly wave. If it's a feeling, the opposite of angry could be happy. Now I need to ask myself to envision or feel or hear the thing that is opposite. So at this point, I would envision the person in the car waiting for me and giving me a friendly wave. I would then notice what this changes in me. If it's a feeling, I may notice that I now feel happy. If I heard something, I might now realize I heard something encouraging. This becomes a powerful part of the process. Now practice this "new experience" a few times.

Using a pattern interrupt (the alphabet game or countless other techniques), we were able to interrupt the "bad feeling trance" and replace it with something else. It's like stopping the Rolling Stones song, even though it played for so long, and reprogramming that track to play Led Zeppelin instead. Or let's look at this fictionalized conversation as another example with the communication of physical pain:

You are carrying a 20-pound dumbbell in the gym, and you accidentally drop it on your foot.

Nerves (from the foot): *Hey, Brain. I think we've got problems here! Bad problems! I don't like the information that is coming through. I'm not sure what it is, but it can't be good. Red alert!*

Brain: *Got it, thanks. But you know what? My guess is that this was simply a result of us focusing our attention on something else we have coming up. I'm going to have to access the database of information to identify this message—sorry, it's classified; you'll just have to take my word for it—can I get back to you on that?*

Nerves: *I'm pretty sure something is wrong here. I'm telling you, this is serious!*

Brain: *Yeah, sorry. I'm almost positive that this has more to do with something else we are dealing with, but I'm not authorized to make a final decision until I've accessed the proper paperwork.*
Nerves: *Hey! I might not have the proper clearance for this "information" you keep talking about, but I really think this is a credible complaint, so I am going to continue telling you about it.*
(About this time, your cell phone alarm goes off. You are supposed to be ready for a conference call in 10 minutes).
Brain: *Oh, great! I've got another message coming through.*
Hormone Production Team: *Hey there, Brain. Yeah, we just received a message from the amygdala that we need to produce some stress hormones ASAP. Is this an accurate assessment? Are we stressed? Should we also send messages to the heart to increase its pressure? I also think it may be important to begin sweating. What do you think?*
Brain: *Okay, foot nerves, the data came back: actually, you're fine. Thanks for trying to warn us. We have it figured out. Please reduce the messages for a while. Also, you are having trouble remembering what the problem is. Hormones, yes, data shows that we were late on the last call, and that did not make the boss happy. This is definitely an all-hands-on-deck situation. Let's see an increase in blood pressure and cortisol, and let's make sure we stay in constant communication. This is too important to let go of—big things are at stake.*
Nerves: *Wait, what was I saying? It seems like I was just about to say something important. Oh well, it's gone now. I'll let you know if it comes back to me.*
Hormone Production Team: *Gotcha, Boss. We are already on it. We will produce feelings of worry and stress to make sure the body understands the importance of the mission. This message will play on repeat until we have this solved. Go team!*

Messages go up to the brain, but they also go down. This "two-way-street" of pain communication holds the key to being able to intercept and completely change the transmitted message.

TRANCE

A little more on the trance concept. We are in a trance much of the time. With an average of up to 50,000 thoughts per day, up to 95 percent of them are the same thoughts we had yesterday. We repeat those same thoughts over and over again, every day. That's a lot of practice! These have all been categorized and now are nearly automatic productions. Driving to work: trance. Performing your work duties: trance. Speaking with coworkers: trance. It's just how you do things. Your brain already "knows how" because it does it, in some form or fashion, every day.

This is why it can seem so hard to change. We are keeping ourselves in the same situations, thinking the same thoughts, producing the same feelings day after day. We have a conscious awareness that we would like to be *different*, but we use the same resources to produce a different result. That is rarely successful. If we can be aware of these programs and make conscious efforts to *interrupt* those repetitive messages, then we are left open to suggestions. The brain has to recalibrate because you are introducing something unknown and unexpected into the feedback loop. Because we already have our Metanoia Manifesto, we can always suggest something in alignment with what we want for the future!

"*If you think adventure is dangerous, try routine; it is lethal.*"

— Paulo Coelho

TYPES OF PATTERN INTERRUPTS

There are countless types of pattern interrupts to help you change your mind. Below, I will list just a few. Used in conjunction with the other concepts, tools, and suggestions in this book, a pattern interrupt is an incredibly powerful tool.

- Say the ABCs aloud.
- Play a great song and DANCE!
- Sing a nursery rhyme.
- Watch a funny YouTube video.
- Fake laugh.

- Stand on your tippy-toes and take big breaths, moving your arms up as you inhale and down as you exhale.
- Recite an encouraging scripture.
- Count down from 47 by threes.
- Do multiplication tables.
- Give yourself a big hug and say, "I love me!"
- Rub your tummy with one hand and pat your head with the other simultaneously.
- Do some gentle stretches .
- Smile broadly and try to tickle yourself.
- Draw circles on your right palm with the fingers of your left hand.
- Write "I love you" in cursive on your left palm with your right index finger.

There really are countless ways to do this. To make it even more powerful, we will revisit the concept of representational systems in a few moments. But before that, I want to take some time to address meridian tapping.

When I first was introduced to the concepts of the body-mind connection with trauma and healing, I was using meridian tapping. Emotional Freedom Technique (EFT) is a well-known and effective method of dealing with negative emotions. EFT theorizes that *the cause of all negative emotions is a disruption in the body's energy system*. For those of you in the energy healing community, this makes complete sense. For the rest of us, this may sound a little nebulous. Though the concept of energy (not the stuff that comes out of our electrical sockets, but the "unseen force" that connects all living things) isn't new, it's still considered rather "woo-woo" in the scientific and Christian communities.

Though I do believe that negative emotions can disrupt the body, we now know that emotions/feelings/sensations are *created* by our body. The thought that "energy," whatever that means to you, can "disrupt" our bodies still puts the power *outside* us. I highly respect the work of the EFT pioneers. Roger Callahan, Gary Craig, Dawson Church, and many others have made undeniable contributions to the healing community. Unfortunately, tapping has been met with a fair share of skepticism in the scientific community. Many doctors and psychologists have been quick to dismiss it due to the lack of research.

Dawson Church, PhD, author of *The Genie in Your Genes*, is one of the many people researching EFT as an evidence-based psychological and medical technique. Here are the results from one of his studies:

> *Church performed two pilot studies of EFT (Emotional Freedom Techniques) for post-traumatic stress disorder (PTSD). They demonstrated highly significant results despite a small sample size, indicating a robust treatment effect. This led to a randomized controlled trial, published in the oldest peer-reviewed psychiatry journal in North America, showing highly significant results. It demonstrated that 86% of veterans with clinical PTSD were subclinical after six sessions of EFT and remained so on follow-up. A concurrent study by an independent research team in Britain's National Health Service (NHS) showed similar findings, indicating that EFT meets the criteria of the American Psychological Association (APA) Division 12 Task Force as an empirically validated treatment for PTSD. An independent replication of Church's PTSD study found similar results.*[89]

EFT has been shown to help create a reduction in many stress-related conditions. The problem that persists is knowing why it works, and also explaining why it *doesn't work* for some or becomes less effective over time. I have an EFT Master Certification and have been greatly influenced by the teachings of EFT. But I am someone who likes to understand the mechanics of something. "Trapped energy," although an attractive and reasonable concept, was not concrete enough for me. It also allowed for too much ambiguity. I needed

[89] Church, Dawson. *Vitae.* https://dawsonchurch.com

more. After studying FasterEFT, NLP, hypnosis, positive thought therapy, and more, the answer became clear to me.

I needed to understand how the brain processes and stores memory and the physiological process of stress and emotion. Once I understood this, it was easy to see why tapping worked for many people. It was the pattern interrupt! The tapping, thought to be "releasing trapped energy," was actually just scrambling the messages that were being played along with painful memories. Scramble them enough, and the messages will no longer play. *Voilà!* The science is revealed. Isn't it amazing how God created our brains to do this?

On occasion, I still use tapping at times in my practice. Whether it's on the meridian points or some random place on the body doesn't matter. There have even been neurofeedback studies showing that tapping on a stuffed animal is just as effective as tapping on meridian points.[90] Why? Because these are all just pattern interrupts! I am acutely aware that its effectiveness is simply due to the brain receiving a kinesthetic message while simultaneously trying to reproduce the known problem. Tapping practitioners accidentally stumbled onto one of the biggest healing tools around. Yet many still attribute it to energy. What I have witnessed, both personally and professionally, is that tapping can become another coping mechanism. People will "tap" when they feel anxious, start to feel a bit better, and then stop tapping. Granted, it's a better coping skill than some others, but it is nowhere as powerful as it could be. Knowing physiologically what is happening in your brain when you tap is crucial to long-term success. When we see that tapping is simply one of many forms of pattern interrupts, it frees us up to be more focused and intentional in our healing.

The idea of tapping on the meridian points comes from the doctrines of traditional Chinese medicine. Chinese refer to the body's energy as ch'i. Since ancient times, adherents have believed that by stimulating these meridian points, they could heal. The concept is similar to acupuncture. Though I believe in the notion of meridian channels, I strongly feel that the real power is in the mechanics of our God-created brain.

---

90 Wood, Linda. *Magic Tapping Bears.* http://www.magictapping.com

REPRESENTATIONAL SYSTEMS: "HOW" WE DO WHAT WE DO

In Part 1, I briefly described our representational systems, better known as our five senses (visual, kinesthetic, auditory, olfactory, and gustatory). This is how data is received. It is through these systems that we experience our world. What we perceive are representations of what each sensory organ transmits to us. All the PNEs that you listed on your PaNE CuRe list were input through one or more of these systems. Everyone utilizes all the representational systems, but we tend to favor one over the rest. This is called our primary representational system. Knowing how the experience was recorded can be very helpful in deciding which pattern interrupt will be most beneficial. As a reminder, let's look at primary systems once again and the way that a memory can be stored based on each system.

"Memory" can be represented in many different ways. Knowing specifically how a particular event was processed and stored can be very helpful in interrupting it. Look at the diagram (on the next page) to be reminded of what happens when we receive any external stimuli.

As you can see, our representational systems are the first set of "filters" that are used with any information we encounter. Let me explain by having you do an exercise.

Representational Systems in Action

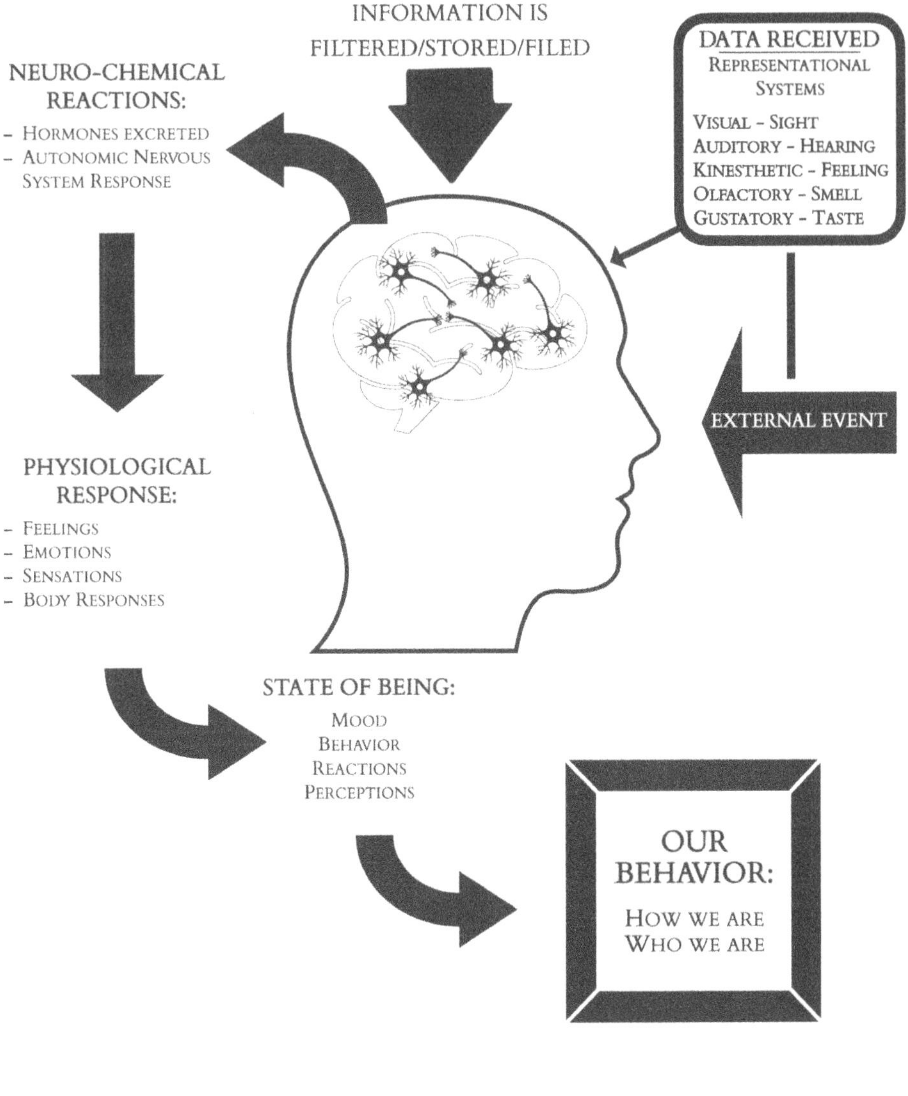

EXERCISE: Close your eyes for a moment and go back to your high-school graduation. Just notice whatever comes up for you.

For the people who stored this memory *primarily* using their visual system, you will have noticed pictures or movies playing in your head. You may remember the color of your cap and gown, or the faces of your friends, or even your face as you sat among your peers waiting to throw your cap into the air.

For the people who stored this memory *primarily* using their auditory system, you will have noticed the sounds of the day. Maybe you will hear the words of the salutatorian giving the speech, your name being called to come up and receive your diploma, or the applause of the audience as each classmate was called. You may remember the music or the words of encouragement from your friends and family.

For the people who stored this memory *primarily* using their kinesthetic system, you will experience the feelings you felt that day. The excitement or nervousness. Maybe even a little sad or even fearful. You might remember how your gown felt or the butterflies in your stomach as your name was called. Feelings of love might be noticed as you think of all the support you had. You may even remember what the temperature was that day or how you felt in the shoes you were wearing.

For the people who stored this memory *primarily* using their audio-digital system, you may hear a dialogue in your mind—recalling each event and the schedule of the ceremony. You may be aware of the wonder you felt and the thoughts that were going through your mind on that day. You may remember the things that you said to yourself, like "*Be sure not to trip on stage*." Maybe you recall *knowing* that things were going to change from this point on and that you had hit a milestone in life.

Assuming that your high-school graduation was not an incredibly traumatic time in your life, there would be no real need to interrupt this memory feedback loop. In fact, if it was a good time in your life, it would be beneficial to go back and spend time in this memory, noticing all the wonderful things that were there. Just by remembering this and replaying it, you can create the same chemicals and results as if it were happening to you *right now!*

If we are dealing with a memory that activated a negative stress response in your body when originally filtered and processed, that is something we would want to interrupt. Because, simply by replaying that memory in your mind, you can produce "feel bad" chemicals, as if it's happening *right now!* If you identify how this memory is stored *primarily*, you can use appropriate pattern interrupts to scramble the message. Let me share a client story to illustrate this point and show you how I used this concept.

DAWN

Dawn came to me as a shy and reclusive woman. She had a strong belief that she was "not good enough," "not smart enough," and a "bad person." As she worked on her PaNE CuRe list, I noticed a few domestic abuse incidents in her past. When probed further, she described her mother being belittled and abused by her father. I asked Dawn how she knew that her mother had been abused. She said that she had heard it. I asked her to go back to one of the instances and describe it for me. Dawn said that she would often be in her room with her door closed when she was a little girl. On the other side of the door, she would hear her parents fighting. A few times, it even escalated to her mother screaming in what Dawn described as pain or fear. She also heard her father say things to her mother like, "You are good for nothing" or "You're so stupid" when they were fighting. It was clear to me that Dawn had input these experiences primarily using her auditory system. As she closed her eyes, she could hear the screaming and insults as if they were being said again right there. She visibly shuddered as she replayed these phrases in her head.

Knowing that we would need to address these memories using the auditory tracks she was hearing, I decided to use an auditory pattern interrupt. I allowed Dawn to get deeply in the trance of this memory, asking her to hear the screams louder and the insults even clearer. I could see her trying to make herself smaller in the chair as she relived this event. This was obviously a very traumatic memory for her. At once, I had her open her eyes and answer a question for me. "Who is your favorite cartoon character?" I asked. Somewhat befuddled, she searched her mind for the answer. Eventually, she landed on Elmer Fudd from

Bugs Bunny. *I asked her if she remembered what he said. Of course, she did. "I'm a'huntin' wabbits," she said with a small smile. I quickly asked her to close her eyes and go back to the memory of her father. I asked her to hear his words and her mother's screams. A small frown appeared on her face, "I can't hear it as loudly," she said, almost disappointed. I asked her to hear it as best she could, and then, mustering my best Elmer Fudd impression, I loudly said, "I got you, wabbit!" Dawn's eyes shot open, and she began to laugh. I asked her to go back to the words of her father and to notice what was there. After a long pause, she said, "I can hear it, but just barely." At this point, I leaned in and whispered in her ear, "You wascally wabbit!" Dawn once again burst into laughter. When I asked her to return to the memory, she quickly responded, "I can't!" When I pushed her a bit further, she smiled slightly and said, "I can only hear Elmer Fudd!"*

I proceeded to further clean up and change any parts of the memory that had been stored with any of the other systems (visual and kinesthetic). Because this memory was primarily auditory remembering, the other systems were even faster to resolve. At the end of our time, I pushed her to try to recall what her father used to say to her mother when she was a child. Of course, she instantly thought of Elmer Fudd and smiled. After that, from some of the other work we did in that session, she was able to remember many of the loving things her father and mother said to each other. In fact, she now realized that her parents' relationship was for the most part encouraging and affectionate. The incident she got stuck on happened to be a singular "rough patch" in an otherwise healthy marriage. But because she was stuck replaying the most traumatizing memory, she hadn't been able to recall the other things. When she began hearing and replaying the good things she heard growing up, her own self-image drastically improved. The next time I saw her, she looked very different. She was sitting a little taller and was much more talkative and animated.

By using an auditory pattern interrupt, we were able to "scratch" the track on that "CD." Also, the deconstruction of that negative neuropathway continued as she began to laugh.

Dawn had been programmed early in life to feel small and "not good enough." Even though Dawn's father never said those things to *her,* he said them to her mother, someone Dawn loved and valued. To make matters worse, because Dawn also loved her father so much, part of her wanted to believe her father was right. This left her feeling guilty and full of shame. A child of four or five years old simply cannot reconcile the grossly mixed messages she was receiving. So she internalized them as a reflection of herself. Now *she* is the "stupid" and "good for nothing" person. Long after her father stopped saying those things, Dawn continued to hear them, only she is just hearing the recordings of her memories.

When she "heard" this over and over, it became a rumination. Inevitably, she began to apologize for herself in all situations, saying, "Sorry! I am just stupid." Now she was declaring. You know what comes next!

RUMINATION + DECLARATION = CREATION.

For memories that are visually held, I find it helpful to create new pictures, movies, or stories. Using new scenarios helps the client "see" a new option and can often totally destroy the previously held visual construct. For kinesthetically held memories, pattern interrupts that involve movement are recommended. Dancing, yoga, deep conscious breathing, or clapping are all good options. Our goal is to be moving the awareness from the old feeling, picture, or sound to a new one. One that is "better" and that is in alignment with what they want more of in their life.

A quick note for those who are new to the concept of representational systems: People often say, "I'm totally visual" or "I'm such a kinesthetic." It is true that the majority of the population will have a *primary* representational preference. But it is important to understand that just because we may be holding something visually, we also *did* hear and feel things about the event. Though I hold many memories in a visual context, my more powerful system is kinesthetic. I usually focus on the visual construct of a memory to avoid *feeling* anything about it. When I work on myself, I often need to change the visual construct first, and then I am able to address any feelings I have about the memory. Remember, our subconscious mind is the smartest part about us. It will do whatever it takes to "protect" us, even if it doesn't make sense consciously. It is important to clean up *all* unpleasant aspects of a memory.

Suppose I remember an abuse scenario with my stepfather and "feel" nothing negative but can still "see" pictures of him hitting me. In that case, I am still holding an unpleasant aspect of this memory. Remember, you will get *more* of what you hold within. If I don't want more of the same, I need to change the pictures and sounds that accompany these memories. The best and most effective "new pathways" will be those that have positive visual images, audio files, *and* feelings.

NEURO REWIRING

> *Low self-esteem causes me to believe that I have so little worth that my response does not matter. With repentance, however, I understand that being worth so much to God is why my response is so important. Repentance is remedial work to mend our minds and hearts, which get bent by sin.*
>
> – John Ortberg

Our brain is constantly learning and adapting to new stimuli. If we are constantly finding what we already know or believe to be true, we aren't necessarily learning anything new. This is just the result of the "firing" of these well-traveled neuropathways. We often hear the phrase "set in their ways" when speaking about older people. Our brain doesn't lose the ability to adapt and change as we get older. We usually just get comfortable with what we "already know and believe." Therefore, we are simply a walking, talking product of these well-worn neuropathways. *But*, if a new thought comes on board, our brain is forced to adapt.

When you think about something in a different way, learn a new task, choose a different emotion, see a different picture, or take a different perspective, you are carving out a new path. Now the brain has two possible pathways to follow. If you keep traveling the new road, your brain chooses this pathway more and more often. The feelings created along with these new pathways become more familiar, like second nature. As the old pathway is used less and less, it weakens and eventually disappears altogether. This is neuroplasticity in action.

As we see with Dawn, her beliefs and corresponding neuropathways were formed early in life. And even though they happened many years prior, they had been reinforced and strengthened over and over. And thanks to the RAS, she found proof for these beliefs again and again. By using pattern interrupts, we disrupted the messages encoded in the deep and well-traveled road. This left Dawn in a suggestible state and open to a different perspective. After it was clear that the former road had become unstable, we were able to rewire or recode the message. Now there is a new pathway—one that has a positive and affirming message.

The goal is to significantly weaken the original neuropathway and offer an alternative route. Once that new path is traveled and the accompanying positive emotions are created, many people realize the benefit of this option. But it is imperative to make an intentional effort to reinforce this message and travel this road daily for an extended time (studies show that a newly formed neuropathway can be made permanent after just 21 days of continual travel/practice).[91] If the new route isn't strengthened by repetition and the old pathway remains, it will be very challenging to change. You can easily fall back into old beliefs, reactions, and patterns. Lasting change comes from our daily practice of choosing which memories we replay and cleaning up anything that doesn't serve us.

Our brains are highly resilient and desire flexibility, functioning optimally when open to new possibilities and learning. We are not only capable of changing the landscape of our lives by creating new neuropathways, but our brains have also highly adapted to make this possible. The human brain is designed by God to heal itself and seems to have a deep desire to do so. Changing deeply encoded traumas and beliefs necessitates a great deal of awareness of our present beliefs

[91] Leaf, Caroline. Switch On Your Brain. Baker Books, Dallas. 2008.

and programs, along with the references held by our subconscious minds. Pattern interrupts are a great way to facilitate the process of change.

I think Jesus used this technique in a well-known story. In John 8, we meet the "adulterous woman." If you are a little rusty on the details, I encourage you to read it again. At the height of the tension, when the Pharisees and the teachers of the Law are formally accusing the woman of adultery before Jesus, he does a very curious thing—he bends down and begins to write on the ground. What?! Why on earth would he do such a thing? I want you to imagine this crowd of people standing around, watching this debacle. Who do you think they were looking at most? Who had everyone's focus? The woman, standing there in shame, likely nude or at least in some state of undress. What do you think happened when Jesus suddenly bent to the ground and began writing on it with his finger? This was an epic pattern interrupt! All eyes were on him now, and for a brief moment, the attention and focus were completely off the woman and her shame. Coincidence? I think not. How do I know? He does it again a few minutes later! I love Jesus for this. Not only does he not want this woman to be publicly humiliated for her transgression (even though she was clearly in a sinful situation), he even cares about her accusers.

Jesus first pulls the focus off the woman (immersed in her guilt and shame), and then pulls it to himself and the ground. With this break in the narrative, he capitalizes on the way the human brain works and provides some perspective. He then stands up again and redirects all that shame and blame, transforming it into a question straight back to the ones who were dishing it out. He puts the ball back in their courts, involving every listener and watcher there. But even then, Jesus doesn't want people to wallow in any shame or blame. So he drops to the ground again and resumes his writing. With this second break in focus, this powerful and unexpected digression from the norm, Jesus is mercifully offering another chance at perspective. It is an ingenious move that is loving but firm. It is full of conviction and mercy, simultaneously. Have you ever considered that there was more behind what seemed like such an odd move from Jesus? Can you see it clearly now?

Pattern interrupts have been used, knowingly and unknowingly, for centuries. It's time for us to learn to harness this God-given tool. With a little practice and a little time, you will come to see how powerful it can be for you and for those around you. In the next chapter, we will pull all the pieces together and outline the basic process of the Metanoia Method.

CHAPTER 18

BASIC METANOIA METHOD PROCESS

If we rebuke our heart by a calm, mild remonstrance, with more compassion for it than passion against it and encourage it to make amendment, then repentance conceived in this way will sink far deeper and penetrate more effectually than fretful, angry, stormy repentance.

– Francis de Sale

Your hunger for growth and desire for change is the reason you've come this far. I am so happy you are on this journey of continual transformation. In this chapter, I want to guide you and walk with you as you learn to put the Metanoia Method into practice. To give you an outline for working on yourself, I will include some helpful scripts and questions to ask yourself. For deeper or more traumatic events, I would highly suggest working with a skilled practitioner.
** *We have created a* Metanoia Method Handbook *that will be very helpful for those who would like to have all of the Metanoia Method outlined in one place. It also has extra tools and tips for self-work, as well as scriptural inspiration. This is available through Amazon and other booksellers.*

There are many ways to approach the way you practice the Metanoia Method. I will go through a few of them here. For more hands-on examples and tutorials, please visit our YouTube channel for continually added, free videos. At most, I would suggest spending no more than one hour a day focused on this work. That would be a very aggressive approach. For others, it may look more like 10–15 minutes a day or 30–60 minutes a few times a week. Even if you start with 5- to 10-minute self-sessions at first, you will be engaging in a powerful and intentional activity. In any case, be gentle and loving with yourself in the process.

WORKING THROUGH YOUR PaNE CuRe LIST

One approach to the Metanoia Method would be to work through your PaNE CuRe list. Prepare yourself for the session by taking a moment for prayer or meditation, using this time to give thanks for the ability to do this work and for the healing that will happen. Next, choose a calm, quiet area where you will not be disturbed. Set a timer for the amount of time you would like to spend. Now is an excellent time to have your GPS handy! Or if you have invested in your "safe haven" (Chapter 15), this would be a great time to go there and spend a minute or so indulging in the good feelings. As you do this, engage in some deep breathing. Deep, three- to four-second inhales through the nose, followed by four- to five-second exhales through the mouth. Do this four or five times as you are in your "feel good" state.

PICK A MEMORY

Either chronologically, by intensity, or by perceived importance, pick a memory or "problem" to work on. Take a minute to notice how you know it's a problem. Allow any pictures, feelings, or sensations to surface. You may notice that one or more memories surface. If so, write those down. Even if you think they are unrelated, just trust the subconscious mind and work through what comes up. Write the title of this memory on a piece of paper in front of you. Close your eyes, and "go there." Notice what you notice. *How* do you know this happened? Do you see pictures? Hear voices or words? Does a feeling emerge? Maybe it's a mixture of these. The most important part of this is "knowing *how* you know."

Under the title, write the letters V, A, K, A-D. If you see pictures, movies, or snapshots, circle the V (visual) on your paper. If you hear things within the memory, circle A (auditory). If you have feelings, sensations or emotions arise, circle K (kinesthetic). If you have an internal dialogue that you can hear or a "knowing" that it happened but nothing else, circle the A-D (audio-digital). *Note: You may have more than one way that you are holding this memory. Just circle all that apply.* For each letter that you circled, write two or three things you notice from that category. If you happen to discover the core belief behind the event, you can write that down as well. It might look something like this:

Memory: Dad yelling about my mom

V:	I see myself as a scared little boy, 5 y/o, cowering in the corner. I can see Dad standing over me, face red, eyes bulging.
A:	I hear the scary tone of his voice.
K:	I feel scared and helpless.
A-D:	I am lazy. Dad doesn't love me. I deserve this.
Core Belief:	I can never be good enough.

RATE YOUR MEMORY

Once you've identified *how* you know this event happened, notice how much it bothers you. Now you can give the memory a rating to acknowledge how much it bothers you. On a scale of 0–10, 0 being you feel nothing at all and 10 you feel as if this is happening again right now, how much can you make this memory bother you? Write this number down beside the title on your paper.

Don't worry if you find it difficult to select a rating. A common subconscious defense mechanism that can arise when we are working on ourselves is distraction. We get distracted by small, inane details, and we allow this to cause unnecessary friction within us. This is the mind's way of trying to "delay" the process. Just be aware of that and move forward. You can thank the subconscious mind for its constant desire to protect you and affirm that you are safe. No need to spend an undue amount of time worrying if the memory is a 2 or a 4. Just give the memory a number. Make it your best guess if you need to, and be fine with that. The rating eventually comes more naturally. It is simply a benchmark for where you were when you started and will be used to see the progress you are making.

Now think about or recall the problem or event in detail. Notice the emotions, feelings, sounds, and specific images that are present in this memory. Allow it to "happen" as if it's happening right now. If it's safe to do so, step into the memory, imagine yourself really there, see what you saw, hear what you heard, and feel what you felt. This is the time to make it as strong as possible, because it will only last a short time. This should take you no longer than thirty seconds to one minute. Any longer, and you begin "practicing" the feelings because the feedback loop has already been playing.

As soon as you reach this place, it's time to open your eyes and engage a pattern interrupt. The optimal pattern interrupt will be one that corresponds with the representational system that you used to most fully recall this memory. For instance, if you have a mental picture of the memory, open your eyes and look through your GPS. Or you can visit your mental safe haven. Alternatively, you can watch a quick YouTube video of funny animals. Spend thirty seconds or so in any one (or more) of these activities. The most important thing is to completely shift your focus from the memory (picture, feeling, sensation, sound) you are working on to the pattern interrupt.

As soon as you are ready, close your eyes and take two deep breaths (three-second inhales through the nose, followed by five-second exhales through the mouth). Notice that your breathing automatically brings you back to a grounded place. Now go back and check your memory that you are working on. Notice what has changed. Notice that the intensity has lessened, or the picture has changed. Maybe the feeling has reduced or moved to another part of your body. Just notice what is left of the memory. Now go to any part of the memory that still bothers you, notice how you know it bothers you, intensify it if you can, and see what you see/feel what you feel/ hear what you hear. Now use a pattern interrupt again.

THE DEVIL IS IN THE DETAILS

It is very important to notice the details of any memory/problem. The details are like the building blocks of the memory. If we change the details, the whole memory can change. So if you notice that you or anyone in the memory is "not happy," go from the general to the specific, "*I'm not happy because* _____," to even more specific aspects.

Here are some examples:

"*I'm not happy because my dad's tone is still rough.*" (This is an "audible" aspect of the event.)
"*I don't like the way his face looks.*" (This is an aspect of the experience, the "visual cue.")
"*The little boy is feeling sad.*" (Here's a "body sensation" to address.)
"*I'm worried he's disappointed in me.*" (A "future fear" to address.)
"*I don't like the way the room feels.*" (A "kinesthetic detail" to address.)
"*I never have good relationships with people.*" (A "limiting belief/past experience" to address.)

And we could go on and on! A person's clearing this experience with their father can have massive positive byproducts on many levels. For example, this person starts with working on and clearing the memory with their father, and as a side effect, they have a better (and less reactive) experience with their spouse later that day.

KEEP GOING UNTIL IT'S GREAT

Continue this process until the memory can no longer bother you. This may happen very quickly, or it may take you the entire time that you set aside. Either is okay. Regardless of the length of time you have spent, notice the fact that you are changing, and applaud yourself! "Great job, me!" Instead of simply seeing what you still need/want to change, take a moment to see how much you have already changed. Notice the good shifts your mind is capable of. Once you can no longer make the memory bother you, it's time to change your mind. If it's a picture, you may notice that the picture has already changed. The brain is amazing that way! If not, you may just notice that you can no longer find the image, or it has gone completely blurry. Now is the time to be intentional about what we hold within. Ask yourself, "What would I rather have seen instead?" If auditory, "What would I rather have heard?" Kinesthetic, "What would I rather have felt?" Make it good, because you will get more of what you hold. In the example above, maybe the picture changes to the little five-year-old boy sitting on his daddy's lap. His dad's face is gentle and loving. Notice everything that comes with the new memory—the good sounds, words, and feelings that come with this new picture. Allow yourself to really be there. If anything negative or uncomfortable arises, just interrupt that pattern and then return to the new memory.

When everything is good, and nothing can bother you about this memory, you may think you are done. But this is the point to go in and make it even better! Go back into the memory and "redecorate" a bit. Maybe now you see Daddy playing your favorite board game with you, and you *win!* Perhaps he is now telling you all the things you needed to hear. Maybe you are wrapped tightly in the arms of your daddy, and you can feel all the love. Even better, perhaps it's all these things mixed together.

Don't worry if other memories come up during the time you are working on this one. Simply take a moment to jot them down and thank your subconscious mind for giving you more resources that have been supporting this belief/ problem. You can work on them after this memory is cleared, or you can save them for another time.

If you are working on a memory and find resistance, that is okay. It doesn't mean it didn't work. It only means you have a little extra investment in this belief. It's likely foundational and may require one or two sessions of self-work. Take a break and come back later. You may find that the memory is now changed. If not, you will likely find less resistance when you revisit it. Remember that it probably took you many years to develop such a deeply rooted response. Or you have practiced this memory thousands of times, therefore reinforcing it daily. It may take you a few hours or even days to rewrite some of these events, but it is well worth it!

For any of you who were at our very first live training that we hosted, I (Kent) sat in front of the audience and demonstrated how to work on yourself. I worked on a painful memory of my college girlfriend breaking up with me on my voicemail. Now all I can do is laugh out loud because all my mind thinks about and remembers is adventuring through New York City with Yoda on my back!

For me, this image popped into my mind as I was doing the work, and I decided to use it to help me laugh and relax. Though it might sound silly, it was a powerful tool to help me shift my feelings. Thank you, voicemail breakup, for flooding my mind with joy!

If you remember from before, I (Heather) had an old memory of a physical abuse event with my stepfather when I was about 10. I no longer have any emotional connection to that original memory (other than a vague awareness that it may have happened). Though I can tell the old story, it really doesn't *feel* real to me any longer. It feels as though I am telling the story about someone else. When I recall this memory now, the first thing I see is my stepfather taking me out for ice cream. I have a cone with 10 scoops of different ice cream flavors towering above me! I can even smell the ice cream shop and feel the cone in my hand and the melted ice cream running down my wrist. I wrote this memory down so that I could rehearse it and replay it any time. A lot of healing has come from this singular event! But my GPS is *full* of these "rewritten" memories.

The first time you rewire a memory, you may be shocked. The first few times might feel a little bumpy or awkward, but the more you do it, the more your brain gets the hang of it. At this stage of my journey, I can often change painful memories simply with the intention of doing so. My brain is so accustomed to letting go of the painful things that do not serve me that just the acknowledgment of needed change stimulates the change! Of course, some things are still very rooted in my belief system, and those things take a little more work. I still utilize sessions with colleagues on a regular basis to help me clean up some of the things I am unaware of or that are particularly stubborn beliefs.

A word of caution: though this method has been used to tackle some of the most devastating traumas, it is advised that you work with a skilled practitioner if you find that the emotional "charge" of the memory is too high. The trance of the painful memory can sometimes be so powerful that you have a challenging time breaking it on your own. This is where an experienced professional can utilize different protocols to break that trance. This is very deep work, and it can be extremely beneficial to work with someone who has been trained to handle any situation that may arise. It is the goal of any practitioner (trained in the Metanoia

Method) to empower and enable clients to work on themselves eventually. Therefore, starting out with a practitioner can be very helpful.

For more information and instructional videos on using pattern interrupts, please visit our Mind Change YouTube channel. This should give you a good start on how to use these tools yourself.

CHAPTER 19

THE END...OR THE BEGINNING?

Correctly understood, repentance is not negative but positive. It means, not self-pity or remorse, but conversion, the re-centering of our whole life upon the Trinity. It is to look, not backward with regret, but forward with hope—not downwards at our own shortcomings, but upwards at God's love. It is to see, not what we have failed to be, but what by divine grace we can now become; and it is to act upon what we see. To repent is to open our eyes to the light. In this sense, repentance is not just a single act, an initial step, but a continuing state, an attitude of heart and will that needs to be ceaselessly renewed up to the end of life.

– Kallistos Ware

We have reached the end of this journey. I hope you have enjoyed the ride. I want you to know that this is probably not the end for you, but likely the beginning. This book is just the introduction to a longer conversation. Some of you are deeper into the conversation already, but some of you never even knew you needed to *have* a conversation.

It wasn't easy to know where to stop. There is so much more. There is always so much more! We are ever-changing, ever-evolving beings. Science is daily revealing more astounding things through research. The frontier of our minds has only barely been explored. For me, this journey has been eye-opening to my faith. This information challenged some long-held (yet deeply unbiblical) doctrines I unknowingly adhered to. Though it was difficult, I am encouraged by the refining of my faith. This has given me an avenue to reevaluate my beliefs from a completely different perspective.

I believe I've accomplished what I set out to do—to provide you with a foundation of how the mind works, some powerful tools to change it, and a biblical framework for this method. But it's not the end. Even though I have found incredible healing and power with this information, I am still learning. I am always looking for faster and better ways to change and grow. I intend to continue to share that information with you.

For some people, the information in these pages will be enough for them to move forward, heal their past hurts and traumas, and create their future by design. For others, it will be just enough to be intriguing, but they are left wanting more. Wherever this finds you, I want you to know that I am grateful that you joined me on this journey. You are not alone. Hundreds of thousands of people around the world are ready for change. You are in good company.

Or perhaps you are not ready yet. Maybe this is all a bit "too much" right now. That's okay. I've been there too. I want people to know that there is hope for everyone, not just the lucky few. Remember Jesus' words, "*I have come that they may have life, and have it to the full*" (John 10:10). Life to the full is not a one-time gift. It's ever flowing and ever constant, as we "*remain in the vine*" (John 15:4). One way or another, God gives us windows to see his truths and his promises. "*The Lord is not slow in keeping his promise, as some understand slowness. Instead he is patient with you, not wanting anyone to perish, but everyone to come to repentance*" (2 Peter 3:9). And this is precisely how the Son represents the Father: Jesus meets us wherever we are at in order to give us the best chance we can at living life to the full.

No matter what you have been through, no matter where you are now, it is possible to find freedom, health, and happiness. It won't come in the form of a pill, a diet, a fad, or a distraction. It won't be popular and isn't always easy. It may be maligned, mistaken, and misjudged. But the good thing is that it is within every person's reach. It will involve *letting go* of anything that does not serve you and looking beyond the mask you put on daily. No one can make you do it, but no one can take it away either. A changed mind is a changed life. Only you can change your mind.

So let's keep up the conversation. Be the adventurer of your own destiny, the surveyor of your own mind. Make friends with your subconscious mind and learn the language of your soul. If you need help, reach out. Read more. Listen more. Become an expert in the art of *you*.

If you want more, there is an extensive reading list at the end of the book. We are adding more and more relevant and inspiring information via blogs, podcasts, and products on our site. We also have online training for the Metanoia Method (www.MindChangeInstitute.com). The first module is to train people to work on themselves, and the second module introduces the concept of working on other people. I'll do my best to keep you up to date on what I am learning and finding. In the meantime, there is no better time to start than now. Thank you for your company. Thank you for your heart to grow and overcome. Thank you for your willingness to expand your heart, mind, and spirit.

In closing, I would like to share two stories with you describing transformation: Chinese Bamboo and The Common Household Radish. It is said that Chinese bamboo starts out as a hard-shelled seed. Once it is planted, it needs good soil, sunshine, and water. After the first year, there are no visible signs of growth; not even a seedling or sprout. In the second year, it's the same outcome. In the third and fourth years, still, there is nothing. The grower just continues to water and nurture the plant from the surface. But in the fifth year, the Chinese bamboo finally peeks through and then shows miraculous growth—often 80 to 90 feet in six weeks! Was the little plant really dead and inactive for five years? Of course not! It was busy creating an entire foundational structure that could eventually support its enormous growth.

Contrast this to the radish. I grow these in my garden and have witnessed their growth cycle. Within days of sowing the seeds in the ground, little seedlings pop up. In 20 to 30 days, the radishes are fully developed and ready to harvest. Depending on the amount of rain and sunshine they get, it can be even faster. I can pull them up and drop in a few little seeds, and the whole process starts over again. They are easy to grow and relatively worry-free. And they taste amazing!

Understand that some of the things that you work on will be like those radishes. Dr. Caroline Leaf, author of *Switch on Your Brain*, says it takes around

21 days for all the necessary changes in your brain to create a long-term memory.[92] Those new little memories and neuropathways need to be fed and watered. They need to be practiced over and over in a short period to build a strong root system in your mind. Other things, like core belief systems and generational mantras, may take a little longer. They may be the "bamboo" of your life. Keep watering.

You will likely see a bunch of new little sprouts in your life as you apply these principles. Harvest them and enjoy. Don't forget to keep planting. Other things will reveal themselves slowly, doing the deep foundational work under the surface. Both are important.

The Metanoia Method is crucial and sacred work. Welcome to the end...and the beginning.

> *As long as man does not convert it into action, it does not matter how much he thinks about this new repentance... Wallow in it... Write a book about it; that is often an excellent way of sterilizing the seeds which the Heavenly Father plants in a human soul... Do anything but act. No amount of piety in his imagination and affections will harm the cause of evil if it is kept out of his will... The more often he feels without acting, the less he will ever be able to act, and, in the long run, the less he will be able to feel.*[93]
>
> – C.S. Lewis

> *Accomplishments don't erase shame, hatred, cruelty, silence, ignorance, discrimination, low self-esteem or immorality. It covers it up, with a creative version of pride and ego. Only restitution, forgiving yourself and others, compassion, repentance and living with dignity will ever erase the past.*
>
> – Shannon L. Alder

---

[92] Leaf, Caroline. *Switch On Your Brain.* Baker Books, Dallas. 2008.

[93] Lewis, C. S. *The Screwtape Letters.* London: G. Bles, 1952.

APPENDIX

RECOMMENDED RESOURCES

**All opinions held within these recommended reads do not necessarily reflect the beliefs, theology, and doctrine held by Kent and Heather McKean or MindChange, LLC. Please use your own judgment and discernment when accessing references.

Mind Change: Changing the World One Mind at a Time
by Heather McKean

Mind Change Handbook: The Companion Guide to Mind Change
by Heather McKean

The God-Shaped Brain: How Changing Your View of God Transforms Your Life
by Timothy R. Jennings

How God Changes Your Brain: Breakthrough Findings from a Leading Neuroscientist
by Andrew Newberg M.D.

Lifetime Guarantee: Making Your Christian Life Work and What to Do When It Doesn't
by Bill Gillham

Your Miracle Brain: Maximize Your Brainpower, Boost Your Memory, Lift Your Mood, Improve Your IQ and Creativity, Prevent and Reverse Mental Aging
by Jean Carper

The Divided Mind: The Epidemic of Mindbody Disorders
by John E. Sarno

Healing Crisis and Trauma with Mind, Body, and Spirit
by Barbara Rubin Wainrib EdD

Rare Leadership: 4 Uncommon Habits For Increasing Trust, Joy, and Engagement in the People You Lead
by Marcus Warner & Jim Wilder

Authority to Heal
by Ken Blue

The Power to Heal
by Francis MacNutt

Appendix A: Recommended Resources

A More Excellent Way, Be in Health: Spiritual Roots of Disease, Pathways to Wholeness
by Henry W. Wright

Beyond Willpower: The Secret Principle to Achieving Success in Life, Love, and Happiness
by Alexander Loyd PhD. ND

You Are the Placebo: Making Your Mind Matter
by Dr. Joe Dispenza

Becoming Supernatural: How Common People Are Doing the Uncommon
by Dr. Joe Dispenza

The Biology of Belief: Unleashing the Power of Consciousness, Matter & Miracles
by Bruce H. Lipton

The Body Keeps the Score: Brain, Mind, and Body in the Healing of Trauma
by Bessel van der Kolk M.D.

The Deepest Well: Healing the Long-Term Effects of Childhood Adversity
by Nadine Burke Harris M.D.

When the Body Says No: Understanding the Stress-Disease Connection
by Gabor Maté M.D.

Deadly Emotions: Understand the Mind-Body-Spirit Connection That Can Heal or Destroy You
by Don Colbert

Switch On Your Brain: The Key to Peak Happiness, Thinking, and Health
by Dr. Caroline Leaf

Your Healing Is Within You
by Canon J Glennon

Forgiveness is Healing
by Dr. Russ Parker

The Healing Code: 6 Minutes to Heal the Source of Your Health, Success, or Relationship Issue
by Alexander Loyd PhD ND & Ben Johnson MD DO ND

The User's Manual for the Brain
by Bob G. Bodenhamer & L. Michael. Hall

How Healing Works: Get Well and Stay Well Using Your Hidden Power to Heal
by Wayne Jonas M.D.

What did you think of The Metanoia Method?

First of all, thank you for purchasing this book. I know you could have picked any number of books to read, but you chose this book, and for that, I am extremely grateful.

I hope that it added value and quality to your everyday life. If so, it would be really nice if you could share this book with your friends and family by posting to Facebook, Instagram, and Twitter, or Pinterest.

If you enjoyed this book and found some benefit in reading this, I'd like to hear from you and hope that you could take some time to post a review on Amazon. I want you, the reader, to know that your review is very important. Your feedback and support will help me continue to help as many as possible.

Can this help a friend, family member, or church? Please spread the word and share about the amazing metanoia moments you are already seeing in your life. I wish you all the best in your future success as you draw closer to God and continue to step into the amazing *you* that God created!

FOR OUR SECULAR AUDIENCE

AN IN DEPTH NEUROSCIENCE APPROACH FROM HEATHER'S HEALING JOURNEY

AVAILABLE ON AMAZON

RANKED #1 BESTSELLER IN NEUROSCIENCE & NEUROPSYCHOLOGY
THE FIRST WEEK OF RELEASE!

Printed in the USA
CPSIA information can be obtained
at www.ICGtesting.com
CBHW070925130424
6869CB00016B/1450

9 781733 422055